SCIENCE IN SPACE
L. V. BERKNER and HUGH ODISHAW

What do we actually know about space?
What is the role of man in space?
What immediate benefits does space
exploration offer to mankind?
These and other pertinent questions are fully
covered in this unique exploration of the
many ways science can utilize the greater
opportunities of experimentation and
observation in space itself and thereby
broaden our understanding of meteorology,
communications, the universe, man himself.

McGRAW-HILL PAPERBACKS
SCIENCE, MATHEMATICS AND ENGINEERING

Science in Space

edited by
Lloyd V. Berkner
Hugh Odishaw

McGRAW-HILL BOOK COMPANY, INC.
New York   Toronto   London

SCIENCE IN SPACE

PREFACE

The spectacular growth of space activity since the launching of Sputnik I on October 4, 1957, requires careful assessment of the opportunities that space exploration provides so that emphasis on those opportunities is reasonably optimized. Among the space activities of exploration, application, and scientific research, the last is precedent to man's other space endeavors. Space applications and man-in-space ventures depend for their success on adequate knowledge of space. Consequently, the necessary antecedent research must be completed before dependent space activities can be most effectively pursued. In addition, space offers a whole new vista of scientific advancement which before was inaccessible. Scientific experiments in many exciting fields of knowledge can now be planned, and these can supplement older methods of research in a very critical way.

This volume presents a review of the new scientific opportunities offered by space science. It is directed to research workers whose scientific activities may be influenced by the new opportunities for experiment offered by growing access to space. In some cases, such as astronomy, new opportunities promise to revolutionize the science. In other cases, space research can critically supplement existing methods. Therefore this volume endeavors to put these new opportunities afforded by space science in some perspective. If our space science program is to be optimized, it must take root across a broad segment of scientific activity in our universities, our scientific laboratories, and our industrial life.

This volume may also be of interest to general readers who are concerned about the national space effort. While some of the chapters admittedly are somewhat technical, others present few if any difficulties. They will suggest the nature of the scientific challenges afforded by the tools of the space age, the types of applications in the offing, and the questions that must be faced if our space endeavors are to be well conceived and executed.

The material of this volume has been contributed from a broad spectrum of American and foreign scientists. All members of the Space Science Board and of its committees have contributed through discussion, criticism, and editorial comment. In addition, many scientists outside the formal organization of the Board have given freely of their time and assistance. Therefore, full recognition to all those who have taken part in writing the volume is beyond the capabilities of the editors. We particularly express our appreciation to the President of the Academy, Dr. Detlev W. Bronk, who has sat with the Board during critical discussions, for his advice and guidance.

We are indebted to several members of the Board's secretariat for assistance in the planning and preparation of the volume: G. A. Derbyshire, E. R. Dyer, Jr., J. Orlen, J. P. T. Pearman, and R. C. Peavey. We are also much obligated to Miss Hope Marindin and Miss Grace C. Marshall for their devoted secretarial, proofreading, and indexing help.

Lloyd V. Berkner
Hugh Odishaw

Washington, D.C.
January 1, 1961

CONTENTS

PART 1

A GENERAL REVIEW

1 ≡

DIMENSIONS AND PROBLEMS

L. V. Berkner and Hugh Odishaw

1. THE NATURE OF SPACE ACTIVITY

Perhaps no venture in man's history has proclaimed its immediate challenges and problems as quickly and clearly as space exploration. In part this has come about because there are at hand and in the offing rocket systems capable of reaching out far into the solar system with significant cargoes. This capability points directly and compellingly to a host of important scientific problems and applications whose solutions call for satellites and space probes.

In the past, man has been tied to the Earth. What he has learned of the universe until very recent times has been based upon Earth-bound observations. From these observations, he nonetheless has learned much about the very high atmosphere, the solar system, stars in our own galaxy, and about galaxies beyond. When we consider the remarkable knowledge of the universe attained by astronomers, dependent upon only a thin slit in the electromagnetic spectrum, we can sense the excitement engendered by prospects of more direct contact with the universe. Even if we add the radio-frequency window to the narrow light-wave window, the sum gives astronomy about twenty octaves (above 100 kilocycles per second) of the electromagnetic spectrum with which to investigate the universe from the Earth because atmospheric attenuation precludes use of the whole spectrum. Yet an additional forty octaves are in principle available to instruments flown just above the Earth's masking atmosphere. The radiations in this heretofore hidden spectrum contain some of the most important information that the universe provides.

Space tools afford even further opportunities. They permit the transport of measuring devices into interplanetary space, there to record directly particles, fields, and radiations. They can carry instruments to the moon and to other planets for *in situ* detection and measurement. They will ultimately take men to these regions and bodies. In short, space carriers open up prospects that lead to the following generalization, if we are to sense how it is that the current challenges of space science are so clear and compelling: in the past man has largely had immediately before him the small, finite Earth alone, along with its lower atmosphere, for *direct* investigation; he now has, in principle, an infinite volume of space and matter accessible to him.

Consequently this ability to penetrate directly into the interplanetary medium and to reach other bodies in the solar system has a special meaning. It means a vast extension of opportunities for detection and observation above the Earth's interfering atmosphere. But even more, it means that man is now equipped to *conduct experiments* in contrast to *making observations*. The conduct of controlled experiments leads to deduction; the passive taking of observations only permits inference.

Observation is characterized in most fields of the geophysical sciences by superimposition of many variables in the collected data. Thus voluminous quantities of data are required, over years and centuries, if the many parameters are to be separated and defined; and the data reduction and processes of analysis are complex, protracted, and arduous. A specific phenomenon under study may be buried in the mass of accompanying other variables, analogous to the presence of a desired but weak radio signal in a "hash" of radio noise: the high noise level masks the wanted signal.

The ability to conduct an experiment, however, permits the gifted experimenter to devise his measurements in such a fashion as to separate the variable of interest from the many unwanted ones. Perhaps after decades and perhaps centuries of conventional observations, the Van Allen Radiation Belts might have been inferred, but the conduct of appropriate experiments quickly and directly established their existence and defined their character. Similarly the Argus experiment, by injecting into the high atmosphere a *known* quantity of charged particles at a *known* time and place permitted the conduct of a unique experiment dealing with the control mechanism of the Earth's magnetic field. The interior structure of the Moon and other planets will never be within reach until seismic and related experiments can be conducted from their surfaces: no amount of observation from the Earth can ever penetrate these mysteries.

Science is not the only claimant upon the energies that man is even now devoting to space efforts. Tools at hand, and projects already under way, point to three principal and overlapping areas of space activity:

First, *exploration.*

Second, *application.*

Third, *research.*

In spite of the inevitable overlap among these three categories, each can be said to have its own rationale and urgency, and each is best considered independently from the point of view of support.

Exploration. Perhaps the basic motivation behind the exploration of space affecting the generality of mankind is adventure. Even if space endeavors did not embrace science and application, this unparalleled adventure would be pursued, for man's history is at least in part a recital of the curiosity which has led him to voyages of exploration and discovery on his own planet from ancient days to the present. But exploration is more than adventure: it is the act of searching, the quest for discovery; and exploration has no lasting value except for critical studies that advance man's knowledge step by step. The hazards and cost of adventure and leadership through space exploration call for careful and critical analysis by the makers of policy: the effort and priority in this area should not be for personal aggrandizement at the expense of important work that lies before man in research and application.

Thus the pursuit of even this activity—exploration by man—should be integrated as closely as possible with research. The reasons are several and self-explicit. For example, if we had been able to launch man into space five years ago and had done it successfully, without prior physical experiments, man would have perished there, a victim of our lack of knowledge of certain radiations in space. Sound exploration must go hand in hand with research.

Application. It is patently clear that several applications are within grasp: no new principles, yet to be discovered, are called for; no recondite technological problems stand in our way. Rather straightforward problems in rocket-vehicle systems and technology, amenable to reasonably prompt solution, are all that we face—plus the decision to pursue the objectives with vigor. The applications include meteorology (and here TIROS I is the brilliant precursor), communications, and geodesy.

Weather satellites, reporting cloud cover and storm patterns, are of obvious day-to-day significance to the peoples of the world. Communications satellites afford the promise of extending, in effect, the available frequency spectrum by as much as several orders of magnitude. Geodetic satellites will provide more accurate means for navigation and mapping.

Research. From unique information about the solid Earth itself to new insights into extragalactic astronomy, space research affords innumerable opportunities for advances in science. To these opportunities and problems are devoted the bulk of this book, which suggests how much can be undertaken if suitable spacecraft are available, if a broad program of background and flight-directed research is undertaken, and if the full potential of creativity among scientists throughout the nation is developed. Achievements in this area are ultimately the proper first objectives of space efforts and the basis of true exploration. Their attainment —whether as contributions to knowledge, or ultimately to applications, or to national leadership—represents substantive accomplishment as against the ephemeral and already discounted "stunts" that are attempted from time to time.

What has been learned of the upper atmosphere and near space so far? What does this knowledge mean as a guide to further efforts? What is the status of development of space systems upon which future efforts depend? What are the prospects of practical applications of Earth satellites? What is the role of man in space? Why is science deeply concerned about the research prospects afforded by spacecraft? How can we best go about the complicated business of properly and economically planning and conducting meaningful space activities? These and similar questions are pertinent and timely. Yet answers are not easy because the sum total of all that is involved in our current space endeavors represents an evolving, intricate complex of interests, forces, and activities. Yet answers to questions such as those above must be pursued, and the remainder of this chapter is concerned with such problems in a preliminary, tentative way in the hope that responsible public debate may be stimulated.

2. ROCKETS, SATELLITES, AND PROBES

The use of sounding rockets, which rise almost vertically and return to Earth directly, for measurements in the upper atmosphere is significant because it has yielded important and unique data and because it was the necessary precursor to space systems. Moreover, satellites and space probes do not relegate sounding rockets to obsolescence, for sounding rockets have unique virtues in studies of the lower and higher reaches of the atmosphere. They provide a means for examining a large region above the reach of balloons and below the altitudes where satellites can long endure. They permit the investigation of events and processes as a function of altitude. They also afford a useful tool for trying out, in a meaningful way, space instruments before their commitment to more expensive space flights.

Direct access to the upper atmosphere for scientific observation and experiment has come only in the past two decades. Before then, knowledge of the upper atmosphere depended upon *indirect* measurements. For example, scientists had probed the ionized layers of the atmosphere between some 80 and 500 km above the Earth's surface, largely by sending short bursts of radio energy skyward and by examining the reflections. From these reflections, which yielded the virtual heights of the reflecting layers as a function of frequency, the gross features of the ionosphere and its behavior were mapped. The knowledge gained thereby has been helpful to man's utilization of radio waves in their many forms and applications. Yet this hard-won knowledge has depended upon indirect observations: the region itself was not penetrated and thus *in situ* measurements were impossible. These limitations have been removed with the advent of atmospheric sounding rockets.

Following the first, military utilization of large rockets by the Germans during World War II, the application of sounding rockets to research was developed by several nations, particularly the United States. These experiments led to important advances in our knowledge of the atmosphere, the ionosphere, and the Sun. Early rocket experiments demonstrated the feasibility of obtaining cross-sectional measurements through the atmosphere, thus yielding connecting relationships in the troposphere, stratosphere, mesosphere, and ionosphere.

The results of sounding rocket research are extensive, and a few examples will suggest this. The detection of X rays and of auroral particles in the upper atmosphere and of the penetration of equatorial ionospheric current sheets were made possible by sounding rockets. The first detailed photograph of the solar ultraviolet spectrum was made possible by rocket-borne instrumentation. The first photograph of an earth-invisible, gigantic tropical storm was achieved by rocket technology, presaging the pictorial mapping transmitted by TIROS I.

Pressure, temperature, density, and composition have been measured through cross sections of the atmosphere to altitudes extending some 300 km over many rocket-launching sites. In the ionosphere, electron density data have been obtained, and the diffusive separation of the components of the atmosphere below and above the E-region have been measured. Rockets have soared directly into active auroras, permitting the study of the electromagnetic and particle radiations. Such studies have shown, for example, that the soft radiation flux above 40 km is many times that of the primary cosmic ray count. Rockets have significantly augmented investigations of secondary cosmic rays on ground and of primaries by means of balloons: intensities and compositions of the primary radiations have been determined by instruments above the denser layers of the atmosphere with which the primaries react. The Earth's magnetic field has been measured in the auroral regions while in the equatorial regions electric currents have been observed through their magnetic effect.

Fields of science other than those directly concerned with the upper atmosphere have profited from rocketry. From above the masking layers of the atmosphere, astronomy has gained new knowledge of solar radiations and their spectra and of stellar ultraviolet radiation. Rockets have also made possible the conduct of man-made experiments in the upper atmosphere. The ejection of sodium vapor, for example, has permitted the measurement of its radiations under the stimulus of particle and radiation impact, of atmospheric winds as the vapor was carried along, and of its diffusion. The injection of electrons into the upper atmosphere in the Argus experiment contributed markedly to an understanding of the trapping of charged particles by the Earth's magnetic field.

Some of the above findings were made in the years immediately following the last war, and many were made during the intensified research period of the International Geophysical Year. During the planning of the IGY—an unprecedented attack on problems of our planet and its spatial environment—it was clear that rocket vehicles afforded powerful tools for exploring the upper atmosphere. Accordingly, strong endorsement to sounding rocket programs was given by the international scientific community planning the IGY. But more than this took place: the established body of new knowledge of the high atmosphere, wrested from Nature only by sounding rockets, suggested clearly that extensions of the technique offered even greater insights into the nature of near space, the relationships between solar activity and events and processes near Earth, and into the cosmos itself. These prospects, about which some technically sound conjectures had been made some years earlier, took on a more hopeful aspect because technological advances in rocket system design and construction, in guidance and control, and in related engineering devices and techniques suggested the imminent feasibility of satellites.

Thus the IGY incorporated recommendations advocating geophysical research using space vehicles. The impetus was simple: while sounding rockets provide directly sensed data of the upper atmosphere, their lives are brief and their spatial coverage restricted to a "line slice." Yet the parameters of events in space vary extensively with space and with time: keenly desired were tools of long life, able to map out variations of many phenomena throughout the expanse of space in the vicinity of the Earth and over appreciable periods of time.

Less than four years have passed since the first satellite was launched into near space. During that interval some very significant results have been obtained. Four are noted here not only because they are of intrinsic interest in themselves but because they demonstrate the power of space tools in garnering important data about space and about Earth.

The discovery of the Van Allen Radiation Belts, in which both satellites and deep space probes were used, stands as one of the great discoveries in the history of geophysics. The achievement entails not only the discovery of two vast regions of space and of the particle population of these regions but also provides the basis for a unified description of variations of the Earth's magnetic field, the aurora, and solar particles in a much more realistic and exciting way.

The inner Van Allen Belt was first publicly reported on May 1, 1958, at the National Academy of Sciences in Washington, based on measurements aboard the early Explorer satellites. The Van Allen particles appear above 120 km in northern latitudes and 360 km above the equator and extend over the equator out to about 4000 km. Stoermer's theoretical studies postulated long ago that charged particles could be trapped in the Earth's field and forced to spiral between northern and southern mirror points. But without experiment, the applicability of Stoermer's calculations could not be assessed. Now we find that over a period of time, the number of captured particles can increase appreciably, accounting for the formation of a Van Allen Belt. It is probable that at least some of the Van Allen particles in the inner belt arise from beta decay of cosmic ray neutrons.

Van Allen and his colleagues obtained further striking results from space probes Pioneer III and IV: the second Van Allen Belt was discovered to range from 10,000 to 60,000 km beyond the Earth's surface. The structure and composition of this outer zone are not clear. Solar disturbances appear to play a role. Plasma clouds from the Sun, bearing protons and electrons, reach the vicinity of the Earth and interact with its magnetic field. Particles from the outer zone are released by this interaction into the atmosphere, and this is followed by an increase in the number of electrons (of energy 10 kev or higher) within the outer zone.

The energy has its source in the kinetic energy of the plasma cloud: how the energy is transferred remains unknown, and much further research is called for before the nature of the structure and composition of the outer Van Allen Belt can be satisfactorily established. Yet the existence of the belts and that which is known about their properties are of fundamental significance: first, because a major feature of near space has been discovered and its general nature outlined and, second, because the belts suggest the prospect of an integrating concept of a variety of geophysical phenomena and processes.

The second great achievement made possible by IGY satellites relates to the shape of Earth. Here the first small Vanguard satellite has permitted O'Keefe and his associates to make detailed studies of its orbits. Their findings resulted in the postulation of a "pear-shaped" model of the Earth. The apparent variation from the previous theoretical model is small even in comparison to the 21 km difference between equatorial and polar radii, but it is extremely important in terms of the Earth's structure and surface loading. Moreover, this initial study points out the scientific value of satellites in studying the solid Earth itself because eventual checks on surface distortion may have a profound effect on theories of isostasy and of internal structure and mass distribution.

Satellites of both the U.S.S.R. and the United States also provided valuable data on drag and density and on satellite environmental conditions—e.g., temperatures. Soviet satellites, with transmissions at 20 and 40 megacycles, afford an opportunity for ionospheric studies when the receptions can be coupled with precise positional data. One of the most striking findings in the field of near-space structure relates to drag. Jacchia has established a correlation between the drag on a satellite and solar activity: the correlation between Vanguard I drag and (a) solar flux index at 10.7 cm wavelengths and (b) magnetic activity index is remarkable.

The fourth advance is concerned with meteorology. Rocket photography had some years ago revealed cloud cover over thousands of square miles and had betrayed the birth of a major storm in the structure of cloud patterns—a storm unsuspected from ground observations. Two IGY satellites were devoted to meteorological problems: one to a scan of clouds, the other to measurements of the Earth's radiation balance. With the launching of TIROS I, however, the great potential of meteorological satellites was demonstrated. The striking photographic coverage, over vast expanses and about the Earth, provide data for research as well as information for storm warning purposes. A major initial step in applying satellite tools to problems of meteorology has been taken in this venture.

These examples make meaningful the argument that spacecraft are powerful tools of research. The dominant features of artificial Earth satellites as tools for research are three in number.

First, their sensors can *look down* at the Earth and at what lies between. The photography of cloud cover is a most vivid illustration, but even in meteorology one can look forward to devices yet undeveloped that may measure altitude-dependent parameters. Another example relates to their geodetic utility. Tied to Earth, satellites are in the grip of the Earth's gravitational field, and careful determinations of their orbital perturbations betray variations in the gravitational field, providing new insights into the shape and structure of the Earth.

Second, satellites about the Earth can *look around* and sample their immediate environment. Properly instrumented they can measure particles, radiations, and fields about them. Done systematically this yields a mapping of all such events in the ellipsoidal shell about the Earth form ing the satellite's orbital envelope and, sustained over appreciable periods of time, provides the temporal variation of local events. Thus, "look around" means *in situ* measurements and controlled experiments as a function of space and time. Again the difference between observation and experiment is pertinent, for observation generally includes a confusing complex of unwanted variables that mask the sought-after quantity while sound experiments can be simple and critical, directed to searching out what the experimenter is after specifically.

Third, artificial satellites can *look out* into space, their sensors examining the Moon, the Sun, and other stars, intercepting radiations and particles. It is this attribute which commends satellite vehicles for astronomical observations, beyond the refracting, reflecting, and absorbing blanket of air—provided that less difficult approaches (e.g. balloons and sounding rockets) have been exhausted.

Given these qualities of an artificial Earth satellite, one can readily extrapolate along two lines as to the uses of other types of spacecraft. First, the utility of *space probes* lies primarily in their ability to measure phenomena in their own vicinity over extended trajectories far away from Earth. Space probes provide the only tool we know for direct measurements of the particles, radiations, and electromagnetic fields in the interplanetary medium and in the fantastic space beyond our solar system which these vehicles may some day reach. They also provide a means for better views of other bodies in the solar system—the Moon and the planets—by passing near them. Second, the utility of satellites about the Moon and planets is comparable to that summarized for Earth satellites. Of particular value is the detailed information that could be secured by such satellites about the atmospheres of the planets, about their gross surface features where photographable, and about their gravitational and magnetic fields. Finally, spacecraft that can land on the Moon and the other planets would permit a vast increase in the acquisition of scientific data. Initially such craft can be expected to deliver instrumented complexes whose findings would be radioed back to Earth. Ultimately manned ventures may be undertaken.

3. SPACE VEHICLES

The availability of enough reliable vehicles with varying payload capacities and ranges is an obvious prerequisite to the study of space. The vehicular program of the National Aeronautics and Space Administration—past, present, and future—embraces 13 systems: Vanguard, Juno II, Scout, Thor-Able, Delta, Thor-Agena B, Redstone, Atlas, Atlas-Able, Atlas-Agena B, Centaur, Saturn, and Nova.[1] Eight of these systems are of current interest, and Table 5 presents some of their characteristics. Of these, in turn, six are of greatest interest because they represent the likely systems that will be used for some years by NASA: Scout, Thor-Agena B, Atlas, Atlas-Agena B, Centaur, and Saturn.[2]

The intent of NASA, in its concentration on a few space systems, is to develop an economical family of reliable carriers having among its members sufficient flexibility for a variety of objectives, from those relating to artificial Earth satellites to those relating to heavy-payload planetary investigations. The rule which NASA has imposed upon itself is: "Reduce to a minimum the number of different types of vehicles and components that are developed and thereby increase the frequency with which those that remain are used."[3] The application of this rule to current and coming vehicular needs has led NASA to undertake launch vehicle development in five categories.[4]

Category I. Scout is the system which now meets the requirements of this class. A four-stage solid-propellant vehicle, the Scout was first test-launched on July 1, 1960. Its utility is largely twofold. It can serve a variety of research needs as an Earth-satellite carrier; in this application it can put some 60 kg into an orbit of about 500 km. For near-space probe purposes, the Scout will be able to serve as a high sounding rocket with maximum range of some 6500 km. It is relatively low in cost: production and launching costs are expected to be about one million dollars per firing.

Category II. The vehicle desired here is one of substantially more weight capacity than Scout but less than Centaur. It would serve for heavier Earth-satellite purposes (some 600 kg in a 500-km orbit) and in space-probe applications. Its characteristics will probably be somewhat similar to the Thor-Agena B (see Table 5). Pending the development of the new vehicle, the eight Thor-Agena B's and the Atlas Agena B will fill this gap. The latter is a two-stage vehicle, liquid-propelled, and its capacity ranges from close to 2400 kg in a 500-km Earth orbit to about 300 kg for lunar-probe applications.

Category III. The Atlas-boosted Centaur fills the propulsion needs in this category and provides greater capability than any other vehicle now based on the Atlas booster. This is achieved by the new hydrogen-oxygen–propelled second stage, which was under developmental testing in the latter half of 1960. Centaur is designed to place 3500 kg in a 500-km Earth orbit, lesser payload beyond this; as a planetary probe it is expected to have a payload capacity of close to 600 kg. Aside from its Earth-satellite utility and its uses in lunar and planetary studies, this Centaur could launch a heavy communications satellite into a 24-hour orbit.

Category IV. This system is conceived of as a family of vehicles generically called Saturn. Only the first is "at present under active development," and an operational prototype is scheduled for 1964. Designated the Saturn C-1, it is a three-stage vehicle and, like the whole family, uses chemical propellants. The first stage consists of eight engines and nine tanks in a cluster, the second of four Centaur engines fed from a single tank, the third of a single Centaur. The C-1 is expected to have an approximate payload of 8000 kg in low orbits about the Earth, of 2400 kg at escape velocity, and of 400 to 800 kg for soft landings on the Moon. Plans are underway for subsequent members of the Saturn family.

Category V. The Nova system is an approach to the heavy payload problem—e.g., some 120,000 kg in a 500-km orbit, 24,000 kg in a 24-hour orbit, and 40,000 kg for a lunar probe. This approach is one of three possible: (a) refueling of rockets in space, using later versions of Saturn, (b) direct flight from the Earth using chemical rockets, and (c) use of nuclear engines in upper stages. Nova is an approach of the second kind—with possibly a cluster of six 600,000-kg thrust engines making up the first of four stages. Nova, or its equivalent, is not likely to be realized until late in this decade.

The vehicular program of NASA, outlined above, is significant for many reasons but particularly for the following two:

a. These developments will be technologically significant in themselves. They will represent engineering and industrial activity of billions of dollars. They will produce remarkably powerful rocket engines of several types. The attendant vehicular and component applied research and developmental efforts will have values beyond those pertaining to rocket engines.

b. These developments open up vast opportunities in the investigation of space. The very existence of powerful, high-load systems in the near future raises serious problems as to their full and best utilization by science and technology. To grasp this, it is necessary to look at only a few specifics.

First, a total of 260 launchings are contemplated in the 1960s, an average of better than two launchings per month. Of these, 62 are vehicle test launchings, 41 for man-in-space efforts, 28 for such applications as meteorology and communications, 33 for lunar and planetary investigations, and 96 for research satellites.

Second, in 1958 and 1959 the weight of our satellites in 500-km Earth orbits increased from 4 to 60 kg. By 1967 this will have increased to more than 20,000 kg. By 1970 the clustering of engines may provide some 6,000,000 kg of initial thrust: this means that between 1970 and 1975 space payloads may range some 100,000 to 160,000 kg. To visualize this we may think of the Boeing 707 as our unit: two of these units are represented by the maximum estimate of 160,000 kg.

A vehicular program of the above scope represents a major national effort. NASA's budget is close to one billion dollars for the pursuit of exploration, application, and research; Department of Defense space ventures account for somewhat more than one billion; and the probability that these annual expenditures will rise by appreciable fractions over the next ten years raises legitimate budgetary and policy questions. Prudence dictates that such large sums yield commensurable results. Yet a totally rational approach is most difficult, for the bulk of such expenditures relates to vehicle systems and man in space: here competition for technological leadership in a prestige- and publicity-ridden arena is involved.

The vehicular needs of science and application are susceptible to a simpler approach. These needs, in terms of numbers of vehicles, are approximated in the NASA program for the decade of the 1960s. The payload requirements now appear to be adequately accounted for in the provision of four classes of vehicles, ranging in capacity from small to heavy payloads: (*a*) the Scout, (*b*) the Atlas-Agena B and Centaur, (*c*) the Saturn, and (*d*) Nova. However, for both science and its applications, the crucial considerations relate to reliability and continued availability. Where reliability has not been attained, back-up vehicles are called for in numbers sufficient to assure the flight of experiments. Failure to pursue this course not only means that important work will not be done but that the energies of creative scientists will have been wasted. The latter, in turn, can only lead to frustration and withdrawal of the best minds now engaged in space research and to difficulty in attracting other able scientists, particularly at universities, not now participating but capable of doing so and needed for progress in coming years.

Moreover, launching vehicles of varying payload capacities will be needed for a long time. This means that a successful, reliable vehicle should not be shelved in the expectation of the development of an advanced system. An orderly scientific program cannot be conducted if the unreliability associated with new vehicles is perpetually present. Moreover, prudence dictates that the size of the vehicle should be matched to the job to be done.

4. APPLICATION

Of the three self-evident applications of Earth satellites, the one of greatest interest to the practical man, concerned with economics, is communications. In principle, satellites can multiply the quantity of long distance communications by a factor of perhaps 10,000. The ionosphere provides a band of about 20 Mc: a single satellite may eventually provide a band 100 times wider.

The types of communications that satellites can contribute to are many: telephony, long-range radio communications, and even international TV. An expansion of such services has numerous implications. A major industrial expansion of the communications and electronic industries is one. Quite aside from the meaning of expanded services domestically, the international impact appears potentially very large, providing a unique opportunity for leadership through the satisfaction of genuine, growing needs.

Telephony can serve as an example. According to the American Telephone and Telegraph Company: "Of the roughly three billion people in the world, only 180 million, or six per cent, live in the United States. Yet, at present, the United States, exclusive of Alaska and Hawaii, has 55 per cent of the world's telephones. The telephones outside the United States are rapidly increasing in number, as indeed are those inside the country. We will necessarily expect a tremendous increase in telephones abroad as the 94 per cent of the world's people outside of the United States becomes more industrialized. In addition to talking with many of these people by telephone, we will need to communicate with them by transmitting and receiving data and other business communications, and by means of television."[5]

During the last 40 years, the population of the United States has increased about 60 per cent; the number of telephones has increased by some 500 per cent. In about the same period, the population of the world has also increased by about 60 per cent; the number of telephones outside the United States has increased almost 800 per cent. The number of domestic conversations rose from 17 to almost 88 billion; in the same 40-year period the long-distance messages handled by A.T.&T. rose from 16 to 532 millions, an increase of more than 3000 per cent. These are real trends, and industry is basing its business judgments upon them, extrapolating to future needs as populations grow and as service requirements grow even faster.[6]

The saturation of the conventional radio spectrum precludes recourse to it. Moreover, studies indicate that satellite communication systems are more than competitive. Estimates of the A.T.&T. are germane: " . . . providing basic facilities for 600 telephone circuits from each United States terminal to each European terminal and 600 telephone circuits from Oakland to Hawaii will cost about $50,000,000. This is made up of $30,000,000 for a 30 satellite system and $2,500,000 for each of eight ground stations. The 2400 circuits provided by this plan will cost less than $25,000 per circuit. In comparison, the cost of the latest, most efficient overseas cable now being designed, although less than that for the cables now in service, will still be substantially more per circuit than the indicated cost for satellite communication.

"If television is added to this initial network, the cost of satellites will increase to about $60,000,000 and each ground station will cost about $2,700,000. The total cost, therefore, of providing the basic facilities for television and message service between each of the four pairs of terminals will be about $82,000,000.

"This plan indicates that large cross sections of intercontinental circuits can be provided much more economically than with cable. Satellite communications will also provide transoceanic wide-band television which we cannot obtain today and will provide a most valuable facility for circuit diversity. The advantage of circuit diversity should not be underestimated. In all forms of communication, experience has shown that reliability is best obtained by having more than one route. Satellites will provide this added facility to complement the cable network."[7]

The second application of broad interest has to do with meteorology, discussed in some detail in Chapter 6. The prospect of detecting major storms early in their history and of following them has large human values. Thousands of lives are taken annually by the caprices of weather, and the loss of property and misdirection of effort runs into hundreds of millions. Weather satellites, coupled with international warning services, could provide alerts so that human beings might take suitable protective measures or estimate their actions more suitably. Ultimately, further research with storm and cloud cover data from satellites and related meteorological studies, both experimental and theoretical, may lead to a genuine understanding of weather and climate, to vastly more effective forecasting services, and perhaps to an amelioration by man himself of the destructive energies of major storms.

The third area of application concerns the science of geodesy, the subject of Chapter 5. Geodetic satellites can serve both research and application interests. As to the latter, navigation and surveying come closest to the immediate interests of mankind. In principle, satellite navigational systems could become common, universal methods for all forms of surface and air navigation, with accuracies even exceeding requirements. They could also be used for surveying over difficult terrain and for tying together most effectively the geodetic nets throughout the world. Except for research navigation over the seas (for example, leading oceanographers argue that a satellite system is essential for oceanographic surveys over the waters in and near the Indian Ocean), geodetic applications do not appear to have the urgency of communications and weather forecasting: work on them may thus probably be reasonably pursued as part of broader programs.

Taken as a whole, the significance of satellite applications appears as follows:

1. They are attainable in the near future at reasonable cost.

2. The commercial value of applications in just the communications area will probably not only be self-liquidating but may provide revenue, directly and indirectly, for all prudent space activities relating to applications and to fundamental research.

3. Their successful achievement represents significant national contributions to the public welfare, at home and abroad. Leadership in these areas appears most meaningful internationally.

In addition, the area of military applications must be noted even though this volume is concerned with civilian aspects of space. Quite clearly space developments in communications, weather forecasting, and navigation are of operational interest to the military services. In these areas the military represent another set of users of the results of research and development whose applications are general. In other areas there are far more specific military interests—for example, in observational and early-warning satellites. To ignore such potential applications of space vehicles in a world of antagonistic powers is unrealistic: if reconnaissance and warning satellites are feasible, they will be developed by nations having the capability and need. History shows that the major powers have not refrained from exploiting the applications of science and engineering, from the crossbow to atom-bomb-tipped guided missiles.

Finally, the applied research and development associated with vehicle systems themselves will have applications in other areas, aside from their utility in advancing the art of rocketry. The chemistry of fuels, the development of high-temperature alloys and ceramics, the design of guidance and control systems—these and similar rocketry efforts will have value, sooner or later, in industrial technology. There is even the possibility that some day rocket systems themselves might prove useful in some form for commercial purposes.

5. THE EXPLORATION OF SPACE BY MAN

Three kinds of manned space ventures may be considered: orbital flight about the Earth, travel through the interplanetary medium, and exploration of the Moon and the planets.

It is not likely that man can contribute much if anything to knowledge or application either by simple orbiting about the Earth or mere travel through the interplanetary medium. It is most probable that instruments can do all that is necessary. Such instrumented payloads will be much lighter than those required for man and cost vastly less. Any argument that man might contribute in some way—e.g., repair or maintenance—must demonstrate that automation and redundancy of instruments cannot do at far less cost what the inclusion of man entails.

Nevertheless, man in orbit is worth pursuing for several reasons. First and above all, the ultimate exploration of Moon and planets will be done by man. This means that experience must be gained, step by step, and the orbiting of man is the first of this long sequence of steps. Second, auxiliary devices crucial to manned spacecraft will prove useful in other programs. Third, some time in the future men on orbiting scientific laboratories may prove to be useful in connection with stabilization and orientation problems and in altering scientific programs. Fourth, the knowledge and experience gained from man-in-orbit efforts may turn out to have applications, direct or indirect, in travel and transport between points on the Earth.

The significant and exciting role of man lies in the exploration of the Moon and planets. We can speculate on the prospects for planetary exploration by man in the relatively near future by considering the system that might initially take him to, say, Mars. This system, noted earlier, provides for a maximum payload of some 160,000 kg; if its development is pursued with reasonable vigor, perhaps the venture may be possible in the 1970s, but the cost of a single venture will be some hundreds of millions of dollars.

Of the 160,000-kg payload, at least one quarter will be needed for the fuel system and fuel to permit landing on the planet. One half of the payload will be used for the return rocket system. Most of the remaining quarter will be used for food, water, and oxygen to sustain some two to four men (and these provisions probably must be enough to last for a number of months if the costs are to be justified); for auxiliary equipment, including radiation shielding, electric power supply, and radio trans-mitters; and, finally, for scientific equipment with which to tackle the problems of exploration of the planet.

The critical question is this: what might be done by automation and remote control? In both the manned and unmanned cases, about 40,000 kg of the total payload will be used in landing. But the unmanned system has available about 120,000 kg for automatic instrumentation, including transmitters for radioing back findings, because it need not return. In contrast, the manned craft can devote only a fraction of some 40,000 kg to instrumentation. No proper answer can be given to the question until suitable studies are made and the concerted development of automatic equipment is undertaken. Following these efforts, it should be possible reasonably to appraise the alternatives. During this neces-sary research period, also, the problems of planetary exploration will be better understood as a result of space probe studies and soft landings of relatively simple instrumental payloads. Yet we can conjecture that ultimately, for detailed exploration of the planets, man will be needed to define the useful range of instrumentation and to direct complicated technical operations.

The success of these prospective ventures of man into space—from orbital flights about the Earth to landings on planets—is far from simple or, at present, assured in spite of the pronouncements of space enthusiasts. Success can come and it will come. When it comes, what failures precede achievement, how high the costs: these depend upon many factors and many decisions.   For example:

1. Development of suitable spacecraft for man.   This is most certain because the progress of engineering and technology is in a sense straightforward and also because of national preoccupation with rocket technology, for and in itself.

2. Solution of the physiological problems.   These include such topics as acceleration, vibration, and ecology.   One could adopt, bearing in mind the development of aviation, a somewhat casual attitude toward these problems, but there is danger that when large vehicles become available in the next decade unwarranted risks will be assumed.

3. Research on the physical environment in space.   This has several aspects, and a few examples may be of interest.   The nature of particles and radiations in space is an obvious one.   Not only the Van Allen Belts but the sporadic ejection of solar protons represent very real although resolvable hazards.   However, we do not yet know as much as we should about the interplanetary medium.   If we turn from man in orbit and man in pure space to man on the planets, clearly the greater advantage that man can take of the planetary environment after landing, the greater his chance of success.   Therefore the more knowledge of this environment, the better.   This knowledge should be acquired as far as possible in advance of ventures, and it should be acquired in the simplest, most economical way: (a) much can be learned of the planets from observatories on Earth and from balloons and rockets and (b) much can be learned from unmanned, instrumented spacecraft—from Earth satellites, from Moon and planetary probes, from satellites orbiting about the Moon and planets, and from soft landings of automatic instruments.

The question of man in space thus hinges on the value of manned exploration of the Moon and planets.   We believe that men and nations place a very high value on satisfying man's curiosity about the unknown, for this is a genuine human and scientific objective.   The pursuit of this endeavor is unparalleled in man's history, its nature is difficult and daring, and it is costly, for before its realization billions will have been expended. Such expenditures raise legitimate questions of several kinds whose resolution calls for intelligent debate.   If a nation proceeds with man in space, there is a responsibility on the part of the government (1) to assess as carefully as possible the costs, (2) to outline the possible schedules that appear as reasonable alternatives, and (3) to admit the hazards.

1. Costs.   We doubt that man-in-space expenditures, from Project Mercury to, say, the successful landing of man on Mars, will be less than

25 billions. This estimate might well be exceeded by two or three times if repeated failures occur.

2. Schedule. The timetable or rate of activity must at least take into account (a) the annual expenditures we wish to devote to this effort and (b) the rate of advance in other areas of space. As to (a), a decision could be made to pursue the program at a much slower tempo, stretching out costs over, say, an added decade. As to (b), it would be foolish to adopt an accelerated program if vehicular reliability cannot be guaranteed, if intermediate steps prior to the availability of large payload vehicles like Saturn are based on sheer competitive motives and do not represent sharply defined and stated steps of progress, or if research by instruments is so insufficiently supported that our knowledge of planetary environments is inadequate to appropriate, conservative planning and design of the manned space system so as to ensure a reasonable chance of man's survival.

3. Hazards. The history of geographic exploration on Earth tells over and over again of the deaths of bold explorers. To ignore this in the far more difficult and hazardous area of man in space is foolish; men will perish in space as they have on the high seas, in Antarctica, in the heart of Africa, and whenever they have ventured into unknown regions.

In view of the magnitude of the effort and its hazards, serious thought should be given to the possibility of an international effort. The head of the astronautics section of the Soviet Central Air Club, in a radio discussion of problems of manned ventures to the planets, observed: " . . . the preparations and performance of such flights will involve huge expenditures. Naturally, if the whole world cooperated not only in the scientific work but in bearing the cost, that would be a big help. In any case we can be sure that the difficulties connected with the mastery of outer space will be overcome much better and sooner if several countries, and especially the U.S.S.R. and United States, pool their material and intellectual resources."[8] The Soviet scientist L. I. Sedov is quoted as saying: "There are so many experiments which are so difficult and so expensive they demand cooperation between several countries."[9]

An international effort would have important values. It would eliminate the essentially absurd question of international planetary claims. It would eliminate a race whose scale is so gigantic as to raise questions of justification on the part of individual nations. It would simplify the problem of protection against possible contamination of the planets and of the Earth. It would have a unifying effect among nations as they worked together in a great effort. If the nations of the world, through their scientists, were able to cooperate in the IGY, whose magnitude approached some one billion dollars all told, they can also undertake in the same way and in the same spirit the conquest of outer space by man.

6. SPACE RESEARCH

The incredible vastness of space and bulk of its content mean that the research prospects before man are infinite. This great scope, however, makes it difficult to categorize the opportunities. Certainly and truistically, two large categories exist: (1) the category of opportunities and problems yet to be disclosed, and (2) the category of currently known ones.

The second category is, by and large, the subject of this volume. Succeeding chapters present the state of man's knowledge in many fields of the most pertinent branches of science. They propose experiments and types of experiments which can profitably be undertaken now and in the near future, based upon a solid foundation of current knowledge—(a) knowledge of some aspects of cosmic phenomena and processes acquired over hundreds of years of experimental and theoretical research conducted on the Earth itself and (b) knowledge more recently acquired by high-altitude balloons, sounding rockets, Earth satellites, and space probes.

These two reservoirs of knowledge permit us to ask a host of intelligent questions, of great scientific significance, whose answers require space research. They also allow us to go beyond the asking of meaningful questions. As the following chapters demonstrate, present knowledge permits us to specify the nature of hundreds of experiments and of their instrumentation. Many of the experiments present essentially minor difficulties in the design and construction of measuring devices; others require appreciable effort although they do not represent instrumental extensions beyond the edge of known principles.

From the future conduct of these experiments will come the clues to questions and specification of problems now unknown: the category of the unknown will step by step become revealed as to the problems and questions of interest and importance. In this way, as throughout the history of science, new opportunities to advance knowledge will unfold.

The more general questions that confront us today, as we attempt to make the best possible use of spacecraft for research, include the following: What are the objectives of science in space research? How shall we tackle these challenges intelligently and economically? These questions can be looked at from several points of view—e.g., in terms of a vehicular capability, or of the classical fields of science and their branches, or of regions of space. Whatever the point of departure, overlapping exists and, because some simplicity is gained, we shall first look at the subject sectorially: Earth and near space, the interplanetary medium, the Moon and the planets, and the Sun and other stars.

Earth and Near Space. Perhaps paradoxically at first glance, the solid Earth itself can be studied by instrumented spacecraft. Satellites circling the Earth are affected by the Earth's gravitational pull, which varies in accord with the Earth's interior composition and structure. Thus it is that artificial Earth satellites, of long duration so that precise determinations can be made of orbital variations, can contribute in a basic way to geodesy on such topics as the size and shape of the Earth, its gravitational field, and its hidden structure. What can be learned about the Earth in this way has a twofold significance: new data of this kind will yield new insights respecting our own planet, but these experiments will also prepare the way for analogous studies of the Moon and other planets.

Between the surface of the Earth and about 30,000 meters above, 99 per cent of the atmosphere is present. This is a zone of paramount interest to the meteorologist, for here are at play the gross forces that make up weather and, ultimately, climate. Only within the last decade have meteorologists been able to probe this region to altitudes of about 20,000 meters using balloons instrumented to measure temperature, pressure, humidity, and winds as they vary with altitude. Only since the start of the IGY have meteorological balloons been available for ascents to some 30,000 meters. Three sets of atmospheric problems confront observational and experimental meteorology:

1. Geographical coverage by sounding balloons even to 20,000 meters is inadequate. Over some land masses, enough data are secured; over other land masses, tools and skills are, for one reason or another, lacking; over the seas almost nothing is done. Useful steps along two lines are called for: first, a better geographic coverage over all of the Earth by balloons and, second, an extension of balloon altitudes to 30,000 meters and higher insofar as feasible.

2. Although the gross forces determining weather are probably at play beneath some 30,000 meters or so, the atmosphere is a continuum, and knowledge of its nature beyond 30,000 meters is of fundamental value to research meteorologists. Here rockets can be productive. A small synoptic rocket chain has recently been established in the United States: its extension domestically and abroad should be pressed. Suitable and standardized measuring devices and simple, inexpensive rockets are called for. Their development, already begun, merits intensification.

3. The application of Earth satellites to cloud-cover photography has

its forecasting justification, but the information is also useful in research. Provided that full analyses are made of these vast bodies of data, much can be learned of the dynamics of the atmosphere. In the application of basic physics, applied mathematics, and electronic computing techniques lie the solutions. Moreover, auxiliary instruments (for example, devices that measure incoming and outgoing energy) yield further fundamental data. Finally, the development of new devices that might look to the Earth from satellites and measure the altitude variation of several meteorological parameters merits investigation.

Beyond the lower atmosphere—from about 50 to 1600 km—stretches the upper atmosphere. Here the attenuated atmosphere under the direct glare of the Sun absorbs the major portion of particles and radiations from the Sun and space. Here lie the ionospheric layers, the zones of auroral displays, the region where primary cosmic rays begin their transformations into secondaries, and that part of the Earth's magnetic field in space most intimately linked to human affairs. Much has been learned of this envelope from ground-based studies, balloons, and rockets. For direct observations of the lower levels of the upper atmosphere, rockets provide the means: balloon technology and costs preclude ascents much beyond 35 km while satellites cannot generally survive long below some 350 km.*

Above some 350 km, satellites in circular and elliptical orbits represent powerful tools for investigating the upper atmosphere. Its composition, its structure, its variability: these are the objects of research into a region that is closely linked to life and activity on Earth. The manifestations of the upper atmosphere embrace such events as the auroral lights, the airglow, the reflection, transmission and absorption of radio waves by the ionosphere, and magnetic storms that often influence communications. The phenomena of interest include the constituents of the attenuated atmosphere itself, such particles as cosmic rays and their impact-produced progeny, visible and invisible radiations from the Sun, and solar particles. Their interplay, often in the grip of the Earth's magnetic field, presents a complex array of questions to the physicist, the chemist, the geophysicist, and the astronomer.

The Interplanetary Medium. As between the lower and upper atmospheres, no sharp line of demarcation exists between the upper atmosphere and the region beyond it which we call "near space," referring

---

* This is, of course, a figure intended to be suggestive of the problem, for satellites with highly elliptical orbits can have perigees considerably below 150 km and last long while even in circular orbits satellites some 60 km above the Earth will have productive lives much longer than that of a sounding rocket.

to space from approximately 600 km above the Earth out to perhaps half the distance to the Moon. Some purpose is served by these terms for we can look at the upper atmosphere as that region close to the Earth characterized by the presence of an appreciable number of atmospheric atoms and molecules in an ionized state—a dynamic state in which ionization and recombination are continuously going on. Beyond this region, we cannot recognize the Earth's atmosphere but the Earth's magnetic field is still powerful enough to establish a zone of influence. Thus the Van Allen Radiation Belts, stretching out some 60,000 km, exist because the Earth's field exists, exercising its influence upon the charged particles present there, arriving from the Sun and cosmos. Beyond this range, the magnetic field of the Earth is lost, enmeshed with fields in space.

The mapping of this vast sector of space near Earth, the identification of particles and radiations, their quantitative measurement and characterization, their study in relationship to the Earth's magnetic field, to fields of other origin, and to solar processes: these searches have only begun. Their proper pursuit calls for satellites and space probes, in generous number but with light payloads, thoughtfully instrumented; and these experiments, based on current estimates of the nature and magnitude of our problems, call for studies over many years—perhaps at least one complete solar cycle of eleven years but probably two or three such cycles. Once we have established the nature of this region and have developed sound theories to account for the phenomena and processes, we can think of restricting our effort to monitoring—systematically checking to see the changes that may occur over long periods.

Beyond the region of near space, where the Earth's magnetic field exerts its influence, we are plunged into the interplanetary medium. Here the interests of science closely parallel those relating to near space: atomic and nuclear particles, electromagnetic radiations, and magnetic fields concern us. Contrary to earlier notions, this space is not empty. Tenuous gases, mostly hydrogen, occupy space at pressures far below those attained in the best "vacuums" produced in the laboratory. It is conjectured that the Sun's corona, enveloping and extending perhaps far beyond the Earth, accounts for the hydrogen. This great volume is also traversed by cosmic rays, those high-energy charged particles whose sources largely lie far beyond the solar system. From time to time, after periods of violent solar activity, the Sun ejects streams of particles (including some of cosmic-ray energies), and these too travel through the interplanetary medium, often reaching the Earth's upper atmosphere. Magnetic fields in space await exploration: some, transient in nature, are

created by streams of particles, for charged particles in motion constitute
an electric current which induces its own magnetic field.

Interest in the interplanetary medium has several purposes, quite aside
from the quest for sheer knowledge. For example, knowledge of events
in this expanse of space will shed light on events in near space and the
upper atmosphere. It will afford a basis for coping with difficulties in
exploring, whether by instruments or by man, the interplanetary medium
and its content in greater detail and over extended range in the next
decade and beyond. It will afford a basis for surer extrapolations from
our increased knowledge of the solar system to other, similar systems
elsewhere in our and other galaxies. These general objectives and those
somewhat more specific noted in the preceding paragraph can be attained
with spacecraft of modest payloads: (a) satellites in large or very elongated orbits and (b) space probes, launched in predetermined sequences
and patterns adequately to sample the breadth of the interplanetary
medium.

The Moon and the Planets. Within this decade automated instruments will land on the Moon and some of the planets. During the next
decade it may be possible for man himself to reach one of these bodies.
Why is science concerned with these bodies? The planets of the solar
system are part of a whole—in their origins, in their present states, and
in their futures. For the first time in history, man has it within his power
soon to investigate these other bodies, and what he learns will be a significant addition to man's total knowledge. Unquestionably the possibility
that some form of living matter exists on another planet is the most exciting prospect: the origin of life under radically different conditions of
environment and ecology is a subject of unprecedented significance to
fundamental biology. As to this, Mars is the most exciting by virtue of
its astronomically known character, which suggests the possibility of
some form of living matter.

The Moon is an appropriate object of study because it is tied to the
Earth, in origin and history. Yet its surface layers have not weathered
as have those of the Earth, and in them lie clues both to its and to the
Earth's early history and development. Even on the Moon, the remote
possibility of some form of life cannot be ignored completely. Although
the surface is uncongenial, with temperatures of 100°C on the side facing
the Sun and −125°C on the dark side, and unprotected by an atmosphere
from high-energy particles and the full spectrum of solar radiations, simple forms of life may exist beneath the surface or in cavities. Biologists
are much interested in this possibility, an interest that argues strongly
for a policy of protection against contamination of even the Moon.

The types of problems and questions relating to the physical characteristics of the Moon can be classified by the various space approaches possible: observations from satellite orbiting about the Moon, from instruments on hard and soft landings, from samples returned by automated rocketry systems, and from manned landings. Thus lunar satellites could carry devices to detect the presence of potassium, uranium, and thorium; mass spectrometers could determine the composition of the very tenuous lunar atmosphere (estimated at less than 10^{-6} g/cc); and the mass and mass distribution can be calculated from the orbital constants of the satellite.

Soft landings of instruments would permit the taking of photographs of surface details; the televised pictures should shed light on whether the surface material was produced by solidification from a melt or by consolidation of conglomerates. X-ray analyses of the surface, hardness tests, detection of any magnetic substances, spectroscopic analyses of rocks, seismic and gravimetric determinations: such studies appear feasible by instruments landed softly on the Moon, automatically measuring the desired quantities and sending their records to Earth by radio. If the return of an automated rocket system becomes feasible, a variety of specimens should be accumulated: samplings of different surfaces, corings, and lunar dust would be invaluable for terrestrial analyses. The eventual landing of man on the Moon would open up the Moon to that kind of scientific exploration which has been carried out on Earth.

The more distant planets pose problems for exploration which lie far in the future. Mars and Venus, however, are accessible by spacecraft, in one way or another, within this decade. The compositions, depth, densities, and temperature distribution of their atmospheres can be studied by space probes and planetary satellites. An artificial satellite orbiting about Venus would permit the conduct of such important experiments as a study of the composition of the clouds of Venus, determination of its mass and mass distribution, measurement of the spectrum of its dark side, photography at various wavelengths, and such physical measurements as those associated with magnetic fields and charged particles. Similar experiments should be conducted aboard a Martian satellite. Both planets should be investigated for the presence of living organisms, but especially Mars. TV observations from a planetary satellite may yield some information as to this, but more promising and detailed examinations are possible when automatic instruments can be soft-landed. Hard, soft, and ultimately manned landings: each approach will extend the range of possibilities in the study of these planets, analogous to the lunar prospects.

In brief, the kinds of observations that are of the highest significance are those that shed light on the nature, origin, and evolution of the planetary system and of life within it. The Moon, Mars, and Venus are now on the verge of meaningful accessibility by space tools, and eventually it should be possible to turn also to the other planets.

The Sun and the Stars. Interest in the Sun is obvious: from it stem life and activity on Earth, dependent upon solar energy from primordial times. Light and heat are but a small portion of the full range of radiations and particles ejected by the Sun, many of which reach at least the higher zones of the Earth's atmosphere. Interest in the Sun is thus strongly motivated by interest in the Earth in an immediate sense but it is also motivated by the fact that the Sun is our nearest star, an average star whose study is relevant to our notions of other stars.

From Galileo until the closing years of the nineteenth century solar astronomy was largely observational, statistical, and descriptive. Spectroscopy and atomic theory have led to major advances during the last 80 years, providing quantitative knowledge of many aspects of the Sun, but much remains to be done. For example, the whole range of solar short-wave radiation—ultraviolet, X rays, and gamma rays—calls for measurements from beyond the interfering layers of the Earth's atmosphere: line spectra to the shortest possible wavelength and greatest resolution, measurements of radiation intensity for the entire run of spectral bands from X-ray to radio frequencies, profiles of intense lines such as Lyman-alpha and their variation from center to brink, X-ray intensity measurements from flares and other sources. The extreme short-wave radiations originate in high-temperature solar processes about which we know practically nothing. Moreover, in contrast to the better-known aspects of the Sun—light and heat radiation, which are thought to be quite steady—the high-frequency radiations are extremely variable on a short time scale.

Balloons and rockets can provide some of these data, as they have already done to a limited extent, and these tools should be used more extensively because they are relatively inexpensive. Space probes can also be useful—not so much because our problems require proximity to the Sun but because the mapping, say, of unusually intense solar corpuscular streams requires observation and experiment posts other than the Earth itself or an Earth satellite. Thus a probe, either in or out of the equatorial plane, but some distance away from the Earth, would allow us to track a solar corpuscular stream.

When, however, time and space variations are important, satellites and space probes are called for. For example, it is most important that several otherwise invisible solar parameters be monitored systematically, and satellites afford the means. For only thus can we continuously observe and measure the Sun's radiation across important spectra, invisible from Earth, that may provide totally new insights as to the Sun's behavior, variations, and activity.

As with the Sun, so too with all stars: until recent years astronomy has been limited to that information transmitted by light radiation. With the development of powerful telescopes like that of Mount Palomar and of theory, during this century, enormous progress has been made in our concepts of the universe. Radio astronomy has appreciably extended the range of the electromagnetic spectrum available to Earth-bound astronomy. Now space tools afford a further extension which will permit us to measure and study events in that part of the spectrum invisible on Earth, accessible only above the Earth's atmosphere.

Invisible short-wave radiations can tell us much about the high-energy processes in stars and of the influence of very hot stars on interstellar gas around them. For by measuring the absorption of stellar ultraviolet radiation, it should be possible to deduce the quantity of hydrogen in interstellar space, its location, and its motions. Studies of stellar infrared radiation may turn up the existence of very cool or invisible dark objects like extinct stars and protostars. This prospect is of fundamental interest to cosmology for it deals with the total amount of matter in the universe. Very-low-frequency radio waves, undetectable below the ionosphere, may also alter current astronomical theories. These waves are nonthermal in origin, come from the agitation of plasma, and betray the motion of these aggregates of charged particles. The aggregates range from small ones like the Crab Nebula, some 10 light years across, to the gaseous filling of an entire galaxy, some 100,000 light years in diameter. What energy mechanism drives the plasma? Where does it come from? What happens to it? The answers to such questions, with which the study of these very-low-frequency radio waves is concerned, may shed light on theories of star creation.

7. THE CONSERVATIVE ROLE OF RESEARCH

Research underlies every area of meaningful space activity: (a) The pursuit of new insights into the universe is research. (b) The exploration of the planets makes sense only if that exploration, whether by man or by instruments, is a scientific one. (c) The applications of science now within reach are based upon past research and are linked to current and future research.   Accordingly, efforts in space should be oriented critically to substantive objectives.

The difficulty in a logical analysis of the over-all space program stems in large measure from the following: even if science and application were in no way involved in space, the adventure of space would lead men to space flight.   The early voyages of discovery can serve as useful analogies. These voyages fulfilled the need for adventure, glory, and personal and national aggrandizement.   In similar fashion, manned adventure in space would fulfill the same objectives, and even the most unsystematic and ill-directed efforts would yield some new knowledge.

Experience has shown that the scientific approach maximizes the rate of acquisition of new knowledge and minimizes the chance of error.   If space endeavors were cheap, one could be tolerant of the ancient attitude. But they are enormously costly, and therefore every effort must be made to reduce hazards and errors and to increase the quantity and quality of results.

It is in this sense that research—which by its very nature is revolutionary—serves as a conservative force.   One expects the end results of scientific attack upon the mysteries of space to be radically new insights into the nature and properties of the universe, and these tend to yield substantial value for expenditures.   But the scientific method is rooted in a concern with substantive objectives, pursued in an orderly, logical manner and sequence: this is an essentially conservative approach.

Economically and intelligently to maximize the results of our space effort requires that primary attention be transferred from hardware and launchings to the real objectives of space activity.   To this end three considerations are relevant.

First, emphasis should be placed upon the conduct of important experiments in space.   Support of specific experiments must therefore be adequate and timely.

The vast impetus involved in the development and launching of space vehicles carries great momentum—a momentum directed to system exploits.   This means that vehicles command primary interests, and only secondary attention can be given to experiments.   If a meaningful payload is not available, any package conveniently at hand will be used. So comes into being a disease, known in science as "projectitis," characterized by a cancerous encroachment of technology over the sound objectives of space ventures.   When science is ahead of vehicles, the absence of such a large and imaginative research program is not so dangerous. As more vehicles, in number, capacity and reliability, become available in coming years, the danger of "projectitis" becomes real. It is the policy planners and budget formulators who must see to it that a research program is supported so that important experiments are available for flight. In short, vehicles and launchings are *the means, not the ends, of space efforts: research and experiment are the ends and must be determinative.*

Second, a large space effort must be supported by a broad and extensive program of underlying basic research. Economy, good future experiments, and systematic advances in knowledge depend on this.

The variety and quality of experiments in space conducted so far have been excellent. Much of this work has as its basis prior research and experimentation, concerned with the upper atmosphere. There is no guarantee that good experiments will materialize automatically: really worthwhile experiments grow out of broad, continuous research efforts. Moreover, the coming capacity of space vehicles poses real problems as to the availability of enough first-class experiments to justify the very large costs of the rocketry and launching: only a solid, imaginative, basic research effort provides assurance that these vehicles and their opportunities for discovery will be properly capitalized upon, for man's permanent benefit. At least two general areas of research may be cited as illustrative:

1. **Research Relating to Planetary Exploration.** A large program of research directed to the full range of problems associated with the scientific exploration of the Moon and planets is a necessary precursor to the conduct of worthwhile experiments on and near these bodies: this program must not be oriented to payload packages, for it must be basic and back-up in nature. Out of it will develop the ideas, experiments, and devices that will yield the results expected of lunar and planetary launchings.

The problems of lunar and planetary investigations are not simple. Our terrestrial environment conditions the nature of the ideas, experiments, and instruments with which terrestrial problems have been attacked. There is no guarantee that these will succeed, at all or as well, in other environments. Difficult and novel situations will be encountered on other bodies in the solar system. Intelligent formulation and adaptation of terrestrial experimental techniques is called for. Differences in environment may affect techniques; different ranges of phenomena will be encountered; the time available for conduct of planetary experiments will generally be much shorter than that on Earth, and yet the data must be good enough to permit the drawing of at least some conclusions so as to guide subsequent efforts. Thus a whole range of ideas and techniques must be devised for and adapted to new requirements. This requires careful study, the organization of hypotheses, the formulation of experiments, and simulated tests of the instrumentation. All of these steps must be taken long in advance of the preparation of experiments for planetary payloads.

2. Research on or Near the Earth. The problems of space are not restricted in their solutions solely to utilization of costly space systems: ground-based observatories, balloons, or rockets provide a means of investigation into many of these problems. Because these approaches are relatively economical, they should be fully exploited. This calls for a major research effort on Earth in astronomy and geophysics.

Planetary astronomy has not been pursued vigorously during this century. Heightened interest in space and the prospects of planetary vehicles indicate that this area merits support. As much knowledge as possible should be acquired of the Earth's upper atmosphere, interplanetary space, the Sun, and the planets by conventional astronomical and geophysical techniques, by balloons, and by rockets. These approaches not only cost a fraction of space experiments but will lead to (1) fewer requirements for space launchings and (2) improved quality of space work. Examples of the kinds of ground-based investigations are numerous: high resolution studies of the sun and the surfaces of planets, the spectroscopy of planetary atmospheres, composition and structure of meteorites, systematic studies of the cloud cover of Venus, and the shifting caps of Mars, photochemistry of the far ultraviolet, infrared studies in those spectral regions for which absorption in our atmosphere takes place at a fairly low level, extended studies of the surface temperature of Venus by passive radio astronomy, and radar studies of Venus (reflectivity, range, line-of-sight velocity, rotation rate).

Moreover, ground-based, balloon, and rocket studies of the Earth's atmosphere should be intensified. First, because much remains to be done before we shall have mastered the problems of this region. Second, because fuller knowledge of the upper atmosphere through these methods reduces the demand for Earth satellites and will guide investigations of planetary atmospheres by spacecraft.

Researches of the above kinds—experiments in space and both basic and back-up investigations on and near the Earth—are not now receiving adequate support in spite of their relative economy and in spite of their direct relevance to the expensive launchings later in this and throughout the next decade. Both the National Aeronautics and Space Administration (NASA) and the National Science Foundation have authority for supporting back-up and fundamental research, but the problem persists.

NASA is confronted with the pressures and costs of vehicle development and launching: its research emphasis is on flight packages. Yet a broad program of research is mandatory for its objectives. The example of other agencies, dependent upon science and its applications, shows that agencies with specific missions must assume responsibility for the basic research upon which those missions depend and which is long precedent to application.

The National Science Foundation is oriented to grant procedures in the traditional disciplines of the natural sciences, on a competitive basis. Review and selection procedures are not adapted to support of research that may be relevant to space problems. The Foundation's difficulties are essentially administrative and two steps could be of value to it: first, the recognition of space research as a legitimate administrative and budgetary activity; second, the establishment of divisions devoted to the geophysical sciences and space research.

In this way the Foundation would be in a position to assign suitable staff and appropriate funds to fundamental research in two important areas of contemporary activity. The administrative acts themselves would help to resolve some of the problems. Meanwhile the NASA should adopt an imaginative policy for the support of those fundamental studies and back-up research upon which its missions will depend increasingly. The total expenditures for all such research support, it should be noted, are but a fraction of the space effort—a fraction that will determine whether or not space activity is really meaningful and not trivial.

Third, space is so vast, and the problems are so many, that participation should be on as broad a basis as possible. The best creative minds everywhere must be attracted.

Domestically this requires a program based extensively upon participation by universities. The greatest reservoir of creative scientists is to be found in the universities, and it is there that the scientists of succeeding years are trained and tested. The present and future interests of space investigations depend upon attracting these groups. To do so calls for specific policies:

1. Support of space experiments must carry with it assurances of flight. The interest of experimenters cannot be sustained if years of work are vitiated by vehicular unreliability, lack of back-up vehicles, or engineering payload difficulties.

2. Support of research should, in general, be directed to fundamental objectives. It should not be a transaction of purchasing payload

packages. Its essence should be research. Such research will lead to space experiments: then suitable arrangements for flight packaging and launching can be made.

3. Research is characterized by its long-range nature. University support must meet this requirement, for the environment is conducive to continuity of imaginative research, hinging on the nexus between senior scientists and graduate students.

4. Research is not confined to launching capabilities. Its subjects relate the whole gamut of investigations, experimental and theoretical, and range from Earth-bound studies to experimental ideas and developments that may far exceed vehicular capabilities at a given time. Support should be granted imaginatively enough to embrace these aspects of research.

To summarize: In the pursuit of knowledge about the universe, research is understandable. In the area of applications, the connection is intimate: what can be done now in communications, for example, depends upon research of the past; but what might be developed in the future will depend on further research. Moreover, there is a bond between research and technology, and advances in one affect the other. Thus cloud-cover satellites will not only permit the tracking of storms for forecasting but will yield data important to the research analysis of atmospheric dynamics. Ventures by man in space receive their ultimate justification, in the light of current knowledge, because they are linked to exploration of the planets. But exploration is really not exploration without careful recording of significant observations and the conduct of sound experiments.

8. INTERNATIONAL COOPERATION

The opportunities before scientists everywhere are far greater than suspected either by most of these scientists themselves or by their governments. The fact that only two nations in the world are now engaged in the launching of space vehicles appears on the surface restrictive, but this is not fully so.

First, space researches themselves increase the interests in and potentialities of research on Earth. Studies from the Earth itself in a variety of fields can be more profitably pursued. Examples are planetary astronomy, ionospheric physics, aurora and airglow, geomagnetism, and cosmic rays. Investigations in many of these fields have long been underway in many countries: their intensification and expansion is now far more significant in the light of current space interests. Much experimental and theoretical work remains to be done on and near the Earth, and this work is of great intrinsic significance in itself, can valuably augment space experiments, and assumes even greater importance than in the past.

Second, the increased use of balloons and rockets for studies above the masking layers of the atmosphere represents a very large area of activity that merits support by many more nations. Significant discoveries are unavoidable using these techniques, for science has only scratched the surface of our ignorance in terms of a detailed knowledge of the upper atmosphere and of information about the universe that can be acquired by instruments above the denser layers of the atmosphere. Perhaps of particular interest is the use of small rockets for meteorological observations: it is quite likely that such rockets will become standard tools for meteorology within a decade.

Third, much of the data from satellites and space probes can be acquired, either directly or indirectly, by scientists everywhere. These data are suitable for analysis and theoretical research. Much has been done in this area of research by scientists of such nations as England and Japan: much more can be done by scientists elsewhere. As a matter of fact, an increasing number of experiments aboard satellites and space probes can be construed as universal experiments: scientists can receive the telemetered data,* reduce and analyze it, and interpret it just as though the experiment in space had been designed and planned by themselves.

Fourth, experimental ideas and experiments themselves, conceived and developed by scientists elsewhere, have good prospects of realization at least in the space program of the United States. Arrangements have already been made with groups abroad for inclusion of their experiments in future satellites.

Fifth, sooner or later nations other than the United States and the Soviet Union will develop launching capabilities. To this end their prior activity in balloon and rocket launching and in fundamental research will be most useful.

Thus the opportunities before science and mankind for a truly concerted, international space effort are many. Mechanisms are at hand for achieving these ends. Within the scientific community itself, the Committee on Space Research (COSPAR) of the International Council

---

* This requires, of course, (a) knowledge of the transmitted frequencies and the codes and calibrations and (b) continuous transmission, if scientists everywhere can interpret the signals. Some satellite experiments are not conducive to this approach, but enough have been—and the number will grow—to justify the statement above.

of Scientific Unions is already in being and has made appreciable progress, continuing and extending the IGY cooperation in rocket and satellite research.

It is fortunate that the space age was ushered in by the International Geophysical Year,[10] for the IGY engendered a spirit of harmonious cooperation in a period of political tensions. This unprecedented enterprise, sponsored and carried out by the International Council of Scientific Unions, made possible a coordinated assault upon man's ignorance of his planet and its surroundings. It saw some 30,000 scientists, observers, and technicians engaged in studies from pole to pole in thirteen areas. Three of these concerned the solid Earth: seismology, gravity, and longitude and latitude determinations. Three dealt with interface phenomena: oceanography, meteorology, and glaciology. Five investigated aspects of solar-terrestrial relationships and the upper atmosphere: cosmic rays, ionospheric physics, aurora and airglow, geomagnetism and solar activity. Two additional programs utilized new tools to explore the upper atmosphere and near and far space: these were the IGY programs in sounding rocket and satellite research.

The IGY was instrumental in extending sounding rocket research. The program of the United States and probably that of the Soviet Union were intensified during the IGY period. The number of nations engaged in rocket launchings and research increased, from the stimulus of the IGY, from two or three to seven. Moreover, a satellite effort was initiated by the IGY: how this came about is of interest as we look toward further international cooperation.

The International Council of Scientific Unions (ICSU), a nongovernmental organization, is composed of its constituent thirteen subject-matter unions and more than forty adherents (usually academies of science) from as many nations. Of the unions, two were particularly concerned with problems of the upper atmosphere and near space: the International Scientific Radio Union (URSI) and the International Union of Geodesy and Geophysics (IUGG). In 1954, at their general assemblies, first the URSI and then the IUGG adopted resolutions on the subject of satellites. These resolutions were then considered by the Special Committee for the IGY (CSAGI), established by the ICSU for the planning and coordination of the IGY, and the following resolution, in substance essentially like those of URSI and the IUGG, was adopted at the Third General Assembly of CSAGI at Rome on October 4, 1954:

"In view of the great importance of observations, during extended periods of time, of extra-terrestrial radiations and geophysical phenomena in the upper atmosphere, and in view of the advanced state of present rocket techniques, CSAGI recommends that thought be given to the launching of small satellite vehicles, to their scientific instrumentation, and to the new problems associated with satellite experiments, such as power supply, telemetering, and orientation of the vehicle."

Two nations agreed to undertake the responsibility of launching instrumented earth satellites. The United States intention to attempt the launching of an earth satellite in response to the resolutions of the international scientific unions was announced on July 29, 1955. At the Fourth Assembly of the CSAGI at Barcelona on September 11, 1956, the intention of the U.S.S.R. to launch instrumented earth satellites was declared.

The CSAGI Conference on Rockets and Satellites held in Washington from September 30 to October 5, 1957, brought about detailed discussions and plans for satellite research and culminated in the announcement on October 4 of the first successful launching of an instrumented earth satellite by the Soviet Union. This was shortly followed by the launching of Sputnik II by the U.S.S.R. on November 3, 1957, and by the United States with the launching of Explorer I on January 31, 1958, and Vanguard I on March 17, 1958. The complete list of satellites launched up to now is shown in Tables 1-4.

The initial IGY period of eighteen months, from July 1, 1957, to January 1, 1958, was extended for another year under the designation IGC-59 (International Geophysical Cooperation–1959). During this two-and-a-half-year period hundreds of sounding rockets were launched by or from Australia, Canada, France, Japan, the U.S.S.R., the United Kingdom, and the United States. In this same interval 17 scientific satellites and space probes were launched by the U.S.S.R. (6) and the United States (11). In accord with IGY agreements, provisions were made for descriptions of rocket and satellite programs of the various countries, for data interchange, and for publication.

The value of continued, cooperative rocket and satellite research was recognized more than two years before the end of the IGY-IGC program, and resolutions were submitted by the IGY to the International Council of Scientific Unions recommending that suitable means for continuing planning and cooperation be established. In October, 1958, the ICSU established the Committee on Space Research (COSPAR) for this purpose.

The primary purpose of COSPAR is that of providing the world scientific community with the means whereby it may exploit the possibilities of satellites and space probes and exchange the resulting data on a cooperative basis. It accomplishes this objective by working through

Table 1. U.S. Scientific Satellites*

Designation: Popular, Scientific	Launch date; inclination to equator	Telemetry stopped	Initial values			Payload weight (kg)	Experiments
			Apogee (km)	Perigee (km)	Period (min)		
Explorer I 1958 Alpha	31 Jan. 1958 33.34°	28 Feb. 1958	2,532	360	114.8	13.9	Cosmic rays. Micrometeorites. Temperatures.
Vanguard I 1958 Beta	17 Mar. 1958 34.25°	still broadcasting (1 Jan. 1961)	3,948	658	134.29	1.47	Geodetic. Temperatures.
Explorer III 1958 Gamma	26 Mar. 1958 33.37°	10 May 1958	2,810	195	115.87	14.1	Cosmic rays. Micrometeorites. Temperatures.
Explorer IV 1958 Epsilon	26 July 1958 50.29°	19 Sep. 1958	2,221	262	110.27	16.82	Corpuscular radiation at several intensity levels.
Vanguard II 1959 Alpha	17 Feb. 1959 32.88°	15 Mar. 1959	3,322	558	125.85	9.8	Cloud cover.
Explorer VI 1959 Delta	7 Aug. 1959 46.9°	9 Oct. 1959	42,418	251	~750	64	Radiation. Cloud cover. Magnetic field. Micrometeorites. Behavior of radio waves.
Vanguard III 1959 Eta	18 Sep. 1959 33.3°	11 Dec. 1959	3,748	515	130.2	45	Magnetic field. Solar X radiation. Temperatures. Micrometeorites.
Explorer VII 1959 Iota	13 Oct. 1959 50.3°	still broadcasting (1 Jan. 1961)	1,094	550	101.33	41.5	Earth's radiation balance. Heavy primary cosmic rays. Solar ultraviolet and X radiation. Micrometeorites. Cosmic rays and less energetic particles. Lifetime of unprotected solar cell. Temperatures. Ground-based studies of ionosphere.

Table 1. U.S. Scientific Satellites* (Continued)

Designation: Popular, Scientific	Launch date; inclination to equator	Telemetry stopped	Initial values				Payload weight (kg)	Experiments
			Apogee (km)	Perigee (km)	Period (min)			
Tiros I 1960 Beta	1 Apr. 1960 48.327°	17 June 1960	750	690	99.19		122	Photographs of cloud cover.
Sunray 1960 Eta 2	22 June 1960 67.5°	still broad-casting (1 Jan. 1961)	1,057	615	101.5		19	Solar Lyman-alpha and X radiation.
Echo I 1960 Iota	12 Aug. 1960 47.24°	still broad-casting (1 Jan. 1961)	1,688	1,521	118.3		75.9	Passive communications relays.
Explorer VIII 1960 Xi	3 Nov. 1960 49.9°	27 Dec. 1960	2,290	415	112 7		40.89	Ionospheric electron concentration. Positive ion concentration and mass distribution; electron temperature; charge distribution on satellite surface. Frequency, momentum, energy and erosive effects of micrometeorite impacts. Temperatures.
Tiros II 1960 Pi	23 Nov. 1960 48.53°	still broad-casting (1 Jan. 1961)	729	623	98 37		127	Photographs of Earth's cloud cover. Earth's radiation in specific infrared and visible spectral bands.

* In addition to the research satellites listed, other U.S. satellites have been successfully launched: Discoverers I, II, V, VI, VII, VIII, XI, XIII, XIV, XV, XVII, XVIII (recovery of capsule); Transit IB IIA (all-weather global navigation system); Midas II (test of missile-launching detection system); Courier IB (active communications relay); Project Score (transmission of recorded speech).

Table 2. U.S. Scientific Space Probes

Designation: Popular, Scientific*	Launch date and inclination	Maximum distance of radio contact (km)	Flight result	Payload weight (kg)	Experiments
Pioneer I	11 Oct. 1958	112,600	Achieved altitude of 113,800 km.	38.3	Radiation in space. Magnetic fields of Earth and Moon. Density of meteoric matter. Temperatures.
Pioneer III	6 Dec. 1958	102,000	Achieved altitude of 102,320 km.	5.87	Radiation in space.
Pioneer IV	3 March 1959 0.127° to ecliptic	653,000	Entered heliocentric orbit; Perihelion: 147,600,000 km. Aphelion: 173,600,000 km. Period: 406.9 days	6.1	Radiation in space.
Pioneer V 1960 Alpha	11 March 1960 3.35° to ecliptic	36,000,000 (at last radio contact 26 June 1960)	Entered heliocentric orbit: Perihelion: 120,500,000 km. Aphelion: 148,500,000 km. Period: 311.6 days	42.9	High energy radiation. Total radiation flux. Micrometeorites. Magnetic fields in space. Temperatures.

* Space probes were not included in the Greek-letter designation system until 1960.

Table 3. Soviet Satellites

Designation: Popular, Scientific	Launch date; inclination to equator	Radio life	Initial values			Payload weight (kg)	Experiments
			Apogee (km)	Perigee (km)	Period (min)		
Sputnik I 1957 Alpha	4 Oct. 1957 64.3°	23 days	947	228	96.17	83.6	Internal temperatures and pressures.
Sputnik II 1957 Beta	3 Nov. 1957 65.4°	7 days	1,671	225	103.75	508.3	Cosmic rays. Solar ultraviolet and X radiation. Test animal (dog). Temperatures. Pressures.
Sputnik III 1958 Delta	15 May 1958 65.4°	over 16 months	1,880	225	105.95	1,327	Atmospheric pressure and composition. Concentration of positive ions. Satellite's electrical charge. Earth's electrostatic and magnetic field. Solar corpuscular radiation. Cosmic rays. Micrometeorites. Temperatures.
Lunik III 1959 Theta	4 Oct. 1959 80°, just after passing Moon		480,000*	40,000*	15 days	435	Photographs of far side of Moon.
Sputnik IV 1960 Epsilon	15 May 1960 64.9°		368	303	91.1	4,540	Test of life-support systems and re-entry of cabin.
Sputnik V 1960 Lambda	19 Aug. 1960 64°57'		340	306	90.7	4,600	Test of life-support systems and re-entry of cabin.
Sputnik VI 1960 Rho	1 Dec. 1960 64°58'		249	180	88.47	4,563	Tests of life-support systems and re-entry of cabin.

* Varied widely due to perturbations of Moon and Sun.

41

Table 4. Soviet Space Probes

Designation: Popular, Scientific*	Launch date and inclination	Flight result	Payload. weight (kg)	Experiments
Lunik I (Mechta)	January 2, 1959 1° to ecliptic	Entered Heliocentric Orbit: Perihelion: 146,400,000 km. Aphelion: 197,200,000 km. Period: 450 days	1,472	Radiation in space. Magnetic fields of Earth and Moon. Density of meteoric matter. Gas components of interplanetary matter.
Lunik II	Sept. 12, 1959 65° to equator	Impacted Moon at 5:02:24 PM, EDT September 13, 1959	390.2	Magnetic fields of Earth and Moon. Cosmic rays. Meteoric particles. Temperatures and pressures.

* Space probes were not included in the Greek-letter designation system until 1960.

Table 5. Launching Vehicles and their Capabilities

Vehicle	Availability	Approximate payload weights in kg*	
		Into 500 km Earth orbit	To escape Earth's field
Juno II	Now	43	7
Scout	Now	70	(10)
Delta	Now	230	30
Thor-Agena B	Now	725	
Atlas	Now	(About 1000 kg to 200 km for manned orbital flight)	
Atlas-Agena B	1961 (est.)	2300	340
Centaur	1962–63 (est.)	4000	1100
Saturn	1964 (est.)	8600	2300

* Derived from official compilation of launch vehicle characteristics by NASA of 6 October 1960, except figures in parentheses which are independent estimates.

ICSU, its adhering national academies, and its constituent scientific unions. COSPAR was also asked to report to ICSU on measures needed to bring scientists of countries not now actively engaged in space research into the international program. Intergovernmental responsibilities for problems of international control were recognized by asking COSPAR to keep informed on the activities of the UN in this field and to make recommendations to ICSU relative to measures of control that would affect scientific research.

Since its first meeting in London during November, 1958, COSPAR and its executive committee have met several times. In these sessions its charter and procedures have been developed and effective scientific work has been achieved. Annual sounding rocket and space programs of the various nations have been collected, and a COSPAR space bulletin has been initiated. Arrangements have been made for continuing the exchange of information along the lines of the IGY but in a somewhat more complete way, using the rocket and satellite subcenters of the on-going IGY World Data Centers. An annual series of International Rocket Intervals has been successfully established. Special topics have been examined—notably a study of the remarkable geophysical events of July, 1959,[12] the development of reference tables for properties of the upper atmosphere, and the needs of space experimenters for radio frequency allocations (directed to the attention of the International Telecommunications Union).

The First International Space Science Symposium, convened by COSPAR at Nice, January 11–15, 1960, gathered 300 leading scientists from 20 countries. Some 100 papers were presented in sessions devoted to the Earth's atmosphere, the ionosphere, cosmic radiation and interplanetary dust, solar radiation, the Moon and planets, meteorites, and tracking and telemetry. The agenda of a second symposium, meeting in Italy, April 7–18, 1961, included telemetry and data recovery problems, radio and optical tracking, geodetic and ionospheric topics, space biology, magnetic studies by rockets and satellites, the international reference atmosphere, and a further examination of the July, 1959 event and associated phenomena.

COSPAR also provides an important forum for science in other ways. The offer made by the National Academy of Sciences, on behalf of NASA, to launch space experiments of scientists of other nations, was appropriately made within the COSPAR. Progress has been gratifying in the preparation of the first of three United Kingdom instrumented satellites, which will be launched by means of a NASA Scout vehicle beginning about 1962. Canadian scientists are preparing an ionospheric-sounder package for a Thor-Agena B satellite scheduled in 1962. Other joint projects are also under consideration. In a cooperative program with NASA, the Space Committee of Italy has undertaken rocket firings from Sardinia for studies of the high atmosphere by ejected sodium vapor. Similarly, NASA and Australia are considering the joint use of British rockets at Woomera for mapping ultraviolet radiation in the southern skies.

Neither COSPAR nor its IGY predecessor in space arrange for bilateral or multilateral efforts of a specific hardware type. But both have provided harmonious environments for expert discussion and exchange, for indicating needs, and for endorsing international objectives. Thus during the IGY, the United States was assisted by many countries in establishing a score of optical and radio tracking and telemetry stations abroad. This spirit of cooperation has continued and today close to thirty NASA tracking and communications stations are scattered in some twenty regions abroad. More than half of these stations are operated wholly or in part by nationals of the cooperating country. Moreover, scientists from many nations are engaged in space research and technology at laboratories and facilities in the United States.

Thus COSPAR affords a basis for extending the cooperation begun effectively during the IGY and whose pattern may be helpful as space activities grow. To realize fully the opportunities before the world will call for major efforts by COSPAR: the encouragement of scientists everywhere to participate by the information and stimulus that can come from general assemblies similar to the First International Space Science Symposium; the extension and expansion of the activities of COSPAR's three current working groups on scientific experiments, tracking and telemetry, and data and publications; and the formulation and coordination of needed, specific international programs along the lines of the IGY. In these and related ways COSPAR can serve the needs and interests of science and mankind, for international cooperation in space research holds promise both of scientific progress in man's most ambitious venture and of contributions to world amity.

The control of the uses of outer space has been recognized as an intergovernmental problem. Measures to ensure that space shall be used for peaceful purposes have been discussed by major powers and within the United Nations although no agreements have been reached. In December of 1958 the UN established an Ad Hoc Committee on the Peaceful Uses of Outer Space. The Committee was asked to study the role of the UN in this area, to assess existing space activities and organizations, and to consider legal problems. The Committee met in the summer of 1959. Following the submission of its report later that year, the UN General Assembly created a broader successor committee on December 12, 1959, to examine practical means for fostering international cooperation, including the permanent continuation of space research carried out by the IGY, to study legal problems that may arise in space exploration, and to convene in 1960 or 1961 an international congress on peaceful uses of outer space.

Important problems of control and regulation confront the UN and its specialized agencies. The possible military use of space is probably the most important one. The allocation of radio frequencies for space research and applications is another critical subject which the International Telecommunications Union has already taken up and must act upon in the near future (e.g., the Extraordinary Administrative Radio Conference, scheduled for 1963). In preparation for the regulatory conventions, the International Scientific Radio Union of ICSU has organized a special symposium to develop the technical basis for such regulations in the field of communications.

In the area of cooperation, two specialized agencies of the UN are working closely with COSPAR: the World Meteorological Organization, which is studying the application of satellites to forecasting, and the UNESCO, which has broad and general interests in the sciences and which has close liaison relationships with the International Council of Scientific Unions and COSPAR.

But the important steps taken so far must be considered as preliminary in the light of the enormity of the challenge and scope of space. The problems of planetary exploration ahead are many and costly, and they are tied to a host of precedent researches which are in themselves extensive and important. These objectives might best be pursued on an international basis, and the successful pattern of the IGY may be useful in considering how mankind can approach cooperation in space. The principal organizational and administrative characteristics of the IGY were the following:[13]

1. The organization of the research was achieved through national machinery. Consequently, the governments of the world responded favorably to requests by their own scientists and committees for the support of specific activities within their capabilities that were planned and endorsed by the world's scientific leaders.

2. The international planning and coordinating committee was entirely nonpolitical. This was possible because of the essentially nongovernmental, purely scientific nature of ICSU. The IGY committee accordingly stated objectives, planned requirements, and arranged the interchange of data but made no recommendations for work by one nation within the territories of another. Nor did it attempt to pool national resources, which would have created a host of administrative problems. It encouraged bilateral negotiations where cooperation between specific nations was advantageous. Above all, it welcomed participation of all national groups.

3. The planning function was international, and it was necessary that

the planning be financed internationally. UNESCO properly played a leading role in this, particularly in the beginning; when added funds were needed for the operational phase, national contributions by adherents to ICSU (academies of science and research councils) provided an international fund of a grant nature, devoid of any semblance of political control or connotation. The amount of administrative funds was small (some two hundred thousand dollars over a period of about seven years), and it represented a fraction of the hundreds of millions devoted by nations to the effort, catalyzed by this international stimulus.

4. The method was successful in catalyzing extensive research, for the specification of international objectives inspired the desire for participation by national groups everywhere, satisfying a sense of national aspiration. Consequently, research that would otherwise not have been done was accomplished. The scientific exploration of Antarctica by twelve countries is an example.

5. The method captured the imaginations of the world's best research scientists. The planning by scientists of many nations toward a common objective inspired enthusiasms for otherwise unrealizable goals. Creative scientific work of international scope can best be achieved by the world's leading scientists themselves, assessing genuine needs, problems, and opportunities.

No a priori reasons preclude the utilization of this pattern for the exploration of space. During the last decade scientists and nations, with genuine enthusiasm, embraced the IGY program. Tired of war and dissension, men of all nations turned to "Mother Earth" for a common effort on which all found it easy to agree.[14] Now mankind has the vastness of space within its reach, and the opportunities for rewarding international cooperation are multiplied limitlessly. "Those ingenious insights into the real meaning behind a set of observed facts that lead to real advances in the understanding of our universe are not the prerogative of a single nation or group but come from every quarter of the world where men are seriously occupied with scientific research. So vast is the challenge of space research and exploration and so great is the promise to mankind in the way of increased knowledge and ultimate benefits that no nation can afford to neglect or slight the opportunities that lie before it."[15]

Chiseled in the oak above the entrance to the library of Carleton College are the following words of the great Norwegian explorer, Fridtjof Nansen:

The history of the human race is a continuous struggle from darkness toward light. It is therefore of no purpose to discuss the use of knowledge—man wants to know and when he ceases to do so he is no longer man.

In man's brief history, the challenge of cosmic space stands unparalleled. What endeavor in the pursuit of knowledge more compellingly invites the assembly of men and of nations in common creative cause?

REFERENCES

1. NASA-Industry Program Plans Conference (July 28–29, 1960, Washington, D.C.), 36.
2. *Ibid.*, 41.
3. *Ibid.*, 44.
4. *Ibid.*, 43–47.
5. James B. Fisk, Testimony of: *Frequency Needs for Space Communication*, Testimony and Exhibits of American Telephone and Telegraph Co. before the Federal Communications Commission (Docket No. 11866, July 6, 1900, Washington, D.C.), 4.
6. Charles M. Mapes, Testimony of: *Ibid.*, 3–5.
7. Charles M. Mapes, Testimony of: *Ibid.*, 13–14.
8. "U.S. and U.S.S.R. Should Pool Space Efforts," Soviet North American Science in English, Moscow, Jan. 26, 1959, 2300 GMT.
9. United Press dispatch of August 15, 1960, from Stockholm, as cited in the *Baltimore Sun*, August 16, 1960.
10. For the story of the IGY see Sydney Chapman: *IGY: Year of Discovery* (University of Michigan Press, Ann Arbor, 1959). See also Hugh Odishaw and Stanley Ruttenberg (editors): *Geophysics and the IGY* (Proceedings of the Symposium at the Opening of the IGY conducted by the U.S. National Committee for the IGY, National Academy of Sciences, Washington, D.C., June 28–29, 1957), American Geophysical Union Monograph No. 2, Washington, 1958. Many articles deal with the IGY in a general way—e.g., L. V. Berkner: "International Scientific Action: The International Geophysical Year 1057–58," *Science, 119*, 569 (1954); Hugh Odishaw: "International Geophysical Year: A Report on the United States Program," *Science, 127*, 115 (1958); and Hugh Odishaw: "International Geophysical Year," Part I, *Science, 128*, 1599 (1958) and Part II, *Science, 129*, 14 (1959).
11. For a report on the early development of the satellite program in the IGY, see Joseph Kaplan and Hugh Odishaw: "Satellite Program," *Science, 122*, 1003 (1955).
12. *July 1959 Events and Associated Phenomena*, Monograph No. 7, International Union of Geodesy and Geophysics (Paris, 1960).
13. See L. V. Berkner: "International Collaboration in Science," *ICSU Review, 1* (January 1959), and Hugh Odishaw: "The IGY and World Politics," *Journal of International Affairs, XIII* (1959).
14. L. V. Berkner: "International Scientific Action: The International Geophysical Year 1957–58," *Science, 119*, 575 (1954).
15. Hugh L. Dryden: "Future Exploration and Utilization of Outer Space," Seminar on Astronautical Propulsion, Instituto Lombardo, Accademia di Scienze e Lettere, Vienna, Italy (September 9, 1960).

2

RESULTS OF EXPERIMENTS IN SPACE

Bruno Rossi and Robert Jastrow

This chapter presents a brief summary of the scientific results obtained to date[1] in the earth sciences, physics, and astronomy with the aid of artificial satellites and deep-space probes (see Tables 1 to 4 of Chap. 1). Included in this report are a few results obtained with sounding rockets, in so far as they pertain to problems also being investigated with space vehicles. However, no attempt will be made to give equal or extensive coverage to all fields of space science. Also, Russian literature on these problems has not been reviewed as thoroughly as has American literature.

It is, of course, impossible to classify the various problems of space science into sharply defined categories. Broadly speaking, and for the purpose of orientation, one might distinguish four different scientific uses of space vehicles, namely, (1) to explore the environment of the vehicle itself (that is, the particles of various kinds and energies and the magnetic and electric fields present in the distant regions of space that have now become accessible to direct observation), (2) to obtain further information about our own planet by looking at it from above, (3) to study electromagnetic radiation from celestial sources in the spectral regions where the terrestrial atmosphere or ionosphere have heretofore made observations impossible, and (4) to explore the other planets and the Moon.

The first two categories may also be considered in accordance with their contributions to problems of great current interest in the space research program. These are (a) the structure of the earth as a planetary body, and (b) the properties of the atmosphere. The study of atmospheric properties includes the acquisition of basic data on density, temperature, and composition of the thermal population of atmospheric particles and on populations of nonthermal charged particles; the determination of changes in atmospheric structure with time and with location on the surface of the Earth; and the investigation of relationships between solar surface activity and effects in our atmosphere.

The last topic involves the study of the great solar eruptions known as flares, during which the Sun emits clouds of energetic charged particles and radiation into the interplanetary medium. When a solar flare is situated in the right position on the Sun's surface, the particles and radiation travel through the intervening medium to the Earth and interact with its atmosphere. The transfer of energy from the Sun to the Earth through this interaction is only a small part of the energy transferred by radiation in the visible region. In fact, it is less than a millionth part of the total energy transfer in solar radiation. Nonetheless, this small fraction of the total solar-energy transfer produces a number of important effects of great geophysical and practical interest. These effects include communications disturbances, polar ionospheric absorption, magnetic storms, and auroral displays. There has even been some suggestion of a correlation between flare activity and the weather. Flares also produce enormous changes in the intensity of the Van Allen belts, which in some manner as yet not clearly understood are apparently related to other geophysical effects accompanying solar activity. The entire matter of Sun-Earth relationships, including the formation of the Van Allen belts and their possible role in geophysical phenomena, constitutes a relatively new area of research in the geophysical sciences. It is an area which was greatly stimulated by the discovery of the Van Allen belts during the IGY, and an area which is now perhaps the most exciting and fruitful field of research in the present space program. For that reason we shall devote the greater part of our review to the topic of Sun-Earth relationships and the associated observations on energetic particles and atmospheric phenomena, which have been carried out during the IGY and post-IGY periods.

Taking up the above four items in the reverse order, items 4 and 3 can be disposed of briefly because space science has not yet accomplished much in these fields. As to item 4, the U.S.S.R. has carried out the remarkable technological achievement of securing photographs of the back surfaces of the Moon, with the aid of automatic cameras and processing equipment contained in Lunik III.   The U.S.S.R. Academy of Science has published several of these photographs, accompanied by a detailed account of the series of complicated maneuvers which were executed by Lunik III in the course of securing them.[2]   In spite of the blurring of the images, it is still possible to recognize a number of markings resembling the craters and seas that dominate the front face of the Moon.   The most interesting feature is the Soviet Mountain Range, a chain extending 1200 miles across the center of the Moon's hidden face.   The Soviet Mountains resemble the great ranges on the Earth; they do not look like the formations characteristic of the mountains on the front face of the Moon, all of which seem to be crater walls and circular deposits of debris formed by the impact of large meteorites on the lunar surface.

According to our present ideas, terrestrial mountains result from the effects of erosion and the wrinkling of the Earth's crust produced by the slow shrinkage of our planet.   The current opinion is that these mountain-building forces have not been present on the Moon.   The Soviet Mountains may result from the running together of several obscured but independent markings; but we shall have to revise our theories of lunar structure if they continue to appear as a single range in later and more detailed pictures.

Regarding item 3, a start toward astronomy from outer space has been made by means of rockets.   With these devices Friedman, Kupperian, and their collaborators have made important observations of the ultraviolet light from the night sky and of the ultraviolet emission and the X-ray emission from the Sun.[3,4]   To quote one interesting result, they find a strong emission of X rays from the Sun during solar flares.   However, little or no enhancement of the ultraviolet spectrum has been observed at the time of flares, according to measurements made of the intensity of the Lyman-alpha line by Friedman and his collaborators. Several of the Russian and American satellites are equipped with ultraviolet or X-ray detectors, but no results have been available to this date.

Regarding item 2, which includes geodetic measurements, meteorological observations, top sounding of the ionosphere, and the like, observations of the trajectories of artificial satellites have already provided a substantial amount of new and important information on the gravitational field of the Earth and, by implication, on the inner structure of the Earth itself.   The most useful satellite for this purpose has been Vanguard I, launched Mar. 17, 1958, on a 33° orbit, with a perigee height of about 650 km and an apogee height of about 3960 km.   From the observational data on the trajectory of this satellite, it has been possible to determine the first five harmonics of the earth's gravitational field; in this country, the analysis has been carried out mostly by a group of scientists from the National Aeronautics and Space Administration (NASA) and the Smithsonian Astrophysical Observatory.

As is well known, a fluid or plastic earth at rest would acquire a perfectly spherical shape under the influence of its own gravitational field. The Earth rotates with a period of 24 hr, and under the combined influence of the gravitational forces and the centrifugal forces due to its daily rotation, the sphere is flattened into the figure of an oblate spheroid.

The degree of flattening is usually expressed in terms of the fractional difference between the equatorial and polar radii, which is defined as the flattening ratio. Very precise calculations of the flattening ratio have been carried out on the assumption that the Earth has a plastic interior in hydrostatic equilibrium.[5,6] These precise calculations yield a flattening ratio of 1/299.8.

The Vanguard I satellite can also yield a very accurate value for the flattening ratio, independently of the assumption of hydrostatic equilibrium. The satellite measurement of the flattening is derived from the fact that the equatorial bulge of the Earth exerts a torque on the satellite, which causes a precession of the plane of its orbit about the polar axis. The rate of precession of the orbit plane has been measured with particular accuracy in the case of the Vanguard I satellite,[5] and the data on the precession rate for this satellite indicate a flattening ratio of 1/(298.2 ± 0.2).

The discrepancy between the observed value of the flattening and the value obtained on the assumption of hydrostatic equilibrium is substantially greater than the probable errors in the observations and indicates that the interior of the Earth is not in hydrostatic equilibrium. It appears that the Earth is not plastic, but has instead a mechanical strength within its interior sufficiently great to support the stresses at the base of the mantle which must be associated with the departure from the figure of hydrostatic equilibrium. O'Keefe has noted that the mechanical strength required at the base of the mantle to support these stresses is 2×10^7 dynes per cm.

The rate of rotation of the Earth is steadily decreasing as a result of the effects produced by lunar tides. The pull of the Moon on the Earth raises tides in the seas, with amplitudes of many feet, as well as smaller tides in the mantle of the Earth, with amplitudes of a few inches at the Earth's surface. The dissipation of energy in the friction produced by these tidal motions gradually slows down the Earth in its rotation. If other influences on the Earth's rotation are neglected, it will continue to slow down until the time is reached, several billions of years in the future, when the length of day is the same for both Earth and Moon and each

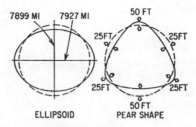

FIG. 1. Shape of the Earth from Vanguard satellite data; the drawing on the left represents the old conception of the spheroidal Earth, with a 28-mile difference between the diameters at the pole and the equator; the figure on the right shows, in exaggerated form, the effect of adding a pear-shaped component to the ellipsoid, as required to fit the Vanguard data; in each drawing the dashed circle represents an equivalent spherical Earth with equal volume. (*From R. Jastrow, Missiles and Rockets*, July 20, 1959.)

keeps an unchanging face toward the other. At that time the length of the day will be about 50 of our current days.

The current rate of change of the length of the day is about 10^{-3} sec per century. From this value we can calculate that the observed value of the flattening, as deduced from the Vanguard I data, would correspond to the figure of hydrostatic equilibrium for a plastic earth some 50 million years ago, when the day was about 23 hr and 30 min in length. Thus it appears that the mantle is sufficiently warm and plastic to respond to the changing stresses associated with the slowing down of the Earth; yet it has enough internal strength to cause the response to lag behind current conditions by about 50 million years.[48]

There are other departures of the geoid from the shape of hydrostatic equilibrium, in addition to the discrepancy in the flattening. These departures, which have also been determined primarily from the analysis of the Vanguard I orbit, include the famous pear-shaped component, or third harmonic in the expansion of the gravitational field (Fig. 1).[7] They also include harmonics of the fourth and fifth order. Higher harmonics than the fifth are lost in the noise level of the orbit determinations, within the accuracy of present tracking systems. The magnitudes of the undulations in the geoid, i.e., the departures from the figure of hydrostatic equilibrium, are shown in Fig. 2 for each harmonic up to the fifth. The variation associated with the discrepancy in the flattening ratio, i.e., the second harmonic, is also shown in Fig. 2. These undulations, which range between tens and hundreds of meters, seem insignificant in com-

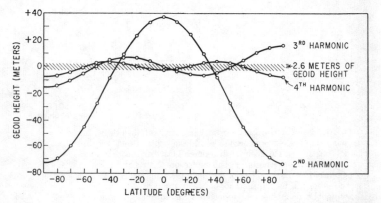

FIG. 2. Effect of second, third, and fourth harmonics on geoid height as referred to a fluid Earth with a flattening of 1/299.8. (*From J. A. O'Keefe, J. Geophys.·Res., 64, 2391, 1959.*)

parison with the radius of the Earth, or even in comparison with the topographic irregularities on the surface.   Nonetheless, they are of very great significance to the student of the Earth's interior because they represent actual variations in the sea level.   The third harmonic, for example, has an amplitude of 17 m at the North Pole, and this means that there is an excess of mass under the North Pole, or some other more complicated variation of the mass distribution in the mantle, sufficient to draw up the level of the sea by 17 m *over an area comparable with the size of the Atlantic Ocean.*   As we have remarked, such variations in the mass distribution probably indicate very large shearing forces in the interior of the Earth.

It is also possible that large-scale convection currents in the mantle are responsible for the undulations of the geoid.   However, the theory of the effects of these currents has never been developed for the case at hand in which the convecting layer contains many scale heights of temperature variation.   Until further theoretical work is done on the problem, the choice between these possibilities must be considered as open.

As a sidelight on the geodetic analysis of satellite orbits, the analysis of the Vanguard I orbit has been refined to such a degree that the very small effects of solar radiation pressure are clearly indicated in the orbital results.   The force exerted by sunlight on Vanguard I is only 3×10^{-7} oz, and yet it has produced an observable change of 2 km per year in the perigee height of the satellite, as Fig. 3 shows.[8]

Two years of tracking observations were required to reveal the effects

of radiation pressure on the Vanguard I orbit, and even at the end of that
time the magnitude of the pressure could be determined with a precision
of only 30 per cent.   The theory of orbital perturbations produced by
radiation pressure, as developed by Musen,[9] constitutes an interesting
addition to the literature of celestial mechanics, and it is fortunate that a
recently launched satellite provides a more accurate means for measuring
the effect of radiation pressure and for comparing the Musen theory with
observation.   This is Echo I, a balloon made of aluminum-coated Mylar
with a thickness of 10^{-3} cm.   It has a diameter of 30 m, a weight of
70.4 kg, and an area-mass ratio of 10 m² per km.   This area-mass ratio is
1000 times greater than typical values for previously launched satellites,
making Echo I a sensitive detector of such small effects as drag and radiation pressure.   The computed variation in the orbit of Echo I produced
by radiation pressure amounts to an initial decrease of 2 km per day in
the perigee height, some 300 times greater than in the case of Vanguard I.
This perigee decrease shortens its lifetime from 20 years to about 1 year.

Figure 4 shows the comparison between the calculated and observed
variations of perigee height for Echo I.[10]   The agreement shown in Fig. 4
confirms the Musen analysis with an accuracy of about 3 per cent.   The
variation shown in Fig. 4 is produced by a momentum transfer whose
integrated magnitude over the entire skin of Echo I amounts to a force
of only 0.02 oz.

Regarding meteorology, the first meteorological satellite, Tiros I, was

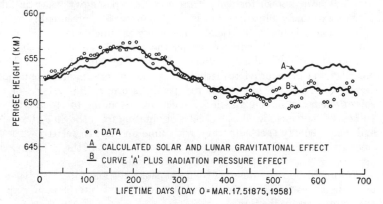

FIG. 3. Effect of solar-radiation pressure on the orbit of
Vanguard I. (*From P. Musen, R. Bryant and A. Bailie, Science,
131*, 935, 1960.)

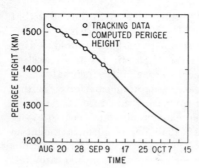

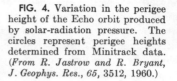

FIG. 4. Variation in the perigee height of the Echo orbit produced by solar-radiation pressure. The circles represent perigee heights determined from Minitrack data. (*From R. Jastrow and R. Bryant, J. Geophys. Res., 65,* 3512, 1960.)

placed in orbit on Apr. 1, 1960, and performed beyond the expectation of its designers until June 17, 1960.   The success of Tiros I led to the launching of Tiros II on Nov. 23, 1960.   This satellite contains videcon systems for securing images of cloud-cover patterns; as in Tiros I.   In addition, Tiros II contains a set of infrared detectors which constitute an important source of weather information and a second major objective of the meteorological satellite system.   The infrared measurements provide the fundamental data required for calculations of the transfer of radiant energy within the atmosphere.   Meteorological aspects are discussed in greater detail in Chap. 6.

The rest of this paper concerns item 1, that is, direct observations of the environment of space vehicles.

It has been known for some time that interplanetary space is filled with an extremely dilute gas that is, for the most part, presumably hydrogen.   It also contains particles with energies much greater than the kinetic energy corresponding to either the thermal agitation or the bulk motion of the individual particles of the interplanetary gas.   These particles will be referred to hereafter by the generic name of energetic particles.   They include cosmic-ray particles originating outside of the solar system and having an energy spectrum extending to at least 10^{18} or 10^{19} ev.   They include, also, particles originating from the Sun whose flux and whose energy spectrum vary with time and are correlated with the solar activity.   Ordinarily, only a very small fraction of the solar particles have energies greater than several hundred Mev.

Presumably, in the inner part of the solar system and at sufficiently large distances from the planets, the conditions of interplanetary space are dominated by the Sun.

Ultraviolet rays from the Sun ionize the interplanetary gas.   Because of its low density and consequent slow rate of recombination, this gas must be practically 100 per cent ionized. It thus must form an almost perfect "plasma," whose behavior is determined by the long-range electric and magnetic interactions rather than by the short-range forces that appear during the collisions between gas particles.

Gravitational attraction by the Sun determines the trajectories of meteorites and micrometeorites. It also must play an important role in the distribution of density of interplanetary gas, at least in the inner part of the solar system. Another factor to be taken into account is solar-radiation pressure. In fact, it has been shown that even the trajectories of artificial satellites are influenced appreciably by it (see Fig. 3).

Presumably, the solar gravitational attraction not only tends to prevent the escape of interplanetary gas into interstellar space, but it also produces an infall of gas from interstellar space toward the Sun. Thus part of the matter in interplanetary space may be of extrasolar origin. Most of it, however, probably originates from the Sun, being ejected in spurts on the occasion of solar eruptions and, perhaps, also continuously through some sort of evaporation processes.

The Sun has a dipole magnetic field, as well as local and much stronger magnetic fields related mainly to sunspots. Ionized plasma flowing out of the Sun distorts and stretches the magnetic lines of force, thus carrying and spreading the magnetic field of the Sun throughout the solar system.

As we approach the Earth, we pass gradually from a region of space where the Sun is the dominant agency into a region of space where conditions are controlled primarily by our planet, while the Sun, of course, still exerts an influence.

The terrestrial effect that is felt at the largest distance is the magnetic field. In the vicinity of the Earth's surface, the Earth's magnetic field resembles that of a dipole. The magnetic-field lines that cross the Earth's surface near the equator do not go very far, and they return to the Earth practically undisturbed by whatever conditions prevail in interplanetary space. As we consider magnetic-field lines that cross the Earth's surface at increasingly higher latitudes, we find that they reach farther and farther into space where 'the strength of the Earth's dipole field is no longer large compared with that of the general interplanetary field. They are thus more and more distorted, until eventually they no longer return to the Earth, but join with the magnetic lines of the interplanetary field.

The Earth's magnetic field affects cosmic-ray particles, producing the well-known latitude effect and E-W asymmetry. It also affects the motion of the interplanetary plasma and is, in turn, affected by it. For when a mass of ionized gas approaches the Earth, it will be brought to a stop gradually while it compresses the lines of force (and this will happen whether or not the plasma is originally magnetized). Notice that the effect of the gravitational attraction of the Earth on the motion of the plasma is small compared with that of the magnetic field.

As we come closer to the Earth, terrestrial gravitational attraction becomes the dominant factor. It prevents the escape of gases filtering through the Earth's crust and of those originating from inorganic chemical reactions or from the metabolism of living organisms. These gases, together perhaps with some residue of the original terrestrial atmosphere, form the present atmosphere of the Earth.

The upper layers of the atmosphere are strongly ionized by ultraviolet and X rays from the Sun, and occasionally by energetic particles of solar origin. They form the ionosphere.

The ionosphere stops rather abruptly between 80 and 60 km, because atmospheric absorption prevents the ionizing radiation from penetrating to lower altitudes. Thus the Earth's surface is separated from the ionosphere and from the interplanetary plasma beyond by an electrically insulating blanket of air.

Some of the experimental investigations will be discussed in the framework of this broad picture.

One of the interesting results of these studies has been the discovery of a variability in the air drag on artificial satellites, showing corresponding changes in the air density at a given altitude. This fact was first noticed by Jacchia of the Smithsonian Institution by studying the orbit of Sputnik II. The more accurate tracking data on Vanguard I, which became available some time later, and the orbital observations on Sputnik III confirmed these results and showed that the drag fluctuates with a period close to the 27-day period of the solar rotation. This led Jacchia to correlate the changes of air density in the upper layers of the atmosphere with the periodic changes of solar activity brought about by the Sun's rotation. Presumably, when an active region appears on the visible portion of the solar disk, there is an increase in the flux of solar radiation responsible for the heating of the upper layers of the atmosphere. The consequent increase of temperature causes an outward expansion of the atmosphere and an appreciable increase of the air density at the apogee of the satellite.[11] Jacchia's conclusions were considerably strengthened by the work of Priester, in Germany, who found that there was a close correlation between the variation of the drag on the satellite and the variation in the 20-cm radio waves emitted by the Sun. This radiation is an excellent indicator of solar activity.[12] Shortly thereafter, Jacchia found a similar correlation between the drag and the solar radio emission at 10 cm.[13]

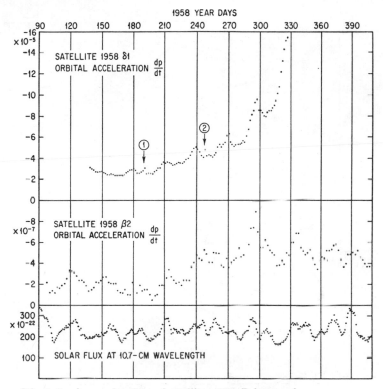

FIG. 5. Secular accelerations of satellites 1958 Delta 1 and 1958 Beta 2 compared with the 10.7-cm solar flux. The dates of the two great geomagnetic disturbances, July 8–9 and Sept. 4, 1958, are marked (1) and (2), respectively. Accelerations computed at intervals of 25 revolutions. (*From L. G. Jacchia, Nature, 183, 1662, 1959.*)

The same correlation was found simultaneously in the orbits of two satellites, Sputnik III and Vanguard I, demonstrating that the effect was associated with atmospheric changes rather than with peculiarities in the drag response of a particular satellite. Figure 5 indicates the drag decelerations calculated and published by Jacchia in support of these remarks.

In the course of his work Jacchia made another interesting observation. He noticed that on two occasions an abrupt increase in the drag on

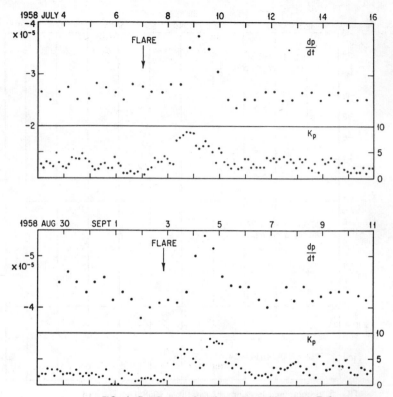

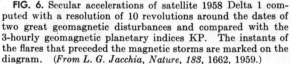

FIG. 6. Secular accelerations of satellite 1958 Delta 1 computed with a resolution of 10 revolutions around the dates of two great geomagnetic disturbances and compared with the 3-hourly geomagnetic planetary indices KP. The instants of the flares that preceded the magnetic storms are marked on the diagram. (*From L. G. Jacchia, Nature, 183, 1662, 1959.*)

Sputnik III occurred about a day after the appearance of large solar flares. The drag increase occurred at approximately the same time as the rise in the planetary magnetic index and the occurrence of the magnetic storm which accompanied the flare. The correlation of these effects is shown in Fig. 6. Since the magnetic storm is usually taken to signify the arrival of a plasma cloud ejected from the sun during a flare, Jacchia suggests that in these particular instances the drag increase may have been the result of atmospheric heating produced by the collisions of solar corpuscular streams with the atoms and molecules of the atmosphere. As an alternative explanation, the simultaneity of the drag increase and the magnetic storm may be fortuitous, and the lag of one or two days between the flare and the drag increase may represent the time required for the atmosphere to come to equilibrium after the heating produced by the absorption of X radiation emitted during the flare.[14]

However, a recent analysis of the Echo I orbit provides an indication that solar *particles* are in fact responsible for the drag increases observed at the time of major flares. As we have noted, Echo has a very large area-mass ratio, making it a sensitive detector of drag changes. In the period Nov. 10 to 15, 1960, a major solar event occurred, including two class 3+ flares and several smaller eruptions. This solar storm was the most severe that has occurred since the great flare of Feb. 23, 1956. It was followed on Dec. 4, 1900, by a second event, including one class 3+ flare. The analysis of the Echo orbit shows that at the time of occurrence of each of these events, the drag acting on Echo I increased by about a factor of 2 and remained at this high value for several days before returning to its previous level for that period[15] (see Fig. 7). The increase in the drag probably indicated an increase in the average density of the air through which the Echo I moves, although it may also have been produced by electromagnetic effects associated with changes in the density and velocity of charged particles in the ionosphere. Regardless of the mechanism which produced the drag increase, it is significant that the response of a satellite to a specific flare has been detected in the cases of Sputnik III and Echo I, whereas it has not been observed in the orbit of Vanguard I. In this connection, Jastrow and Bryant note that the orbits of Sputnik III and Echo I pass through regions of high magnetic latitude, in the auroral zones and in the outer Van Allen belt, whereas Vanguard I is confined to the low magnetic latitudes (less than 44°) and well outside the auroral zones. It is known that the intensity of the outer belt increases as much as a thousandfold after solar flares, according to Explorer VI and VII measurements, and that increased auroral activity occurs at these times. These effects are associated with the channeling of corpuscular streams into the high latitudes by the Earth's magnetic field. If the drag variations do in fact represent density changes, then these variations may be understood easily in terms of a corpuscular heating of the atmosphere by collisions with trapped particles, leading to density increases that are confined to the auroral latitudes for a period of a day or two, before they spread to lower latitudes.

Turning next to the ionosphere, rocket work by American scientists has contributed a large share of the information now available on the electron

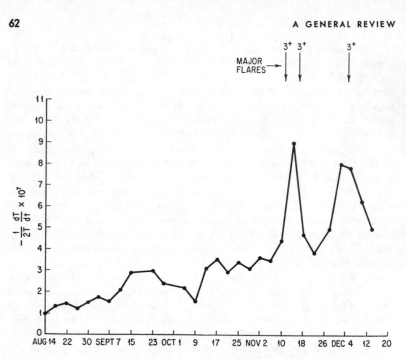

FIG. 7. Drag acting on Echo I as represented by the fractional rate of change of period. The upward trend of the drag is associated with the downward motion of the perigee produced by solar radiation pressure, as indicated in Fig. 4. Sharp increases in drag occurred at the time of solar events in November and early December, 1960. (*From R. Jastrow and R. Bryant, J. Geophys. Res., in press.*)

density and on the relative abundance of the various positive ions, up to about 200 km. The recently launched Explorer VIII satellite contains a variety of plasma probes and field meters for the *in situ* measurement of electron and ion densities and temperatures in the ionosphere. The instruments in Explorer VIII are reported to be working satisfactorily, but data from this satellite have not yet been reduced and published. Russian satellites and space probes have carried such instruments, and some of the results have been made available.[16] Moreover, American as well as Russian scientists have obtained significant data on the density of electrons above the ionospheric maximum by observing the refraction of the waves from radio transmitters carried by U.S.S.R. and American satellites.

Figure 8 summarizes some of the results obtained from whistler data by Smith and Helliwell for altitudes extending out to 5 earth radii.[17] The whistler data indicate an annual variation of 30 per cent in electron density in the exosphere, during the period 1955 to 1959.

Figure 9 shows the electron-density profile to a height of 1500 km, as obtained by Berning by analysis of the propagation of radio waves from a sounding rocket.[18] Other sounding-rocket data, obtained by Nisbet, are shown in Fig. 10. These data resulted from analyses based on Faraday rotation, supplemented by measurements of ionospheric refraction.[19] They were in seven separate flights at various times of day, in the interval between Sept. 20, 1956, and July 9, 1959. The differences shown in Fig. 10 emphasize the great variability of electron densities in the upper atmosphere.

The most impressive scientific result obtained to this date from experiments in space is the discovery of the radiation belt.

When space exploration began, the theoretical background of this discovery had been available for some time. The following facts were known: (1) In the absence of disturbing effects, charged particles can be trapped indefinitely in certain regions of space around a magnetic dipole (Störmer). (2) When the radius of gyration is small compared with the distance from the center of the dipole, each particle spirals about a line of force; as it moves from the weaker field found near the equator to the stronger field found near the poles, the pitch angle increases until it reaches the value of 90°, at which point, the motion is reversed, and thus the particle oscillates back and forth between two symmetrically located "mirror points" (Alfvén, see Fig. 4). (3) Because of the curvature of

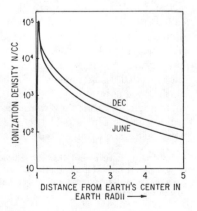

FIG. 8. Electron density to 5 earth radii deduced from whistler data. The data cover the years 1955 to 1959. (From R. L. Smith and R. A. Helliwell, J. Geophys. Res., 65, 2583, 1960.)

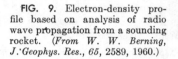

FIG. 9. Electron-density profile based on analysis of radio wave propagation from a sounding rocket. (*From W. W. Berning, J.'Geophys. Res., 65*, 2589, 1960.)

the lines of force and the radial gradient of the field strength, the trajectory of the particle undergoes a slow drift in azimuth, positive and negative particles drifting in opposite directions (Alfvén). There results an electric current, which, in the case of the dipole field of the Earth, would circle our planet from east to west.

Early in 1957 Fred Singer published an article which, for the first time, called attention to the likelihood that there may actually exist in the dipole field of the Earth a trapped radiation, consisting of charged particles which oscillate back and forth along the lines of force while drifting in longitude.[20] Singer had advanced this hypothesis in order to explain the so-called "ring current" which is held responsible for the main phase of the magnetic storms.* Singer suggested that the particles were of solar origin and that they were allowed to enter the normally inaccessible regions of the dipole field because of perturbations in the Earth's magnetic field; he also suggested that the trapped particles, leaking along the

* Actually, it turns out that consideration of the drift alone leads to an incorrect result concerning the magnetic effects of trapped particles. Trapped particles behave like a diamagnetic gas whose polarization makes an important contribution to the magnetic field.

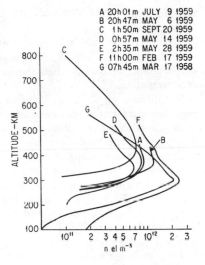

```
A 20h 01 m JULY  9 1959
B 20h 47m MAY    6 1959
C  1h 50m SEPT 20 1959
D  0h 57m MAY   14 1959
E  2h 35m MAY   28 1959
F 11h 00m FEB   17 1959
G 07h 45m MAR   17 1958
```

FIG. 10. Rocket electron-density measurements. (*From J. S. Nisbet and S. A. Bowhill, J. Geophys. Res., 65, 2597, 1960.*)

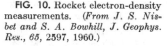

lines of force into the lower atmosphere, would contribute to aurorae, airglow, and ionospheric ionization.

The first satellites carrying detectors of energetic particles were Sputnik II (launched on Nov. 3, 1957), Explorer I (launched on Jan. 31, 1958), and Explorer III (launched on Mar. 26, 1958; see Tables 1 and 3 of Chap.1). For each of the three satellites the detector was a single Geiger counter. Van Allen, whose group had been responsible for the instrumentation of the American satellites, reported his preliminary results at a joint meeting of the National Academy of Sciences and the American Physical Society, held in Washington on May 1, 1958.* He stated that the counting rate of the Geiger counter installed aboard Explorer I was dependent both on latitude and altitude, that it increased with altitude in a more or less regular fashion between 600 and 1000 km, but that, however, no counts were received during several minutes of radio contact while the satellite was above 2000 km. Van Allen interpreted the lack of signal as due to a jamming of the Geiger tube by a radiation of exceptionally high intensity. He figured that the "true" counting rate (such as would have been recorded with zero dead time) must have been greater than 35,000 per sec (as compared with a counting rate of about 20 per sec recorded below

---

* See address by J. A. Van Allen in *Satellites 1958 Alpha and Gamma: High Intensity Radiation Research and Instrumentation*, National Academy of Sciences, Satellite Report Series no. 13, Washington, D.C., January, 1961.

600 km). The data obtained with Explorer III were in agreement with those of Explorer I. They were more complete, however, because Explorer III, unlike Explorer I, had a device capable of recording the counting rates continuously and sending back the information on command from the Earth, when the satellite was in radio contact with a receiving station.

On the basis of these results, Van Allen concluded that a zone of very high intensity radiation exists around the Earth. He called attention to the fact that the radiation is detected through a wall thickness of 1.5 g per cm² and yet does not penetrate to a depth of 600 km. Since the residual atmospheric thickness above 600 km is negligible, Van Allen concluded that the radiation must consist of charged particles that are restrained from reaching the vicinity of the Earth by the Earth's magnetic field. He suggested that these particles are of solar origin, that they penetrate the forbidden region of the Earth's magnetic field through some sort of perturbation of the field, and that subsequently they remain trapped in this region.

Despite Singer's prediction, the discovery of a more or less permanent trapped radiation of the very great intensity revealed by Van Allen's observations came as a major surprise.

Sputnik II, because of its comparatively low apogee (see Table 3 of Chap. 1), had not penetrated deeply into the radiation belt. However, the small increase in counting rate, detected by Sputnik II at latitudes above 60° (and reported by Vernov, Grigorov, Logachev, and Chudakov in a paper submitted on May 4, 1958, to *Doklady Akademii Nauk USSR*) was probably due to the passage through the extreme fringes of the belt.[21]

On May 15, 1958, the U.S.S.R. launched Sputnik III (see Table 3 of Chap. 1). This satellite was equipped with many scientific instruments, among which were various radiation detectors and which saturated only at a much higher radiation intensity than the Geiger counters flown previously. The first results of Sputnik III were made public by Krassowsky, Vernov, Chudakov, and their associates at the CSAGI meeting held in Moscow in July and August, 1958. They confirmed fully the existence of the high-intensity radiation discovered by Van Allen.[22]

On Aug. 7, 1958 (see Table 1 of Chap. 1), the United States launched Explorer IV, equipped with a variety of instruments especially designed by the Iowa group to investigate the radiation belt. The preliminary results, reported late in August, 1958, at the Conference on Peaceful Uses of Atomic Energy in Geneva, dispelled all doubts about the fact that the high-intensity zone was actually due to a magnetically trapped radiation.

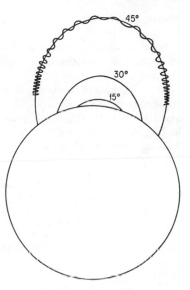

FIG. 11. An illustrative sketch; not to scale, of the spiral path of a trapped charged particle, the guiding center of whose motion lies along the line of magnetic force that intersects the Earth's surface at a geomagnetic latitude of 45°; also shown are lines of force that intersect the Earth's surface at geomagnetic latitudes 30° and 15°, respectively. (*From J. Van Allen, C. McIlwain, and G. Ludwig, J. Geophys. Res., 64, 271, 1959.*)

Fluxes as high as 100,000 particles per cm^2 sec steradian were detected at certain locations. The intensity was shown to depend on the geomagnetic rather than on the geographic latitude. Also, at intermediate latitudes it was found that the radiation was not isotropic, but had a disklike angular distribution such as one would predict in the case of magnetic trapping (see Fig. 11).

Moreover, by the late summer of 1958, United States scientists had succeeded in producing artificial radiation belts by injecting high-energy electrons into the Earth's magnetic field. This experiment, known as the Argus experiment (which was performed by means of three small atomic bombs exploded at a carefully chosen altitude and location), confirmed the theory of magnetic trapping and showed that, under appropriate circumstances, the trapping time in the magnetic field of the Earth could be quite long.[23]

Although the results of the Argus experiment were not made public until the spring of 1959, in the fall of 1958 the existence of a trapped radiation belt was regarded generally as an established fact. However, many questions concerning its nature, its spatial distribution, and its origin still remained unanswered. For example—and this was most important—it was not experimentally known whether the radiation intensity went through a maximum with increasing distance from the

Earth, or whether it kept on increasing asymptotically toward some limiting value.

Some of these questions have now been answered, and we would like to summarize here the most significant results obtained during the last 2 years.

As a working hypothesis, it was assumed from the outset that the trapped radiation consisted mainly of electrons and protons. Sputnik III and Explorer IV carried a number of different detectors, and each of them had a different response to electrons and protons of various energies (see Tables 1 and 2). It immediately became apparent that the ratios of the

Table 1. Instrumentation of Sputnik III

1. NaI scintillator, used (a) as a counter (35-kev bias), and (b) with a current integrator (detects X rays down to about 20 kev)
2. Photomultiplier with thin phosphor, under 4×10^{-4} g/cm² Al foil, used with a current integrator (detects electrons, $E > 10$ kev)
3. Photomultiplier with thin phosphor, under 8×10^{-4} g/cm² Al foil
4. Cerenkov counter (detects heavy c.r. primaries)
5. Spherical ion trap (measures ion densities from 10^4 to 25×10^6 ions/cm³)
6. Mass spectrometer to determine composition of ionosphere
7. Magnetometer
8. Manometers for pressures from 10^{-9} to 10^{-5} mm Hg
9. Micrometeorite detectors
10. Field-mill electrometer
11. Radio transmitters to detect radio "rise" and radio "set"

Table 2. Instrumentation of Explorer IV

A. Plastic scintillator; shielding: 0.4 g/cm² Al; counts:
Electrons, $E > 650$ kev
Protons, $\quad E > 10$ Mev
X rays, $\quad E \gtrsim 400$ kev (low efficiency)

B. CsI scintillator; 0.92 g/cm² thick; shielding: 1 mg/cm²; measures total energy loss of:
Electrons, $E > 20$ kev
Protons, $\quad E > 400$ kev
X rays, $\quad$ (high efficiency)

C. G.M. counter, 1.2 g/cm² wall; unshielded; counts:
Electrons, $E > 3$ Mev
Protons, $\quad E > 30$ Mev
X rays, $\quad E \gtrsim 40$ kev (low efficiency)

D. G.M. counter, 1.2 g/cm² wall; 1.6 g/cm² Pb shield; counts:
Electrons, $E > 5$ Mev
Protons, $\quad E > 40$ Mev
X rays, $\quad E \gtrsim 80$ kev (low efficiency)

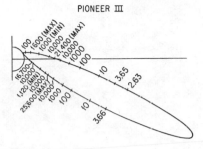

PIONEER III

FIG. 12. A geographical plot, to scale, of the projection on a (rotating) meridian plane of the trajectory of Pioneer III; the semicircle at the left represents the cross section of the solid Earth; polar coordinates are radial distance from the center of the Earth and the geographical latitude; the vertical axis is the geographical axis of the Earth with the north end up; the numbers are true counting rates at selected positions along the trajectory; the outbound leg of the trajectory is the upper portion of the curved line. (*From J. Van Allen and L. Frank, Nature, 183, 430, 1959.*)

counting rates of the various detectors varied greatly from point to point within the radiation belt. In other words, the measured fluxes were strongly dependent, both in absolute and in relative values, on the measuring instrument. It was concluded correctly that the composition and the energy spectrum of the radiation were different at different locations.

Many of the American and Russian vehicles, including Sputnik II, Explorer I, Explorer III, and Explorer IV, carried Geiger counters, with wall thicknesses ranging from a few tenths of 1 g per cm² to slightly more than 1 g per cm² (including the vehicle skin). These counters detect, with practically 100 per cent efficiency, electrons of a few Mev energy,

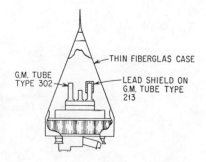

FIG. 13. Physical arrangement of radiation detectors in conical payload of Pioneer IV; base diameter 23 cm; total payload weight 6.1 kg; the arrangement of Pioneer III was identical except for omission of the shield over the 213 tube. (*From J. Van Allen and L. Frank, Nature, 184, 219, 1959.*)

THIN FIBERGLAS CASE

G.M. TUBE TYPE 302

LEAD SHIELD ON G.M. TUBE TYPE 213

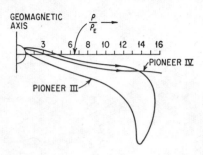

FIG. 14. Plots of the projection of the trajectories of Pioneer III and Pioneer IV on a geomagnetic plane (centered dipole model); unit of distance, $\rho_E = 6{,}371$ km. (*From J. Van Allen and L. Frank, Nature, 184, 219, 1959.*)

and protons of a few tens of Mev energy, which can penetrate the wall. They also detect, with much lower efficiency, electrons down to a few tens of kev energy, through the intermediary of the X rays which they produce in the counter walls.

Late in 1958 and early in 1959, the United States and the U.S.S.R. launched a number of deep-space probes (see Tables 3 and 4 of Chap. 1). Some of them, namely Pioneer III (see Fig. 12), Mechta and Pioneer IV (see Figs. 13 and 14), carried Geiger counters similar to those carried by the satellites. The two most important facts brought to light by these probes were: (1) The high-intensity radiation is confined to a belt around the Earth; at great distances, only the normal cosmic-ray flux is detected. (2) As one moves farther and farther away from the Earth, the counting rate of the Geiger counter goes through two separate maxima; thus there

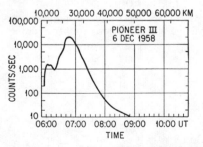

FIG. 15. Semilog plot of true counting rate of the 302 Geiger-Müller tube versus time of observation on the outbound leg of the flight of Pioneer III; radial distance from the center of the Earth is shown at the top of the figure; the geographical longitude during the period shown was 30°W at 0600, 0° at 0630, 5°E at 0700, 4.6°E at 0730, 2°E at 0800, 2°W at 0830. (*From J. Van Allen and L. Frank, Nature, 183, 430, 1959.*)

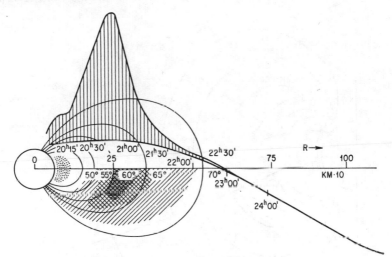

FIG. 16. The trajectory of the rocket in geomagnetic coordinates; Moscow time and the intensity (vertical lines drawn from the trajectory) are shown along the trajectory; the total ionization is used as a measure of the intensity; the magnetic-force lines intersecting the surface of the Earth at latitudes of 50°, 55°, 60°, 65°, and 70° are shown; the magnetic field is taken to be that of a dipole whose geomagnetic-pole coordinates are 78.5°N and 69°W; the inner zone is indicated by the dotted region, the outer zone by the shaded region; the density of shading gives a qualitative picture of the intensity distribution in the second zone. (*From S. Vernov, A. Chudakov, P. Vakulov, and Yu. Logachev, Soviet Physics Dok., 4, 338, 1959.*)

is an "inner zone" and an "outer zone," separated by a slot (see Figs. 15, 16, and 17).

These results were announced first by Van Allen,[24] and then confirmed by the Russian workers.[25] The decrease of the intensity level beyond the maximum was also detected by S.T.L. and Iowa physicists by means of an ionization chamber installed aboard Pioneer I.[26]

Comparing the data of Pioneer III, Mechta, and Pioneer IV, Van Allen established another important fact. Although the population of the inner zone is comparatively stable, that of the outer zone shows large-scale fluctuations, which are presumably connected with solar activity. Figure 18 illustrates dramatically this effect. Note that the flight of Pioneer IV occurred a few days after a period of enhanced solar activity and magnetic storms.

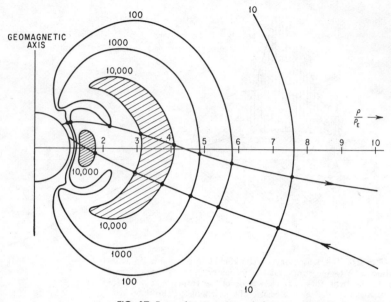

FIG. 17. Intensity structure of the trapped radiation around
the Earth; the diagram is a geomagnetic meridian section of a
three-dimensional figure of revolution around the geomagnetic
axis; contours of constant intensity are labeled with numbers
10, 100, 1000, and 10,000, and these numbers are the true
counting rates of an Anton 302 Geiger tube carried by Explorer
IV and Pioneer III; the linear scale of the diagram is relative
to the radius of the Earth, 6371 km; the outbound and inbound
legs of the trajectory Pioneer III are shown by the slanting,
undulating lines; the intensity structure is a function of detector
characteristics. (*From J. Van Allen, J. Geophys. Res., 64*, 1683,
1959.)

In the meantime, more specific information on the composition of the
trapped radiation was becoming available, through both a detailed
comparison of the counting rates of the various instruments installed on
Explorer IV and Sputnik III and direct observations by means of photographic plates and magnetic spectrometers flown with rockets into the
lower edge of the radiation belt. Figure 19 shows the proton spectrum
between 75 and 400 Mev at the fringe of the inner zone (about 1000 km
near the equator). Figure 20 shows the spectrum of electrons between
80 and 500 kev measured between 600 and 1000 km at high latitude,
where the outer belt reaches down to fairly low altitudes. No protons

with more than 1-Mev energy were found in this region.[28]   Table 3 gives
some tentative estimates of the intensities of protons and electrons of
various energies at the heart of the inner zone (3000 km on the geomagnetic equator) and at the heart of the outer zone (16,000 km on the
geomagnetic equator), according to Van Allen.[29]

On Aug. 7, 1959, Explorer VI was launched; it was followed by Explorer
VII, launched on Sept. 19.   Explorer VI is on an orbit with a perigee height of 252 km and an apogee height of 42,434 km (see Fig. 21).
Explorer VII is on an orbit with a perigee height of 556 km, an apogee
height of 1086 km, and an inclination of 50°.   Explorer VI carries three
radiation packages: (1) a proportional counter telescope within a shield
of 5 g per cm² of lead, built by the Chicago group; (2) a thin-walled
Geiger tube and an ionization chamber built by the Minnesota group; and
(3) a scintillation detector provided by S.T.L. (see Table 3).   Explorer
VII carries two Geiger counters provided by the Iowa group.   One of
them is unshielded and has a wall thickness of about 0.5 g per cm²; the
other is surrounded by 1.15 g per cm² of lead.

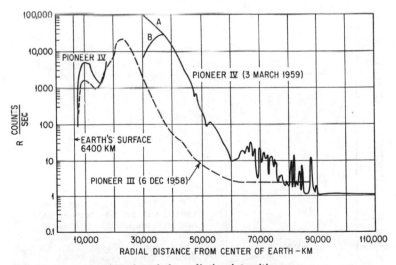

FIG. 18. A comparative plot of the radiation intensities as
measured with nearly identical Anton 302 Geiger tubes in
Pioneer III and Pioneer IV; the trajectories were not identical,
the most important difference being that Pioneer IV cut through
the inner zone several degrees closer to the equator, at a radial
distance of about 10,000 km.   (From J. Van Allen, J. Geophys.
Res., 64, 1683, 1959.)

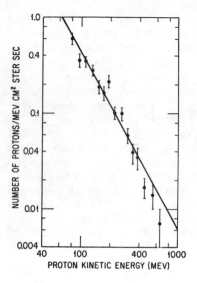

FIG. 19. The absolute energy spectrum of protons above 75 Mev in the lower Van Allen radiation belt at an altitude of 1200 km; the line is a least-squares fit of the equation $N = N_1 T^{-n}$ to the data and gives $N_1 = 2.1_{-0.7}{}^{1.0} \times 10^3$ protons per Mev^{-R} steradian sec cm^2 and $n = 1.84 \pm 0.08$. (*From S. Freden and R. White, Phys. Rev. Letters, 3, 9, 1959.*)

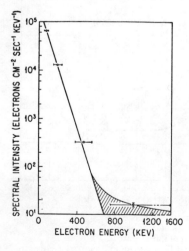

FIG. 20. Electron spectrum measured at high latitude, between 600 and 1000 km altitude. (*From M. Walt, L. Chase, J. Cladis, W. Imhof, and J. Knecht, COSPAR Meeting, Nice, January, 1960.*)

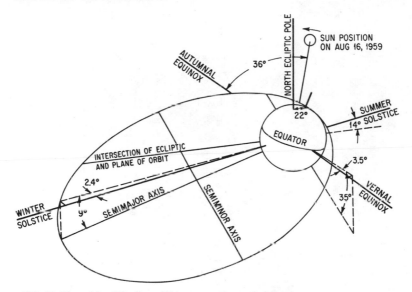

FIG. 21. The orbit of Explorer VI in space; the angle between the plane of the orbit and the Earth's equatorial plane is 47°; the orbital plane is tipped 38° to the plane of the ecliptic; on August 16, during the geomagnetic storm, the major axis was directed about 125° away from the Sun. (*From R. Arnoldy, R. Hoffman, and J. Winckler, J. Geophys. Res., 65, 1361, 1960.*)

A wealth of new information has come from the analysis of the data obtained with these satellites.

Figure 22 shows the threefold coincidence rate of Simpson's telescope on Explorer VI and the single counting rate of the middle counter for a given passage of the satellite plotted against altitude above the Earth's surface.[30] Threefold coincidences are produced only by comparatively energetic particles, that is, protons with more than 75 Mev or electrons with more than 13 Mev kinetic energy, whereas single pulses can be produced also by fairly low energy electrons (down to about 300 kev) through the intermediary of X rays. It is evident that high-energy particles are present only in the inner belt and that the counts recorded by the single counter in the outer belt are due entirely to low-energy electrons.

Figures 23 and 24 represent some additional results obtained from single counting rates of the counters carried by Explorer VI. They show that the outer electron belt has a complex structure. In many passages

Table 3. Van Allen's Estimates of Particle Flux
(From *J. Geophys. Res.*, *64*, 1683, 1959)

Heart of inner zone
(3600 km on geomagnetic equator)

a. Electrons, $E > 20$ kev:
   Max. unidirectional intensity: $\sim 2 \times 10^9/cm^2$ sec steradian
b. Electrons, $E > 600$ kev:
   Max. unidirectional intensity: $\sim 1 \times 10^7/cm^2$ sec steradian
c. Protons, $E > 40$ Mev:
   Max. omnidirectional intensity: $\sim 2 \times 10^4/cm^2$ sec

Heart of outer zone
(16,000 km on geomagnetic equator)

a. Electrons, $E > 20$ kev:
   Omnidirectional intensity: $\sim 1 \times 10^{11}/cm^2$ sec
b. Electrons, $E > 200$ kev:
   Omnidirectional intensity: $\sim 1 \times 10^8/cm^2$ sec
c. Protons, $E > 60$ Mev:
   Omnidirectional intensity: $\lesssim 10^2/cm^2$ sec
d. Protons, $E < 30$ Mev:
   No information

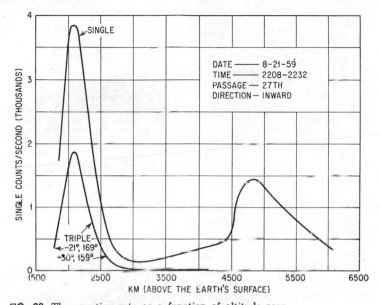

FIG. 22. The counting rate as a function of altitude near perigee for the single-counter channel and for the triple-coincidence channel; the peak at the left is due to protons from the inner Van Allen region having energies greater than 75 Mev; the bremsstrahlung from electrons produces the peak on the right; note that the detection of energetic particles from the triple-coincidence counter is limited to cosmic radiation beyond the altitude of 3,500 km. [*From C. Fan, P. Meyer, and J. Simpson, in H. Kallmann Bijl (ed.), Space Research, p. 956 (Proc. 1st Intern. Space Sci. Symposium), North-Holland Publishing Co., Amsterdam, 1960.*]

FIG. 23. Passage through the two electron regions on Aug. 17, 1959; single-counting rate as a function of time. [*From C. Fan, P. Meyer, and J. Simpson, in H. Kallmann Bijl (ed.), Space Research, p. 957 (Proc. 1st Intern. Space Sci. Symposium), North-Holland Publishing Co., Amsterdam, 1960.*]

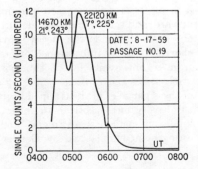

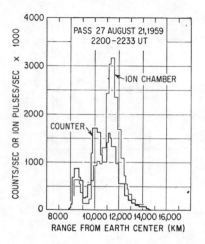

FIG. 24. Radiation levels on the oncoming portion of Pass 27, which shows three distinct radiation regions; the Van Allen inner zone appears at 8500 km, the outer zone at 11,500 km, and the new intermediate zone close to 10,000 km. (*From R. Arnoldy, R. Hoffman, and J. Winckler, J. Geophys. Res., 65, 1361, 1960.*)

two separate peaks appear. The Minnesota instruments indicate that the radiation is softer at the outer than at the inner peak.[31] Both the Chicago and the Minnesota groups remark that the intensity maxima in the electron belt observed at different latitudes lie along magnetic lines of force.

Before continuing this summary of the experimental data, the problem of the origin of the trapped radiation should be discussed. The problem arises, of course, because a charged particle should not be able to enter a captive orbit any more readily than it can leave it, so that some special injection mechanism is required.

One possible injection mechanism, suggested independently by several scientists, is the neutron cosmic-ray albedo. Upon entering the atmosphere, cosmic-ray particles undergo nuclear collisions. Among the products of these collisions are a number of neutrons that are projected upward, and travel, undeflected, through the magnetic field. On the way out, some of the neutrons decay into electrons and protons, injecting these charged particles into trapped orbits. Data on the neutron albedo spectrum are now available; it is thus possible to compute the source spectrum of electrons and protons. Making suitable estimates of the mean lives of these particles in the trapped orbits, it is possible to compute the particle density and spectrum in the radiation belt. Computations of this kind were made first by Singer[32] and refined later by others.[33] An interesting point emphasized by Dessler is the effect of the so-called "Cape

Town anomaly."[34]   In the general area of Cape Town, the Earth's magnetic field is abnormally low.   This should bring the mirror points located on the lines of force that pass through this region into the lower atmosphere.   Atmospheric scattering and absorption would then decrease the population along these lines of force, and the drift in longitude would spread the depletion to a shell around the Earth.

The computed proton spectrum has been found to be in reasonable agreement with that observed in the inner zone by means of photographic plates.[27]   This fact, together with the relative stability of the inner zone, lends considerable support to the assumption that the high-energy particles, found primarily in the inner zone, originate indeed from the decay of neutrons.

It seems very difficult, however, to assume that most of the low-energy electrons, found predominantly in the outer zone, have a similar origin. As pointed out by Gold, this hypothesis is completely ruled out on the ground of energy balance if it is true—as it seems very likely—that aurorae are due to a discharge of the radiation belt along the lines of force into the polar regions of the upper atmosphere, because the energy supplied by the neutron albedo falls short, by several orders of magnitude, of the average energy dissipated in the auroral displays.[35]

Another possible mechanism considered by various scientists is the injection of particles of solar origin, which we have already mentioned. This requires some sort of disturbance of the Earth's magnetic field, brought about, presumably, by the same plasma cloud that also carries the particles.   No detailed theory of this phenomenon exists, but various interesting points have been brought out.   For example, Gold has emphasized the importance of the non-ionized atmospheric layer that insulates the Earth from the highly conducting gases in the exosphere and in interplanetary space.   This makes it possible for the charged particles that, at some time, are contained within a tube of force to be transferred to another tube of force without any expenditure of energy.   Such a transfer of particles might help to explain both the injection of particles and their spread throughout the radiation belt.[36]

Of course, one should also bear in mind that what needs to be injected is *energy* rather than *particles*.   Electrons are certainly produced within the radiation belt by ionization of neutral atoms coming from the atmosphere below.   These electrons have much lower energies than those detected in the radiation belt, but it is conceivable that they may become accelerated by hydromagnetic disturbances induced by the arrival of a plasma cloud.   One might ask, however, whether or not it is reasonable to assume that the plasma cloud should inject its energy into the Earth's magnetic field without injecting, at the same time, the particles of which it is formed.

The problem of the origin of the outer belt is still unsolved. However, certain correlations between intensity variations in the outer belt and solar or geophysical effects offer suggestive clues. It has already been noted that in March, 1959, Pioneer IV detected an increase in the population of the outer belt following solar disturbances. This, of course, is evidence of a solar origin either for the particles found in the belt or at least for their energy. Since that time, further analysis of the data of Explorer IV and new observations by Explorer VI and Explorer VII have provided additional information.

Rothwell and McIlwain, of the Iowa group, relating results of Explorer IV, reported that on the occasion of the magnetic storms of Sept. 3–5, 1958, there was a considerable depletion of the particle population in the "horns" of the outer belt.[37]

During the magnetic storm of Aug. 16, 1959, a number of interesting observations were made with instruments aboard Explorer VI. In comparing these results, one must bear in mind that the various detectors differ greatly in their response to particles of different kinds and different energies (see Table 1). (1) At the beginning of the main phase of the magnetic storm, the S.T.L. group found that the radiation belt was more or less normal up to almost 7 earth radii (geocentric). Around 7 earth radii, however, they noticed considerable structure and some decrease. At the next passage, about 12 hr later, there was a modest increase of intensity (less than a factor of 2) between 3 and 4 earth radii, while there was further depletion and still considerable structure at 7 earth radii. At the subsequent passage, after another 12 hr, there was an increase everywhere in the outer zone, while the structure previously noted at 7 earth radii was disappearing. The intensity continued to increase for another 48 hr; then it began to decrease slowly and, after 2 weeks, was still above the prestorm value.[38] (2) The Chicago group found that, about 2 days after the beginning magnetic storm, the outermost maximum (as measured with the shielded counter) had increased considerably in intensity and had moved to a smaller range.[39] (3) The Minnesota group found that, 1 day after the beginning of the storm, the outer zone was considerably depleted. The radiation dumped into the atmosphere on that occasion was thought to be responsible for the aurora observed at the same time. There was then a gradual recovery of the particle population coincident with the recovery of the magnetic field. For several days after the storm, the particle density was well above the prestorm value.[40]

Finally, the Iowa group reported the following observations made during the magnetic storms of Nov. 28, 1959, and of Mar. 31, 1960, by means of the unshielded counter aboard Explorer VII. To quote from a communication presented at the April, 1960, meeting of the American Geophysical Union:

The effects of the storm (of 28 November, 1959) were, firstly, to greatly deplete the intensity of trapped radiation at high latitudes beyond the peak of the outer zone. The outer zone was thus made much narrower, and it moved towards lower latitudes. Initially very intense fluxes were observed in the peak, and then these gradually disappeared so that on 29 November the counting rate of the counter was only about one-tenth that on 28 November. This effect was noted in both hemispheres. . . .

The (outer) zone was stable on 27 November, but very disturbed on the next day, when a 3-second wide peak at 0336.30 Z was over an auroral arc. Furthermore, a monochromatic 6300 Å sub-visible arc was under the outer zone throughout the night.

It appears that the visible auroral arc may have been generated following a very rapid dumping out of trapped particles. Then over a period of many hours more particles were scattered out and these caused the sub-visible wide red arc. . . .

The most recent and thus far the most drastic observed modification of the outer zone occurred during the period 31 March to 10 April 1960. The time relationship to the very great magnetic storm which began on 31 March leaves very little doubt of the causal association with this event. For several weeks previous to the event the outer zone had been relatively stable in intensity and position. The intensity as observed with the lightly shielded tube was about 200 counts per second. On 31 March–1 April the outer zone as observed at 1000 to 1100 km altitude almost completely disappeared (less than 10 counts per second). Widespread aurorae at low latitudes were reported, favoring the view that the trapped radiation was being precipitously dumped into the atmosphere by magnetic perturbation. The outer zone recovered rapidly in intensity (showing at times considerable detailed structure); by a week later the intensity had built up to over 10,000 counts per second. The intensity then gradually declined toward its pre-storm level.

Another point of considerable significance in connection with the origin of the outer radiation belt is that in its excursion beyond the outer fringes of the belt, Explorer VI has not, so far, encountered any flux of energetic electrons comparable with that found within the radiation belt. This seems to rule out the assumption that the electrons found in the radiation belt arrive from the Sun with their full energy.

The general picture that seems to evolve from all these observations is about as follows. Occasionally a disturbance comes from the Sun, presumably in the form of a fast-moving plasma cloud (or tongue) with a sharp front. The bulk velocity of the cloud may be of the order of 10^8 cm per sec, so that the plasma protons would have energies of the order of 10 kev, while the electrons have presumably, on the average, much lower energies. The cloud interacts with the Earth's magnetic field, and the first effect of this interaction is a dumping of particles from the outer belt into the atmosphere. Subsequently, there occurs, within the outer radiation belt, an increase in the number of electrons of 10 kev or more. The necessary energy must come from the initial kinetic energy of the gas cloud. The electrons that become accelerated may be present already in the radiation belt, or may be injected into it from the cloud. The mechanism of the energy transfer is still obscure. It certainly involves hydromagnetic disturbances, because the collision mean free path is too long for electron-proton collisions to play an important role. However, it has been pointed out that, once the plasma cloud is brought to rest, its kinetic energy of bulk motion (which resides entirely in the protons) may tend to become distributed in equal measure, as kinetic energy of random motion, among electrons and protons.

The great interest aroused by the discovery of the radiation belt has somewhat overshadowed the results concerning cosmic rays obtained by means of space vehicles. And yet it should not be forgotten that detectors of energetic particles had been originally installed on space vehicles for the study of cosmic rays.

Some very significant results concerning cosmic rays have been reported recently by Simpson. They are based on observations made with his counter telescope, installed aboard Explorer VI. This instrument, as previously mentioned, detects only protons of more than 75 Mev energy and electrons of more than 13 Mev energy. Particles of such energies are not found in the radiation belt beyond about 5 earth radii.

Simpson's results have to do with the so-called Forbush decreases. It has been known for many years that often the cosmic-ray intensity on the Earth drops sharply by a few per cent at the beginning of a magnetic storm. This decrease, discovered by Forbush, is ascribed to a modulation of the cosmic-ray intensity by a changing magnetic field. Until recently, however, there was no experimental information on the extension and location of the modulating mechanism. On the occasion of the magnetic storm of Aug. 15, 1959, Simpson observed a Forbush decrease occurring at 6 earth radii simultaneously with a similar decrease on the Earth. This result shows that the modulation does not occur in the vicinity of our planet.[39]

Magnetic-field measurements are also related to the problem. Vanguard III carries a proton-precession magnetometer, whose results are currently being analyzed. They cover a range of altitudes between 500 and 3700 km. To explore the magnetic field at larger distances from the Earth, Sonett and his collaborators[40] at S.T.L. have installed search-coil magnetometers aboard Pioneer I and Explorer VI. The coil is fixed with respect to the spinning vehicle, and thus measures the component of the magnetic field perpendicular to the spin axis. The results of the measurements may be summarized as follows: up to about 5 earth radii from the center of the Earth, the measured magnetic field agrees with that computed from the known dipole moment of the Earth. Beyond 5 earth radii, however, systematic deviations from the theoretical dipole field begin to appear (Fig. 25). They can be accounted for quantitatively by assuming the existence of a ring current of several million amperes, centered at 9 or 10 earth radii. Between 12 and 15 earth radii, there are violent, short-time fluctuations, with periods of the order of seconds, that are ascribed to hydromagnetic disturbances. Beyond about 15 earth radii, the field becomes quiescent and settles down to a value of several gammas, which appears to be characteristic of interplanetary space.

Previous measurements by Dolginov, with a magnetometer installed

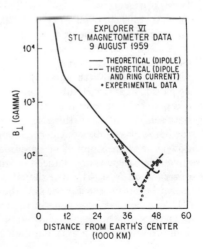

FIG. 25. Measurements of the magnetic-field component perpendicular to the spin axis of Explorer VI, showing the effect of a "ring current." (*From P. J. Coleman, C. P. Sonett, D. L. Judge, and E. J. Smith, J. Geophys. Res., 65, 1856, 1960.*)

EXPLORER VI
STL MAGNETOMETER DATA
9 AUGUST 1959

—— THEORETICAL (DIPOLE)
--- THEORETICAL (DIPOLE AND RING CURRENT)
• EXPERIMENTAL DATA

$B_\perp$ (GAMMA)

10^4

10^3

10^2

0   12   24   36   48   60
DISTANCE FROM EARTH'S CENTER
(1000 KM)

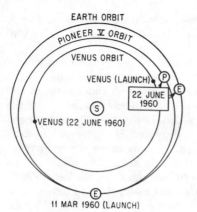

EARTH ORBIT
PIONEER $\overline{V}$ ORBIT
VENUS ORBIT
VENUS (LAUNCH)
22 JUNE 1960
VENUS (22 JUNE 1960)
11 MAR 1960 (LAUNCH)

FIG. 26. Orbit of Pioneer V.

aboard Mechta, had shown an anomaly in the geomagnetic field indicating a ring current at 3 or 4 earth radii.[41]   This anomaly has not been found in the data of Pioneer I or Explorer VI.

The second Soviet Moon rocket, Lunik II, yielded magnetic-field measurements in the vicinity of the Moon up to the time of impact on the lunar surface.   From the Lunik II magnetometer data Soviet scientists concluded that an upper limit of approximately 100 gammas could be placed on the Moon's magnetic field.[42]

Finally, some of the preliminary but very exciting results of Pioneer V (Fig. 26), are now discussed.   This deep-space probe was launched on Mar. 6, 1960, and on May 9, 1960, 1200 UT, was 13,450,000 km away, traveling along a line at approximately 45° to the Earth-Sun line.

Pioneer V carries several radiation detectors and a magnetometer similar to those of Explorer VI.   The magnetometer data obtained in the vicinity of the Earth agree with the previous results of Pioneer I and Explorer VI; in particular, they confirm the systematic deviations from a dipole field beyond 5 earth radii and the region of severe fluctuations between 12 and 15 earth radii.   Beyond this distance, the magnetic field (or better, its component perpendicular to the spin axis) appears to settle down to a value around 2 or 4 gammas.   Occasionally, however, the probe encounters regions of enhanced magnetic field.   Most notable is the event observed on Mar. 31.   On that day, as noted before, a severe magnetic storm began on the Earth, and the radiation detectors aboard Explorer VII showed drastic changes in the outer radiation belt.   Also, cosmic-ray detectors on the Earth showed a Forbush decrease of the intensity. Pioneer V was then about 5 million kilometers away.   The magnetic field recorded by the probe, which had begun to increase late the previous day, suddenly jumped to about 40 gammas, and returned to the normal value after about 24 hr.[43] Simultaneously, Simpson's telescope detected a Forbush-type decrease (Fig. 27).[44] Considerable solar activity occurred at the time. The following day, while the magnetic field was recovering to its original value and almost simultaneously with the appearance of a solar flare, both Simpson's[44] and Winckler's[45] radiation detectors revealed the arrival of high-energy protons and electrons (or photons), presumably produced by the second flare.

These observations appear to confirm the existence of "magnetized plasma clouds" emitted by the Sun and traveling through space, to produce, upon arrival on the Earth, magnetic storms and other geophysical effects. They also confirm Simpson's previous conclusions that the mechanism responsible for the Forbush decreases is not centered at the Earth.

Energetic electrons were detected by Pioneer V in the absence of solar flares. At no time, however, was the flux of energetic electrons in outer space greater than 10^7 per cm^2 per sec, which may be compared with peak values of $\sim 10^{11}$ per cm^0 per sec for the flux of trapped electrons in the outer radiation belt. This is further indication that the trapped electrons are produced by local accelerations, probably in the disordered fringes of the geomagnetic field, rather than by direct injection of solar plasma at the energies detected in the satellite counters.[45,46]

Simpson has discussed additional aspects of the correlation between

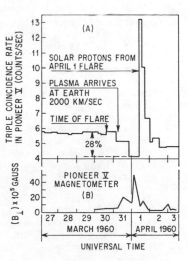

FIG. 27. Measurements of magnetic-field and energetic-particles flux made aboard Pioneer V during the magnetic storm of Mar. 31–Apr. 1, 1960. (*From J. Simpson, Phys. Rev. Letters, 5, 269, 1960.*)

terrestrial events and the magnetic field and particle measurements on Pioneer V.[47]   The magnetic storm and Forbush decrease of Mar. 31, 1960, were apparently produced by the class 2+ flare which occurred between 1455 and 1858 UT on Mar. 30.   A second flare, of class 3, began on Apr. 1 at 0845 UT and lasted until 1222 UT.   At the time of occurrence of this flare, the plasma cloud emitted during the first flare had already enveloped both Pioneer V and the earth.   From the response of Simpson's detectors on Pioneer V it is clear that the second flare emitted an appreciable flux of solar protons with energies greater than 75 Mev.   The fortuitous injection of these energetic protons into the region of the previously emitted plasma cloud provides a means for testing the magnetic-field condition within the cloud.   According to Leinbach, polar-cap absorption set in on Apr. 1 about 0945 UT, indicating that the transit time of the solar protons was approximately 1 hr.   The direct transit time of a 100-Mev proton is 18 min between Sun and Earth.   Thus the magnetic fields in the plasma cloud produced by the first flare lengthened the transit time of the protons by approximately a factor of 3.   It is significant that the solar protons, although somewhat delayed by their passage through the plasma cloud, still arrived with relative rapidity and in great numbers.   From the observed transit time, Simpson concludes that either (1) the magnetic fields within the plasma cloud were disordered and very weak, and in this case he sets an upper limit of 0.5 gamma to the magnitude of a dis-

Table 4. Instrumentation of Explorer VI

A. Counter telescope, 5 g/cm² Pb shielding (Chicago)
   Coincidence rate measures N⁰ of:
       Electrons, $E > 13$ Mev
       Protons, $E > 75$ Mev
   Single rate measures N⁰ of:
       Electrons, $E >$ 13 Mev
       Protons, $E >$ 75 Mev
       X rays, $E \gtrsim 300$ kev (low efficiency)
B. G.M. counter, unshielded, wall 0.02″ steel (Minnesota); counts:
       Electrons, $E >$ 2 Mev
       Protons, $E > 16$ Mev
       X rays, $E \gtrsim 30$ kev (low efficiency)
C. Ionization chamber, unshielded, wall 0.02″ Al (Minnesota)
       Detects: approximately same radiation as B
D. Plastic scintillator, under 3 mg/cm² Al (S.T.L.); counts:
       Electrons, $E > 200$ kev
       Protons, $E >$ 2 Mev
       X rays, $E > 100$ kev (low efficiency)
E. Search coil magnetometer (S.T.L.)
F. Micrometeorite detectors, TV camera to scan clouds, radio propagation experiment

ordered field which would correspond to a transit time of 1 hr, or (2) the field, if strong, must have connected the sun directly with the Earth in an approximately radial configuration. It may be noted that there is evidence for the second alternative over the first in that the flare on Mar. 30 was accompanied by a Forbush decrease, signifying the presence of appreciable interplanetary magnetic fields.

REFERENCES

1. This chapter represents some revision and expansion of the article by Bruno Rossi, "Scientific Results of Experiments in Space," *Trans., Amer. Geophys. Union*, *41*, 410–429 (1960).
2. *The Other Side of the Moon*, issued by the U.S.S.R. Academy of Science, trans. by J. B. Sykes (Pergamon Press, London, 1960).
3. H. Friedman: *Astron. J.*, *65*, 5, 264, 1960.
4. J..E. Kupperian, Jr., E. T. Bryan, T. A. Chubb, and H. Friedman: *1959 Planetary and Space Sci.*, *1*, 3.
5. J. A. O'Keefe: "Determination of the Earth's Gravitational Field," in H. Kallmann Bijl (ed.), *Space Research*, p. 448 (*Proc. 1st Intern. Space Sci. Symposium*), North-Holland Publishing Co., Amsterdam, 1960.
6. S. W. Henriksen: *IGY Annals* (in press).
7. R. Jastrow: *Missiles and Rockets*, July 20, 1959.
8. P. Musen, R. Bryant, and A. Bailie: *Science*, *131*, 935, 1960.
9. P. Musen: *J..Geophys. Res.*, *65*, 1391, 1960.
10. R. Jastrow and R. Bryant: *J. Geophys. Res.*, *65*, 3512, 1960.
11. L. G. Jacchia: *Nature*, *183*, 526, 1959.
12. W. Priester, reported by L. G. Jacchia: *Nature*, *183*, 935, 1959.
13. L. G. Jacchia: *Nature*, *183*, 1662, 1959.
14. M. Nicolet: Private communication.
15. R. Jastrow and R. Bryant: *J. Geophys. Res.* (in press).
16. S. M. Poloskov: "Upper Atmosphere Structure Parameters According to Data Obtained from U.S.S.R. Rockets and Satellites during IGY," *Space Research*, p. 95 (see Ref. 5).
17. R. L. Smith and R. A. Helliwell: *J. Geophys. Res.*, *65*, 2583, 1960.
18. W. W. Berning: *J. Geophys. Res.*, *65*, 2589, 1960.
19. J. S. Nisbet and S. A. Bowhill: *J. Geophys. Res.*, *65*, 2597, 1960.
20. S. F. Singer: *Trans. Amer. Geophys. Union*, *38*, 176, 1957.
21. S. N. Vernov, N. L. Grigorov, Yu. I. Logachev, A. E. Chudakov, *Dok. Akad. Nauk USSR*, *120*, 1231, 1958.
22. S. N. Vernov, A. E. Chudakov, E. V. Gorchakov, Yu. I. Logachev, and P. V. Vakulov: *Planet. Space Sci.*, *1*, 86 (Pergamon Press, London, 1959).
23. Symposium on Scientific Effects of Artificially Introduced Radiation at High Altitude, *Proc. Nat. Acad. Sci.*, *45*, 1141, 1959.
24. J. A. Van Allen and L. A. Frank: *Nature*, *183*, 430, 1959; *ibid.*, *184*, 219, 1959.
25. S. N. Vernov, A. E. Chudakov, P. V. Vakulov, and Yu. I. Logachev: *Soviet Physics Dok.*, *4*, 338, 1959.

26. A. Rosen, C. P. Sonett, P. J. Coleman, and C. E. McIlwain: *J. Geophys. Res.*, *64*, 709, 1959.
27. S. Freden and R. White: *Phys. Rev. Letters*, *3*, 9, 1959.
28. M. Walt, L. F. Chase, Jr., J. B. Cladis, W. L. Imhof, and D. J. Knecht: "Energy Spectra and Altitude Dependence of Electrons Trapped in the Earth's Magnetic Field," *Space Research*, p. 910 (see Ref. 5).
29. J. A. Van Allen: *J. Geophys. Res.*, *64*, 1683, 1959.
30. C. Y. Fan, P. Meyer, and J. A. Simpson: "Trapped and Cosmic Radiation Measurements from Explorer VI," *Space Research*, p. 951 (see Ref. 5).
31. R. Arnoldy, R. Hoffman, and J. Winckler: *J. Geophys. Res.*, *65*, 1361, 1960.
32. S. F. Singer: *Phys. Rev. Letters*, *1*, 171, 1958; *1*, 181, 1958.
33. W. N. Hess: *Phys. Rev. Letters*, *3*, 11, 1958.
34. A. J. Dessler: *J. Geophys. Res.*, *64*, 713, 1959. See also A. J. Dessler and R. Karplus: *Phys. Rev. Letters*, *4*, 271, 1960.
35. T. Gold: *Nature*, *183*, 355, 1959.
36. T. Gold: *J. Geophys. Res.*, *64*, 1665, 1959.
37. P. Rothwell and C. McIlwain: *J. Geophys. Res.*, *64*, 799, 1960.
38. Reports presented at meeting of American Geophysical Union, Washington, D.C., April, 1960.
39. C. Y. Fan, P. Meyer, and J. A. Simpson: *Phys. Rev. Letters*, *4*, 421, 1960.
40. E. J. Smith, P. J. Coleman, D. L. Judge, and C. P. Sonett, *J. Geophys. Res.*, *65*, 1858, 1960.
41. S. Dolginov and N. Pushkov: *Proc. Moscow Cosmic Ray Conf.*, *3*, 30, 1959.
42. S. Sh. Dolginov, E. G. Eroshenko, L. N. Zhuzgov, N. V. Pushkov, L. O. Tyurmina: "Measuring the Magnetic Fields of the Earth and Moon by means of Sputniks III and Space Rockets I and II," *Space Research*, p. 863 (see Ref. 5).
43. P. J. Coleman, Jr., C. P. Sonett, D. L. Judge, and E. J. Smith: *J. Geophys. Res.*, *65*, 1856, 1960.
44. C. Y. Fan, P. Meyer, and J. A. Simpson: *J. Geophys. Res.*, *65*, 1862, 1960.
45. R. L. Arnoldy, R. A. Hoffman, and J. R. Winckler: *J. Geophys. Res.*, *65*, 3004, 1960.
46. J. A. Van Allen and W. C. Lin: *J. Geophys. Res.*, *65*, 2998, 1960.
47. J. Simpson: *Phys. Rev. Letters*, *5*, 269, 1960.
48. W. H. Munk and G. J. F. MacDonald: *The Rotation of the Earth: A Geophysical Discussion*, Cambridge, 1960, Chapter 12.

PART **2**

GRAVITY

$3 =$

THE NATURE OF GRAVITATION

R. H. Dicke

1. BASIC CONSIDERATIONS

Gravitation, the oldest interaction with which man is familiar and the first to be described theoretically, is still but poorly known observationally. Artificial Earth satellites and planets promise to provide a new impetus for research on the nature of the gravitational field.

There has been very little fundamental experimental work done in the past fifty years. This appears to be due in large measure to three causes: (1) the difficulty of performing significant experiments; (2) the rush of competing interests and ideas brought on by the advent of quantum mechanics in the first quarter of this century and the belief that gravitation was too weak to be important for this work; (3) the widely recognized elegance and perfection of Einstein's general relativity, which led many physicists to conclude that it must represent an established part of physics, hence no longer viable.

Whatever the cause, this lack of experimental and observational work on gravitation has resulted in one of the most beautiful theoretical edifices of physics resting upon a very weak observational foundation. While the planetary observations are admittedly accurate, they are generally not accurate enough to exhibit the significant relativistic effects. This is due to the weakness of the gravitational interaction, or equivalently to the low velocities of the planets. Retardation effects of the order of $(v/c)^2$ smaller than the interactions themselves are too small to be observed.

2. THE THREE CLASSIC CHECKS

The only relativistic effect connected with planetary motion which has been unquestionably observed is the perihelion rotation of the planet Mercury. Here, because of the very careful work of Clemence,[1] with a reasonable choice of assumed masses for the planets, it has been possible to account for the motion of Mercury, including the relativistic perihelion rotation, with considerable accuracy. To what extent this choice of adopted masses would agree with the masses resulting from an accurate self-consistent treatment of the motion of the inner planets is not known because such a calculation has never been made. It seems likely, however, that improved planetary calculations will result at most in a relatively small change in the relativistic precession. On the other hand, as will be explained later, small to moderate departures from the Einstein value are to be expected under certain interesting conditions. Hence it is important to obtain a very precise value for the relativistic precession.

The other two standard astronomical checks of general relativity—the gravitational red shift and gravitational deflection of light—are rather poor. The early hope that more observations would result in greatly improved values for these important effects did not materialize. The gravitational red shift of light from the Sun appears to be badly obscured by Doppler shifts resulting from turbulence in the Sun's atmosphere. This effect is not yet quantitatively understood. Observations of white dwarfs are plagued by other troubles.

The discovery by Mössbauer[2] that certain low-energy gamma rays could be produced without the usual Doppler-effect broadening of the spectral line made it possible to make a laboratory measurement of the gravitational red shift. Experiments by Cranshaw, Schriffer, and Whitehead[3] and Pound and Rebka[4] verified the result from general relativity with an accuracy of 10 per cent.[4]

The comparison of the clock rate of a satellite-borne atomic clock with a clock on the earth has been suggested also as a means of investigating the gravitational red shift.

3. POSSIBLE FUTURE DEVELOPMENTS

3.1 Mach's Principle

The great need at present is for experiment and not theory, but theoretical speculation is an important guide to experiment. For all its beauty and elegance there are a number of places where difficulties arise in general relativity. These difficulties range from highly technical questions to straightforward physical and philosophical questions.

One of the more knotty of these questions concerns Mach's principle. The majority of physicists have long believed that completely empty space is without structure. The mathematical concepts of points, lines, geodesics, etc., are believed to be without physical parallel in a completely empty space. Physical concepts must be associated with physical objects. For this reason it is assumed that the geometrical properties of space should be determined uniquely by the matter in the space. The equations of general relativity are such that the geometry is determined only after boundary conditions are stated, and yet it has not been possible to formulate completely satisfactory boundary conditions. Such boundary conditions would, for example, exclude solutions without matter present.

Mach[5] long ago and, even earlier, Bishop Berkeley[6] recognized that from the standpoint of relativity and a structureless space, the very real and commonplace inertial forces which twist at a gyroscope in a rotating laboratory may be regarded as due to the revolution of distant matter about the stationary laboratory. Thus, generally speaking, inertial forces may be interpreted as the interaction of a gravitational field produced by distant accelerated matter with matter in the laboratory.[7] Mach's point of view has been only partially incorporated into general relativity.

A basic difference exists between the point of view of Mach and that of Einstein. In general relativity the gravitational constant is a universal constant that determines the strength of gravity and the motion of gravitationally interacting matter. For Mach, however, the accelerations are determined by the distribution of matter without reference to the strength of the field. Thus, from Mach's point of view, the Earth, accelerating toward the Sun but described in a coordinate system for which the Earth is at rest, is acted on by two balanced gravitational forces: the gravitational pull of the Sun and the gravitational pull of distant accelerated matter. If both forces are doubled as a result of *all* gravitational forces doubling, the acceleration does not change. The acceleration is thus dependent upon the mass distribution only.

For a simplified model of the universe it is easy to obtain an appropriate expression for the acceleration of the Earth toward the Sun. Assume that distant matter in the universe is in the form of a hollow spherical shell of mass M and radius R (both measured in atomic units) and that the Sun, of mass $m \ll M$, is at the center of the sphere. The Earth is at a distance $r \ll R$ from the Sun. The acceleration of the Earth toward the Sun is known to be proportional to m/r^2; it is assumed to depend also upon M, R, and c (assuming the velocity of light for the propagation velocity of gravitational waves).

The unique expression for the acceleration compatible with elementary dimensional considerations is

$$a = \gamma \, \frac{m}{r^2} \frac{Rc^2}{M} \tag{1}$$

where γ is a dimensionless constant which may be assumed to be of the order of unity. From Newton, the acceleration may be written as

$$a = \frac{Gm}{r^2} \tag{2}$$

where G is the gravitational constant. Combining these equations gives

$$\frac{GM}{Rc^2} = \gamma \tag{3}$$

This suggests that G is not a universal "constant" but a function of M/R. Thus G is a field quantity determined by the distribution of distant matter. Equation (3) suggests that for a static distribution of matter the local value of G is given by

$$G^{-1} = \gamma^{-1} \iiint \frac{\rho \, dx_1 \, dx_2 \, dx_3}{rc^2} \tag{4}$$

where ρ is matter density. If this interpretation of Mach's principle is correct, the contribution to G^{-1} at the Earth's orbit due to the presence of the Sun is of the order of 1 part in 10^8.

The real Universe is not a vast spherical shell, but a more or less uniform mass distribution with all parts moving away from each other (an expanding Universe). Because of the Doppler effect, light from distant parts of the Universe is reddened. Matter beyond a certain distance cannot be seen at all. Thus electromagnetic signals arrive from only a finite part of the possibly infinite Universe. If gravitational waves propagate in similar fashion, the inertial forces are to be associated with this finite visible part of the Universe. The M and R in Eq. (3) may be interpreted loosely as the mass and radius of this visible Universe and in Eq. (4) ρ may be defined as an "effective" density. Because of the motion of distant matter, ρ would generally be a function of r.

This interpretation of Mach's principle leads to interesting possibilities: (1) Does the change with time of the mass M and radius R of the visible universe resulting from the general expansion lead to a change with time of the locally measured value of G? (2) Does the locally measured value of G change if we approach the Sun? (3) Does the locally measured value of G depend upon the velocity of the laboratory relative to distant matter? The distribution of distant matter appears to be changed by such motion.

Another possible effect of this interpretation of inertial forces is that the lack of symmetry of the actual Universe (e.g., the pancake shape of the local galaxy) might lead to an anisotropy in the inertial reaction; i.e., the inertial mass of a particle could appear as a tensor rather than a scalar. This possibility has been discussed by Bondi.[8] Cocconi and Salpeter[9] suggested an experimental test for anisotropy. This was followed by other suggestions and experiments, the best of which was that of Hughes et al.[10] They were able to show that the type of anisotropy of inertial mass for which they were searching was less than 1 part in 10^{20}. Because of its great precision, this result is important. It should be noted, however, that anisotropy of inertia is already included in the definition of the metric tensor, and the experiment does not test for anisotropy of inertia generally, but rather it asks whether the anisotropy is the same for all particles and fields in an atomic nucleus. Only a difference in anisotropy from one particle to another would produce a positive effect.

3.2 Dirac Cosmology

Many years ago Dirac[11] noted that, when expressed in typical atomic units such as the mass of the proton and classical radius of the electron, etc., the fundamental physical and astrophysical constants (now all dimensionless numbers) fall into distinct classes. Numbers are of the order of unity, of the order of 10^{40}, or of the order of $(10^{40})^2$. In particular, the reciprocal of the gravitational constant is of the order of 10^{40}, the age of the universe of the same order, and the mass of the universe out to the Hubble radius is of the order of 10^{80}.

We define the Hubble radius of the Universe as the Hubble age of the

Universe times the velocity of light. It is of the same order of magnitude as the radius of the visible Universe. The Hubble age is defined as the age obtained by taking the distance of a galaxy and dividing by its velocity of recession as determined by the observations of red shift (for $v \ll c$).

With the assumption that *now* is a random time,[12] the fact that there are several dimensionless numbers, all about the same size (i.e., 10^{40}) is probably not accidental. This in turn implies that the gravitational constant becomes weaker with time, varying inversely as the age of the Universe, and that the mass of the visible Universe increases with the square of the time. This mass increase is not the result of the spontaneous creation of matter, as in the Hoyle-Gold-Bondi theory, but is due to the inward motion of matter relative to the expanding Hubble sphere.

Being based on empirical evidence involving only orders of magnitude, Dirac's cosmology should not be interpreted too literally. Thus an equally satisfactory interpretation of the empirical data is obtained if one assumes that the fractional rate of change of G with time is inversely proportional to the Hubble age rather than true age of the Universe.

Dirac's cosmology is compatible with Eq. (3) with γ of the order of unity, where M and R are now interpreted as the mass and radius of the universe out to the Hubble radius. Thus, as the universe expands and M and R change, G changes in such a way as to keep Eq. (3) satisfied.

3.3 Other Physical "Constants"

Undoubtedly, a factor contributing to the very limited improvement of our knowledge of gravitation in the past fifty years has been the widespread feeling that gravitation was too weak an interaction to be important to the main stream of physics concerned with the structure of atoms first, then nuclei, and finally particles themselves. While questions of particle structure were important in the nineteenth century, such questions were usually ignored as meaningless upon the advent of relativity and quantum mechanics. Only in the past ten years has it become increasingly clear that an "elementary" particle like the proton is a complex structure with a distributed charge and magnetization. It may be thought of as surrounded by a host of attendant virtual particles in the form of photons, electron-positron pairs, and mesons. It has become clear that the gravitational interaction between these constituent parts may be important, and the reason for some of the divergences which plague quantum field theories may be the failure to include the gravitational interaction.

Landau[13] and his colleagues have shown that subject to their assumptions, including strictly point interactions between particles, there results a zero electromagnetic coupling between charged particles. On the other hand, they show that if elementary particles are given a "size" of approximately a gravitational length

$$\lambda_g = \left(\frac{G\hbar}{c^3}\right)^{1/2} \sim 10^{-33} \text{ cm} \tag{5}$$

the resulting renormalized electric charge of a particle e is in reasonable agreement with that observed. Landau[13] gives the following relation:

$$e^2 = \frac{e_1^2}{1 + (2ne_1^2/3\pi\hbar c) \log (\lambda_c/\lambda_g)} \tag{6}$$

Here e_1 is the "bare" electric charge, whereas e is the "renormalized" charge which is less than e_1, because of partial neutralization by the polarization charge of the "vacuum."

$$\lambda_c = \frac{\hbar}{mc} \tag{7}$$

is the Compton wavelength of the electron. n signifies the number of different kinds of charged particles which exist. In reckoning n, particles of spin $\frac{1}{2}$ count as 1 but spin-zero particles count as $\frac{1}{4}$. If n is assumed to be 12 and $e_1^2/\hbar c \geq 1$, e^2 is found to agree closely with the observed value.

If it is true that the renormalized elementary electric charge and particle masses are affected by gravitation, then a variation in the local value of the gravitational constant might result in a variation of the fine-structure constant, and other coupling constants, possibly also in the dimensionless ratio of the mass of the proton to that of the electron or the mass of the mesons relative to that of the electron. Another possibility[14] is that the anomalous "weak interactions" leading to beta decay and the decay of "strange" particles should have a strength dependent in a sensitive way upon the local value of G.

To what extent these physical constants can vary without contradicting experiments and to what extent a reasonable theory, incorporating such flexibility but remaining compatible with observations, can be constructed are not yet known. Admittedly, there is a strongly speculative character to the assumption that particle structure is dependent on position, time, or velocity. However, the hypothesis is sufficiently interesting that it should be remembered in discussing fundamental experiments on gravitation.

3.4 Theories of a Variable Gravitational Interaction

It has been possible to construct theories which are generally covariant, incorporate the relativity principle, and lead to a variable gravitational interaction compatible with Mach's principle. One of the first such satisfactory theories is that of Jordan.[15] Recognizing that a variable gravitational constant requires an extra degree of freedom, Jordan constructed a five-dimensional gravitation theory having points of similarity to the theories of Klein and Kaluza.[16] In terms of physical content, this theory is equivalent to a scalar theory in which the metric tensor is supplemented by a scalar-field variable, both together comprising the gravitational field. The locally measured gravitational constant is then effectively a function of this scalar-field variable.

Fierz[17] has shown that, by redefining the metric tensor, Jordan's theory can be transformed into other forms. He has also shown that it is generally necessary to consider the direct effect of the scalar field on the motion of matter. It may be shown that for one of these forms particles move gravitationally on geodesics and hence this theory is compatible with the very precise Eötvös[18] experiment. C. Brans at Princeton has been investigating this form of Jordan's theory.

It is a common feature of the various forms of Jordan's theory that the computed value of the Mercury perihelion rotation rate differs somewhat from that of Einstein. The theory contains an adjustable constant, and the size of this constant affects the perihelion rotation rate. A departure from the Einstein value of a few per cent would be not unreasonable.

It is not presently known if it is possible to construct along these lines a theory of a variable gravitational interaction which will give the Einstein value. In any case it is important to attempt to improve the accuracy of the observed relativistic perihelion rotation rate in order to help distinguish between these various alternatives.

The theory due to Milne,[19] developed a quarter of a century ago, should also be mentioned because it may have been the first to incorporate different atomic and gravitational time scales. Some have found the conceptual basis of the theory objectionable as well as its conclusions.

Milne postulated a universe populated by idealized "observers" who can signal each other with an idealized light signal whose velocity of propagation is by definition a constant c. The observers are furnished with identical interchangeable clocks and measure distances by the transit time of a reflected signal. Now, two independent and fundamentally different classes of phenomena are available to the observers as standards of time: (1) electromagnetic, as exemplified by atomic or molecular line frequencies (the "kinematic time" t of Milne's terminology, now often called "atomic time"), and (2) mechanical-inertial, as exemplified by a pendulum clock or the motion of a body in orbit (the "dynamic time" τ of Milne, or, more popularly, "gravitational time").

Milne deduced that the two kinds of time measure are connected by the relation $\tau = T[1 + \ln(t/T)]$ or its inverse $t = T \exp[(\tau/T) - 1]$, in which T is the "age of the universe" by the atomic clock.

4. IMPLICATIONS OF A VARYING GRAVITATIONAL CONSTANT

A varying gravitational constant would have important implications for both astronomers and geologists. Conversely, there is a possibility that geological and astronomical observations can be used to set upper bounds on possible variations in the gravitational constant. Implications of a varying gravitational constant have been briefly discussed previously.[15,20,21] Several important effects are described here, some for the first time, since they are of interest in connection with space exploration.

4.1 Effects Associated with a Secular Variation of G

For purposes of definiteness it is assumed that the age of the universe is 13 billion years and that Dirac's hypothesis is valid; namely, the gravitational constant varies inversely as the age of the Universe. Other atomic constants $(\hbar, c, m, e)$ are defined or assumed to be fixed, and only the gravitational constant varies. This implies that angular momentum is a constant of motion with this set of units.

a. Evolution Rate of the Stars. The radiation rate of a star varies with G as a power between 4 and 7, depending upon central temperature.[22] For the Sun it would be expected that the radiation rate would vary approximately as G^7. As long as the time scale used in discussing stellar evolution is internal, being based only on observations of stellar evolution, no discrepancy should appear. However, an intercomparison with other measures of time could lead to discrepancies. For example, if kinematical considerations were to be used to give an age of a cluster of galaxies and this age were to be compared with the age determined from calculations of stellar evolution,[23] a discrepancy might appear. However, kinematic considerations are usually unable to give a reliable estimate of age. Such discrepancies as have appeared probably have other explanations (see, for example, Oort's discussion of motion and distribution of galaxies in the Virgo cluster[24]).

Rapid evolution in the past and accompanying large radiation rates would be expected to result in large turbulence velocities in the gas content of the Galaxy. This would in turn result in large random motions for stars formed out of the gas. A strong correlation between the age of a group of stars and the dispersion in their motions has been known for some time (Strömgren). However, there are other ways, independent of a possible variation in G, of obtaining early rapid evolution in the Galaxy, such as a possible tendency to form massive stars early in its history.

Better information about the Sun, the solar system, and its age would be of considerable help in setting a limit on a secular variation in G. With the assumption that the present theories of stellar evolution are substantially correct, the observed stellar parameters—radiation rate, mass, and radius—permit, for a stellar model, a calculation of the total energy radiated in the Sun's lifetime. An approximate age of the Sun is provided by meteorite ages (4.5 b.y.). Radiation rates in the past may consequently be inferred. The chief uncertainty in the calculation results from imperfect knowledge of the abundance of primordial helium in the Sun. Unfortunately, helium abundance cannot be determined spectroscopically with any reliability. If it can be assumed that this abundance is quite small ($\ll$20 per cent), a radiation rate in the past compatible with Dirac's postulate and a Hubble age greater than 10 b.y. is possible.[25]

The use of a satellite to determine the composition of the solar wind could greatly reduce the uncertainty in the helium abundance of the Sun.

With the assumption that the gravitational constant is greater in the past, the stellar ages inferred from theories of stellar evolution would be incorrect and could give ages much too great. For example, the 15-b.y.-old stars discovered recently by Wilson[26] would be actually only 4.15 b.y. years old if G varied inversely as the age of the Universe, assumed to be 15 b.y., and the rate of burning were proportional to G^7.

b. Temperature Variation of the Earth and Moon. With G decreasing in accordance with Dirac's hypothesis, the maximum temperature of the Moon's surface (assuming constant albedo) should have varied inversely as the age of the universe to the 2.25 power. This is plotted in Fig. 2. For the Earth it is only feasible to obtain a rough estimate of past temperatures. The water-vapor content of the Earth's atmosphere is a very sensitive function of the Earth's temperature. An increase in the Sun's radiation rate would result in an increase in the water-vapor content. This, in turn, would change the vertical temperature gradient, the distribution of infrared radiators, the circulation pattern, and the albedo of the atmosphere. The effect of these atmospheric changes on the heat balance would result in a change in the surface temperature of the Earth. The sensitive temperature dependence of water-vapor pressure would tend either to stabilize the Earth's temperature or to make it unstable. This can be seen without a detailed understanding of the complicated atmospheric mechanism. A calculation for a simple model of an atmosphere composed of 90 per cent water vapor suggests that the effect of water vapor is to stabilize the surface temperature. The curve for the Earth's temperature shown in Fig. 2 is an estimate based on this calculation. It has no great reliability.

For times in the past greater than some 3 billion years there would have been no liquid water, the whole atmosphere being essentially water vapor and optically opaque. The surface temperature of the Earth would have been high, probably in excess of 1000°C. The formation of sedimentary rocks would have awaited the condensation of this atmosphere.

A point of considerable interest to the exploration of the Moon is whether or not there is evidence of high surface temperatures in the past. Such high surface temperature might be expected to lead to a variety of observable effects. It is conceivable that a higher average temperature 3 to 4 billion years ago would have enabled an isostatic adjustment to take place in craters and mountains where the crust would be now too rigid. It would be interesting to inquire whether the tendency for old craters to be more shallow than young might be due to isostatic adjustment. The absence of central peaks from old craters might also be due to isostatic adjustment. Future exploration of the Moon might answer these questions.

The over-all shape of the Moon, being flattened and having a bulge toward the Earth, does not now appear to be in isostatic adjustment. It may be that the average surface temperature was high enough in the past, when the Earth was closer, to allow a tidal adjustment to take place. This is a very old explanation of the bulge; it is possibly a fossil tidal distortion. The body tide would have damped the Moon's rotation if rapid isostatic adjustment could occur. With a rigid Moon, tidal damping of its rotation would not have occurred.

Another question of considerable interest concerns the evolution of the planetary system. The noticeably different composition of the inner planets from the outer and the variation in density of the inner planets require explanation. If the solar radiation rate were very much greater in the past than now, it would be necessary to assume many other con-

FIG. 1. The southern portion of the moon at third quarter showing both old and young craters. Note vestigial remains of old craters in the highlands, lava-flooded craters in the maria, and young craters in both regions. Lunar explorations may one day enable an unraveling of the thermal history of the Moon's surface (see Fig. 2). (*Courtesy Mt. Wilson and Palomar Observatories.*)

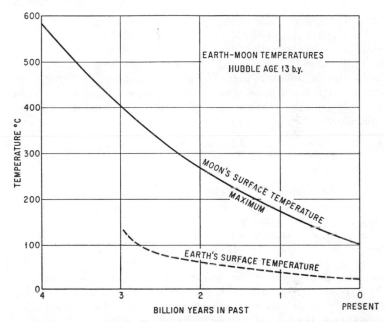

FIG. 2. Hypothetical past surface temperatures of the Earth and Moon under the assumption that the gravitational constant is varying, inversely proportional to the time, with a fractional rate of change now of 7.7×10^{-10} per year.

ditions different also. Thus high-energy corpuscular streams from the Sun could have been so intense as to raise the exospheric temperature of the Earth and other planets to high values. This could in turn lead to noticeable evaporation of even the heavy elements in the atmosphere. Future explorations of other planets could shed new light on this problem.

   c. The Rotation Rate of the Earth. One obvious way in which a secular variation in G should show up is in a time variation of a comparison of atomic and gravitational measures of time. It will be seen later that there are satellite experiments which could assist in making this comparison. For the moment the only source of information which compares these time scales is the Earth's rotation. The Earth's dimensions are determined largely by nongravitational forces, and its rotation is a measure of atomic time. Fortunately, ancient information on solar eclipses enables a comparison to be made between the revolution rate of the Moon and the rotation rate of the Earth over a long time interval.

This type of investigation has a long and venerable history, but is even now not completely satisfactory. Secular accelerations of the Earth and Sun (the secular acceleration of the Sun is a measure of the Earth's rotational acceleration) can be obtained from old eclipse observations, but are unreliable because they are strongly dependent upon a single ancient eclipse described in the following rather ambiguous prose:

Isid-Raki-Rabe of the city of Gozon: "insurrection in the city of Assur. In the month of Sivan the Sun was eclipsed." (Was it eclipsed at Assur? Was the eclipse total?)

On the other hand, the whole situation is greatly improved if modern telescopic observations are used to obtain the secular acceleration of the Moon on an ephemeris time scale. To do this the effect of the irregularity in the Earth's rotation must be eliminated by subtracting from the observed acceleration of the Moon the observed acceleration of the Sun multiplied by the ratio of their mean motions. The use of these modern telescopic observations of the secular acceleration of the Moon on an ephemeris time scale greatly reduces the burden placed on ancient eclipses. It is now necessary only that the ancient observations supply information in the form of a linear relation between the secular acceleration of the Sun and that of the Moon. The accuracy of these old observations seems to be adequate for this purpose. By combining the ancient eclipse observations with modern telescopic observations it is possible to obtain a fair measure of both the secular acceleration of the Moon and the Sun, both on an ephemeris time scale.[27]

The acceleration of the Moon is due to tidal interactions with the Earth. Because of the conservation of angular momentum, the resulting change in the Earth's rotation rate is completely predictable from the observed motion of the Moon. Other predictable changes in the Earth's rotation rate are due to the solar tide (subject to reasonable assumptions) and the solar atmospheric tide. After allowance is made for known effects, the remaining acceleration of the Earth (on a gravitational time scale) can be said to be due either to a changing gravitational constant or other unknown causes.

The result of a detailed study by Munk and MacDonald[28] is that there is a residual acceleration of the Earth's rotation. It is of the right sign and roughly the right size to be accounted for by a secular variation in G. Unfortunately, there are several geophysical effects which could also produce this effect, or obscure it. In particular, a fall of sea level at a rate of a meter per thousand years would decrease the moment of inertia of the Earth and increase the rotation rate by the right amount. Also the effect of interaction of the Earth's magnetic field with interplanetary ionized gas is presently not well understood. It would tend to slow down the Earth in its rotation and compensate for the effect of a secular variation in G.

It must be concluded that at present there is little chance of obtaining reliable information concerning a secular variation in G from the Earth's rotation. However, the uncertainties concerning the torque exerted by the interplanetary gas could be eliminated if there were good information about the interplanetary gas. Satellite observations may provide this information.

d. Expansion of the Moon. A slowly decreasing gravitational constant (at a rate of about 1 part in 10^{10} per year) would result in a release of the gravitational compression of the Moon. The radial expansion rate to be expected is roughly 0.1 per cent per billion years. This should result in the formation of surface cracks. Cracks (rills) are in fact known to exist on the Moon. The use of a large balloon or satellite-borne telescope could give greatly improved photographs of the Moon. Such cracks could some day be looked for on photographs taken from a nearby satellite.

e. Expansion of the Earth. A decreasing gravitational constant would have resulted in a slow expansion of the Earth, the circumference increasing by 300 km in a billion years.[20]

Several geophysicists (Carey,[29] Wilson,[30] Egyed[31]) have suggested that a number of puzzling features of the Earth's topography are explained by an assumption that the Earth has been expanding with time. For example, the Mid-Atlantic ridge and the east and west coast lines of the Atlantic Ocean all have the same shape, suggesting that the medial crack in the Mid-Atlantic ridge is a separation crack and that the Atlantic Ocean was formed through the separation of the Americas from Europe-Africa.

While this explanation may be correct, it is not clear that a general expansion of the Earth is required to cause such a separation. It could also be caused by convection in the mantle. Certainly it must be said that if continental drift has been occurring to the extent indicated by recent paleomagnetic data, the effects of an expansion of radius of 47 km per b.y. would be negligible. Also, the rate of expansion required by Egyed is ten to twenty times as great as this value.

If subcrustal currents are not important, an expansion in radius of only 0.0047 cm per year could produce a medial crack in the Atlantic 2 km wide

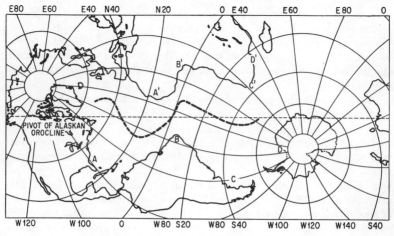

FIG. 3. Map showing the coast lines of the Americas and Europe-Africa in relation to the Mid-Atlantic ridge. (*From W. S. Carey.*[29])

in only 13 m.y., assuming that half the expansion takes place in the Atlantic.*

4.2 Velocity Dependence of Active Gravitational Mass

The possibility that the active gravitational mass of a body depends upon its velocity relative to distant matter suggests an important satellite experiment to be discussed later. We here merely investigate the implications of such a variation.

The Universe may be reasonably assumed to be uniform and isotropic. By symmetry the active gravitational mass, and hence the gravitational constant, would be an even function of v/c, where v is the velocity of the laboratory relative to a coordinate system in which the universe is isotropic. Assuming continuity in the function and its derivatives, the fractional change in G resulting from motion relative to this coordinate system would be in lowest order:

$$\frac{\delta G}{G} = \beta \left(\frac{v}{c}\right)^2 \tag{8}$$

Here β is a dimensionless constant of the order of unity. It may be pre-

* It is a pleasure to acknowledge a number of very helpful conversations with H. Hess on the geophysical questions discussed above.

sumed that β is either zero or satisfies

$$0.1 < |\beta| < 10 \qquad (9)$$

The majority of physicists would bet that β is zero.   This is not the type
of question which can be adequately decided by a wager, however;
experiments are needed.

Purely for purposes of discussion and with no suggestion that this

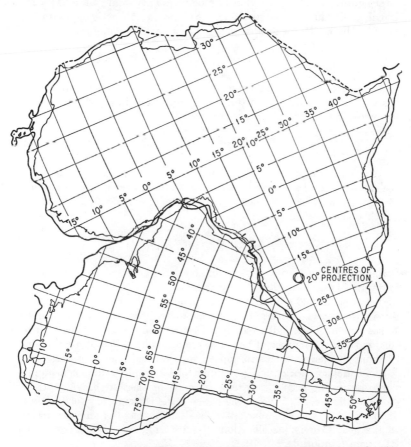

FIG. 4. Map showing the fit between South America and Africa
at the 2000-m isobath along the slope below the edge of the
continental shelf.   (*From W. S. Carey.*[29])

should be accepted, β is for the moment assumed to satisfy Eq. (9). The velocity of the Sun relative to distant matter may be presumed from observations of extragalactic red shifts to lie in the range ± 300 km per sec. For a velocity of 300 km per sec, $(v/c)^2 = 10^{-6}$. It would appear to be rather unlikely that the component of the Sun's velocity in the plane of the ecliptic is less than 30 km per sec. As the Earth moves about the Sun its velocity of 30 km per sec must first be added to, then 6 months later subtracted from, the Sun's velocity. This would result in a fractional amplitude of the resulting variation in the active gravitational mass of the Earth (or locally measured value of G) equal to

$$\frac{\delta G}{G} = 2|\beta| \frac{v_s v_e}{c^2} \tag{10}$$

where v_s refers to the Sun's velocity in the plane of the ecliptic. From these remarks it is clear that the annual amplitude in the variation would be expected to fall in the range

$$2 \times 10^{-9} < \frac{\delta G}{G} < 2 \times 10^{-6} \tag{11}$$

An annual fractional amplitude in G greater than 2×10^{-8}, as seen on the Earth, is not likely, for an anomaly would appear in the timekeeping of pendulum clocks. Hence a reasonable range of $\delta G/G$ due to the Earth's motion about the Sun is

$$2 \times 10^{-9} < \frac{\delta G}{G} < 2 \times 10^{-8} \tag{12}$$

Because of the motion of the Sun about the Galaxy, there should be a variation of G seen in the solar system perhaps as large as 1 ppm, with a period of about 230 million years, if the velocity of the Galaxy relative to distant matter were several hundred kilometers per second. It is difficult to see how such a small effect could lead to anything significant in the solar system. However, it has been remarked occasionally that a period of about this length seems to appear in certain geological processes.[32]

a. Pendulum Clocks. A pendulum clock would indicate an annual variation in the active gravitational mass of the Earth. A statistical study of the record of the clocks in the Paris Observatory for the period January, 1951, to December, 1957, has shown that the annual variation in the gravitational acceleration is quite unlikely to be greater than 0.04 ppm (amplitude 2×10^{-8}).

b. Moon's Motion. Whereas the velocity-dependent interactions between planets are too small to lead to significant effects, satellite systems should exhibit the effect in the form of a periodic error in the longitude of the satellite. In the case of the earth, assuming that its active gravitational mass varies with an annual period and an amplitude of 2×10^{-8}, the amplitude of the resulting annual error in the longitude of the Moon would be only $0''.1$ arc. It is presently impossible to exclude an annual error in longitude this small.[33]

An artificial satellite would allow a much better check for a velocity dependence. The short period and small size of the satellite make such a device particularly suitable. This will be discussed again later.

c. Seasonal Variation in Earth's Rotation Rate. An annual variation in the Earth's rotation rate would result from an annual change in the active gravitational mass of the Earth, for the increased gravitational pull of the Earth on itself would produce a small change in radius with a corresponding change in rotation rate. The change in moment of inertia of the Earth and rotation rate was shown for a simple Earth model to depend upon G as[34]

$$\frac{\delta\omega}{\omega} = -\frac{\delta I}{I} = 0.13\frac{\delta G}{G}$$ (13)

Thus an annual variation in G of amplitude

$$\frac{\delta G}{G} = 2 \times 10^{-8}$$ (14)

would result in an annual variation in rotation rate having an amplitude

$$\frac{\delta\omega}{\omega} = 2.6 \times 10^{-9}$$ (15)

The annual variation in the Earth's rotation rate has a fractional amplitude of 4.5×10^{-9}.

This annual variation is usually assumed to be due to seasonal changes in the angular momentum of the Earth's atmosphere.[35] From the available data it seems quite certain that the variation in atmospheric angular momentum does contribute much of the effect, but it is not believed to have been quantitatively verified that this is the only important contribution. The seasonal variations of the Northern and Southern Hemispheres are opposite and tend to cancel each other. The data for the Southern Hemisphere were taken from the Australian–New Zealand sector only. In view of the highly irregular circulation pattern for the Southern Hemisphere,[36] this approximation is believed to be inadequate.

4.3 Positional Variation of G

If this phenomenon exists, its effects are less important to geophysicists. As discussed earlier, the gravitational constant would decrease if the Sun were approached. The gravitational constant at distance r would be given by

$$G_r{}^{-1} = G_0{}^{-1} + \gamma^{-1} \frac{M_s}{rc^2} \tag{16}$$

Here G_0 is the gravitational constant at great distance from the Sun. M_s is the Sun's mass, and γ has the same meaning as in Eq. (4).

With an orbital eccentricity of 0.017 and with $\gamma = 1$, the annual variation of G at the Earth would have an amplitude of

$$\frac{\delta G}{G} = 1.5 \times 10^{-10} \tag{17}$$

An annual term of small amplitude in the longitude of an Earth satellite resulting from this effect should be no more difficult to detect than the effect due to a secular change in G.

5. PROPOSALS FOR SATELLITE RESEARCH ON GRAVITATION

A number of very interesting ways in which fundamental physical theory can be tested have suggested themselves to various investigators, among them G. M. Clemence (U.S. Naval Observatory), R. H. Dicke (Princeton), H. Lyons (Hughes Aircraft), J. M. Richardson and L. S. Taylor (National Bureau of Standards), M. Schwarzschild (Princeton), S. F. Singer (Maryland), C. H. Townes (Columbia), and Jerrold R. Zacharias (Massachusetts Institute of Technology).

5.1 Secular Change in G

It has been suggested by several people (including G. M. Clemence, M. Schwarzschild, and R. H. Dicke) that an artificial satellite would be an ideal vehicle to look for the secular variation in G discussed above. An intercomparison of the gravitational measure of time provided by the satellite with an atomic measure provided by an earth-bound atomic clock would serve to show the acceleration in the relatively short interval of a year.

It would be necessary to reduce the atmospheric gas drag to low values. In order to achieve interplanetary gas levels, it may be necessary for the satellite height to exceed 2000 km. In addition, if there should be an anomalous drag associated with the Van Allen layers, it may be necessary to go even higher or to take steps to avoid this drag.   It would also be necessary to use a dense satellite to give a small drag-weight ratio.

After all these steps, it still seems unlikely that the gas drag would be negligible, and a measure of this drag would be necessary.   Observations of two separate and independent parts of different density could be used to eliminate the effect of gas drag from the computed acceleration.   To avoid difficulties with time variation, it may be necessary to keep the parts relatively close together.   This seems to present no insurmountable difficulty.

M. Schwarzschild has suggested a very elegant solution to the gas-drag problem.   The satellite would be surrounded by a hollow spherical shell which would eject servo-controlled gas jets to cause the outer shell to stay centered on the inner sphere.   The inner sphere is now shielded from gas drag by the outer spherical shell.   The chief difficulty with this proposal seems to be its complexity.   There may also be difficulty in eliminating residual forces between the inner and outer sphere.

The problem of the precision tracking of a long-lived satellite for gravitation experiments has been discussed by G. M. Clemence and also more recently by Hoffmann, Krotkov, and Dicke[67] (see also Chap. 5). The latter group finds that a small "orange peel" satellite can be photographed directly at 2000 km with a relatively small telescope tracking the stars.   They also find that the illumination of a corner reflector by a pulsed searchlight would give much more light at this altitude, and also enable the satellite to be observed in the Earth's shadow.

Concerning the optimum orbit: it should be high enough to be relatively free from atmospheric-drag effects and factors involving the shape of the Earth, but not so high as to be subject to large perturbations by the Moon or the Sun; it should have low eccentricity in order to minimize the effects of perturbations (which increase with eccentricity) and thus to simplify their calculation; it should have a moderate inclination, enough to be readily observable from a large number of stations in temperate latitudes, but not as great as 60° where certain computational difficulties reach a maximum.   It is to be hoped that perturbations produced by the higher harmonics of the Earth's gravitational field do not produce large resonance effects which would be difficult to handle, as some geodesists believe.   A polar orbit would also be desirable, as factors involving the Earth's figure would then average out.

The gravitational clock, which by international agreement furnishes the fundamental standard of time, is the motion of the Earth around the Sun.   In practice, the motion of the Moon furnishes a more precise and readily available reference on account of its relatively fast angular motion across the background of stars.   These advantages—fast motion and ease of reference to the coordinate system—will prevail a fortiori in the case of an artificial satellite.

If the age of the Universe is taken to be 10^{10} years, then the gain of atomic over inertial time will be 1 part in 10^{10} in 1 year. If the atomic standard is reliable over long periods (months) to 1 part in 10^{11}, as it is hoped, and if the satellite period can be determined to 1 part in 10^{11} in, say, 1 year (an accuracy that appears to be attainable through the use of the most refined modern techniques; see Chap. 5), then the effect of a time-varying gravitational constant should be readily detectable.

5.2 Velocity Dependence of G

It was proposed (R. H. Dicke) that an artificial Earth satellite could be used to investigate the velocity dependence of gravitation discussed above. The requirements are similar to those of the previous section but much less severe. Inasmuch as a velocity dependence, if it exists, is expected to have an annual amplitude greater than 1 part in 10^9, it is probable that an independent measure of gas drag would not be necessary. Thus this experiment, while probably less likely to give a positive result, is considerably simpler and could be tried before one on the secular variation. A negative result for an experiment of this type is just as valuable as a positive result, for it serves to define the terms within which a theory must be constructed.

More reliable measurements of the Moon's position could be used to give information on both the secular variation and velocity dependence. It is conceivable that three well-defined bright spots placed on the Moon artificially could be used to improve the quality of these observations. Small corner reflectors, beads, or reflecting films could be used for fiducial marks. On the other hand, some of the natural markings on the Moon's surface may already define positions sufficiently independent of lighting to make artificial marks unnecessary.

5.3 Positional Variation in G

A satellite experiment designed to look for a variation with gravitational potential of G is virtually identical with that described in the above two paragraphs. However, the expected effect is now so much smaller that all the precautions necessary for an experiment on the secular variation are again needed.

5.4 Dragging of the Inertial Frame

It has been suggested that the effect of the rotating Earth in dragging around with it inertial coordinate systems could be best measured by putting a satellite accurately over the Earth's pole. The effect of the Earth's rotation, according to general relativity, causes the plane of the orbit to rotate around with it. The predicted angular rotation rate of the plane of the orbit is

$$\omega = \frac{1}{2} \frac{Gm_e}{c^2 r} \left[\frac{r_g}{r} \right]^2 \omega_e \tag{18}$$

Here ω_e is the angular velocity of the Earth, r_g its radius of gyration, and r the radius of the satellite orbit. For a satellite at a height of 2000 km, this rotation is only about 0".05 arc per year in the plane of the equator. While this should be observable, there are very serious doubts concerning the possibility of eliminating, in the calculations, the effect of disturbances. The effect of field irregularities due to an irregular Earth would average out for an orbit accurately over the Earth's pole. However, it may not be possible, using presently available techniques, to put a satellite orbit over the poles with sufficient precision.

5.5 Relativistic Advance of the Line of Apsides

This has been suggested by a number of investigators. The effect has already been well established in the case of Mercury's orbit. It would be interesting to put a satellite into orbit with long semimajor axis and eccentricity near unity in order to maximize this effect. The severe difficulty which may make the experiment impractical will lie in calculating and eliminating the terms in the advance of perigee produced by ordinary perturbations, such as those due to atmospheric drag, the oblateness and higher-order harmonics, or, if you like, plain irregularities in the Earth's gravitational field, and the pull of the Sun and Moon (which become appreciable for sufficiently elongated orbits). Aside from the special orbit demanded by this experiment, the requirements are closely similar to those for the other experiments described so far.

Another possible approach to this problem has been suggested (R. H. Dicke). An artificial planet carrying high-frequency pulse-transponding equipment could be used to give continuous, accurate information for the distance between the Earth and the artificial planet. This information could be made to be accurate to a few meters based on an atomic time scale of length (M. Golay, 1958, suggested CW oscillator equipment). Relatively little power would be required. Such an artificial planet traveling in an eccentric orbit could add new dimensions and new standards of accuracy to planetary orbit theory, and it might help clear up the discrepancy between the dynamical value of the solar parallax[38] and the value recently obtained from Venus radar echoes.[39] The planet could, for example, be used to obtain better information about the masses of the inner planets and hence, indirectly, a more reliable value for the relativistic rotation of the perihelion of Mercury. What really seems to be required is a thoroughly self-consistent treatment of the whole system of inner planets. It could itself supply a value for the perihelion rotation. It would also supply very precise knowledge of the Earth's orbit.

5.6 The Gravitational Red-shift Experiment

The general theory of relativity predicts that the frequency of any periodic phenomenon varies with the gravitational potential of the point where the phenomenon takes place. The experiment designed to measure this effect directly has been named after the red shift of the absorption lines in the spectra of stars with strong gravitational fields. This shift has been observed with low precision in the atmospheres of white dwarf stars that are members of binary systems, where the two spectra enable the astronomer to separate velocity and gravitational shifts. It has been suspected in the case of massive O-type stars and of the Sun. Astronomers pretty much concur that a general-relativistic explanation is the correct one; the chief area of dispute arises from the lack of precision of the astronomical observations.

A number of people, notably Zacharias (MIT), Lyons (Hughes Aircraft), Richardson and Taylor (NBS), and Townes (Columbia University), have suggested the possibility of installing a precise atomically or molecularly controlled clock in a satellite and, after it has been placed in an orbit of high gravitational potential energy, of then comparing its frequency with that of an identical clock on the ground. The red shift is of the order M/R; in relativistic units where $c = 1$ and $G = 1$, this relation yields a predicted shift df/f of 7×10^{-10} at the surface of the Earth compared with a clock at $R = \infty$ and correspondingly less compared with clocks in a finite orbit. (In the foregoing, M = effective mass, R = distance from center of potential field, f = frequency.) The detection of so small an effect obviously requires a clock whose frequency stability is reliable to an order of magnitude higher (say, 1 part in 10^{11}) and for moderate lengths of time. This is just about the accuracy claimed for the best experimental clocks today under laboratory conditions. The chief problem here is one of development: the insurance of reliability under other than laboratory conditions, and instrumentation for compactness of volume and weight.

In this experiment, the orbit should be large in order to achieve the greatest possible potential difference from the ground. The smaller resulting velocity would also minimize the special-relativistic time dilation discussed in Sec. 5.7 below. A circular orbit would have the advantage that the time difference between the two clocks can be allowed to accumulate without having to integrate over a range of potentials. On the other hand, if some means can be devised for accurately comparing the clock frequencies by samples of very short time duration, then an eccentric orbit will allow the experimenter to sample the expected red shift over a range of potentials (National Bureau of Standards proposal). It was also suggested by J. Zacharias' group that the experiment could be done with only a crystal oscillator in a satellite moving in an eccentric orbit. The red shift would result in a detectable frequency modulation of the oscillator.

All the various atomic clock systems presently under development have been suggested. Zacharias proposed that a cesium beam clock similar to the Atomochron could be designed to be light enough for a satellite experiment. The Bureau of Standards proposed that the rubidium-vapor-gas cell clock under development by P. Bender be used for such experiments. Townes, Lyons, and Richardson all proposed the use of an ammonia maser.

Each of these clocks has something to be said both for and against it. The cesium beam device can probably be made to weigh 100 lb or less, but there is no way of making the beam tube short without hurting the performance of the device. On the other hand, it is the only one of the three clocks for which there is a considerable body of experience.

The ammonia maser has the advantage of being very simple in principle. On the other hand, the line width of the fundamental ammonia resonance is very much broader than that of the other two "clocks." The result is that the clock frequency is easily pulled by various effects such as cavity tuning and beam loading. With present techniques, a stability of about 1 part on 10^{10} has been achieved.

The rubidium clock, based on work by T. R. Carver, M. Arditi, J. P. Wittke, and P. Bender, has much to be said for it in terms of intrinsic simplicity and accuracy. Its intrinsic line width is less than that of the Atomochron. The clock employs the "buffer gas" technique[40] to eliminate the Doppler broadening. This leads to a small "pressure shift" of the resonance frequency, which is a possible source of future trouble. It is believed that the gas in a properly baked out gas bulb will be sufficiently stable in its composition and density to give a stable resonance frequency. This has not yet been demonstrated, however. It is to be hoped that in a year or two one of the three basic techniques will be seen to be clearly the best approach to a "clock" in space.

If the gravitational red shift were to be measured with considerable precision, it might be used to help decide if the fine-structure "constant" is actually constant. Any departure of the observed red shift from the expected value might be interpreted as due to a change in some one or more of the nongravitational dimensionless atomic constants.

5.7 Velocity-dependent Time Dilatation of Special Relativity

This experiment, suggested by a number of investigators (Lyons, Zacharias, and others), envisions a direct check on the Lorentz transformation of time measurements obtained in two relatively moving coordinate systems. From the standpoint of instrumentation, this experiment might be grouped with experiment 5.6 above, in that it also requires that a satellite-borne clock of the highest available precision be compared with an identical clock on the ground. A velocity of 7 km per sec, corresponding to a small orbit, would produce a frequency shift df/f of about 3×10^{-10}. Higher velocities can of course be achieved in very eccentric orbits. Furthermore, if some means of comparing the frequency of the two clocks over short intervals could be found (see preceding Sec. 5.6), an eccentric orbit would permit measurement of the effect as a function of the velocity.

It goes without saying that time dilatation (decreasing with height) and gravitational frequency shift (increasing with height) will both occur in both experiments; it remains to consider the best way of separating them. If only the accumulated difference between the clocks can be measured, then the most feasible way of handling this question seems to be to launch the satellite in the highest reasonable orbit, where the gravitational shift will predominate, but also make it eccentric so that the drag forces near perigee will shrink the orbit over a reasonably short time, say, 2 years, so that as the orbit becomes smaller, the time dilatation will increasingly dominate.

It is also obvious that, in making frequency comparisons between the clocks, especially over short time bases (nonaccumulative), great care will be needed in eliminating Doppler shifts, ionospheric distortions of the signal path, etc. This problem is not severe, however, if only time signals are generated, i.e., long-term averages are measured.

5.8 Experiments to Measure the Velocity of Electromagnetic Radiation as a Function of Frequency

It was suggested that artificial satellites would be useful in this field in that they provide the possibility of putting either a controlled source of broad-band radiation at an appreciable distance from the detectors, or vice versa. Since broad-band sources of intermittent radiation exist in nature, e.g., eclipsing binaries with a hot component, novae and supernovae, etc., experiments of this type will probably not be attempted with artificial sources unless the natural sources prove inadequate.

REFERENCES

1. G. M. Clemence: *Astron. Papers of the American Ephemeris*, 11, 1 (1943); *Rev. Modern Phys.*, 19, 361 (1947).
2. R. L. Mössbauer: *Z. Physik*, 151, 124 (1958).
3. T. E. Cranshaw, J. P. Schriffer, and A. B. Whitehead: *Phys. Rev. Letters*, 4, 163 (1960).
4. R. V. Pound and G. A. Rebka, Jr.: *Phys. Rev. Letters*, 4, 337 (1960).
5. E. Mach: *Conservation of Energy*, 1872.
6. G. Berkeley: *The Principle of Human Understanding*, 1710.
7. D. W. Sciama: *Mon. Not. Roy. Astr. Soc.*, 113, 34 (1953).
8. H. Bondi: *Cosmology* (Cambridge University Press, 1952).
9. G. Cocconi and E. Salpeter: *Nuovo Cimento*, 10, 646 (1958); *Phys. Rev. Letters*, 4,.176 (1960).
10. V. W. Hughes et al.: *Phys. Rev. Letters*, 4, 342 (1960).
11. P. A. M. Dirac: *Proc. Roy. Soc.*, A165, 199 (1938).
12. R. H. Dicke: *American Scientist*, 47, 25 (1959). What is meant by *now* in the passage under consideration is conditioned by the necessity for an environment satisfactory for the existence of man. In current evolutionary models of the Universe, these conditions can be met when the age of the Universe lies in the range 10^9 to 10^{13} years.
13. L. D. Landau: In W. Pauli (ed.), *Niels Bohr and the Development of Physics* (McGraw-Hill, 1955).
14. R. H. Dicke: *Nature*, 183, 170 (1959).
15. P. Jordan: *Schwerkraft und Weltall* (Brunswick: Vieweg, 1955).
16. P. G. Bergmann: *An Introduction to the Theory of Relativity* (Prentice Hall, 1942).
17. M. Fierz: *Helv. Phys. Acta*, 29, 128 (1956).
18. R. V. Eötvös: *Ann. d. Physik*, 68, 11 (1922).
19. E. A. Milne: *Kinematic Relativity* (Oxford, Clarendon Press, 1935). See also M. Johnson: *Time, Knowledge, and the Nebulae* (Dover, 1947).
20. R. H. Dicke: *Rev. Mod. Phys.*, 29, 355 (1957); *American Scientist*, 46, 213 (1958).
21. P. Jordan: *Zeits. f. Physik*, 157, 112 (1959).
22. E. Teller: *Phys. Rev.*, 73, 801 (1948).
23. M. Schwarzschild: *Structure and Evolution of the Stars* (Princeton University Press, 1958). The author is grateful for a number of helpful conversations with Professor Schwarzschild.
24. J. H. Oort: "La structure et l'evolution de l'Universe," in R. Stoops (ed.), *1958 Solvay Conference Report* (7678 Condenberg, Brussels, 1958).
25. M. Schwarzschild: Private communication. The author appreciates a number of helpful conversations with Professor Schwarzschild on stellar evolution.
26. O. C. Wilson: *Astrophysical J.*, 130, 496 (1959).
27. This method of reducing the data is due to G. J. F. MacDonald.
28. W. H. Munk and G. J. F. MacDonald, in a study to be published soon in book

form.   The editor is grateful to the authors for the opportunity to examine a copy of the manuscript.

29. W. S. Carey: In *Continental Drift: A Symposium*, p. 177 (University of Tasmania, 1958).
30. T. J. Wilson: *Nature, 185*, 880 (1960).
31. L. Egyed: *Zeits f. Geoph., 24*, No. 4/5, 260 (1959).
32. J. H. F. Umbgrove: *The Pulse of the Earth* (The Hague, Nijhoff, 1947).
33. G. M. Clemence: Private communications.
34. G. Hess: Physics Department thesis, Princeton University, 1957.
35. Y. Mintz and W. H. Munk: *Mon. Not. Roy. Astr. Soc., Geophys. Suppl., 6*, No. 9, 566 (1954).
36. H. Riehl: *Tropical Meteorology*, p. 9 (McGraw-Hill, 1954).
37. W. Hoffmann, R. Krotkov, and R. H. Dicke: *I.R.E. Trans. on Military Electronics MIL, 28* (1960).
38. E. K. Rabe: *Astron. J., 55*, 112 (1950); *Astron. J., 59*, 409 (1954).
39. R. Price, P. E. Green, Jr., T. J. Goblick, Jr., R. H. Kingston, L. G. Kraft, Jr., G. H. Pettengill, R. Silver, W. B. Smith: "Radar Echoes from Venus," *Science, 129*, 751 (1959).
40. R. H. Dicke: *Phys. Rev., 89*, 472 (1953).

PART **3** ≡

THE EARTH

4

KNOWLEDGE OF THE EARTH
FROM SPACE

Harrison Brown

About 4,500 million years ago a series of events took place which led
to the formation of our Earth together with the other planets of the solar
system. In spite of the fact that scientists have been studying the Earth
intensively for many years, the processes involved in the formation, the
subsequent evolution to its present form, and many of the processes now
taking place beneath, on, and above its surface are but poorly understood.

Until recently man has been confined to the Earth's surface, with the
result that the types of observation which he has been able to make have
been severely limited. The airplane liberated him to some extent and
made possible a variety of photographic and meteorological measurements. High-altitude rockets increased further his capabilities for
measurement. But the development of satellites and space probes
without question is adding a new dimension to his capabilities. It seems
likely that in the years ahead we shall learn more about the Earth by
leaving it than by remaining on it.

One of the areas of greatest potential yield of new knowledge will be
that of the exploration of the Moon and planets. By studying their
physical features, tectonic activities, magnetic fields, and chemistries,

121

we shall be able to learn a great deal more than we know now about the forces which operate on and within the Earth itself and of the processes which led to its formation.   These particular aspects of the problem of earth formation are discussed in Chaps. 9 and 10 on the Moon and planets. In this chapter we shall confine ourselves to a discussion of the tremendous potentialities which the coming of artificial satellites has opened for the scientific investigation of the Earth's solid body (geodesy), its lower atmosphere (meteorology), and upper atmosphere.   For a similar discussion of the geomagnetic field and its interaction with the particle radiation impinging on the Earth, the reader is referred to Chaps. 11–16, Fields and Particles in Space.

To some extent, the new observations that satellites make possible are extensions of classical procedures.   But they have also made feasible observations of a kind which have simply not been possible until now.

There are many questions concerning the Earth which satellites can help us answer.   They can enable us to determine more exactly the size and shape of the Earth.   In principle, sufficiently exact data can be obtained to enable us to say whether the Earth's figure can best be described as a spheroid, a triaxial ellipsoid, or perhaps by a figure in which the higher-order spherical harmonies are not negligible.   The detailed lumpiness of the geoid can be measured as a function of latitude and longitude.   The Earth's parameters can be measured as a function of time with the end in view of determining their stability.   It is possible that such measurements can shed light on the Earth's elastic and plastic properties, upon the true causes of the seasonal variation in the rate of rotation, and of the currently unpredictable terms in the rotation rate.

Measurements of the Earth's magnetic field from satellites can help us understand its nature.   If it is induced by currents, what is its mechanism?   What are the causes of its secular variation, of its quasi-periodic variations, of the detailed irregularities?   How is the magnetic field affected by interaction with external fields and by streams of charged particles?

Similarly, the Earth's electrostatic field can be studied, with the end in mind of determining the Earth's capacity and the magnitude and origin of its electric charge.

Artificial satellites can greatly increase our understanding of the Earth's atmosphere.   Whereas today our synoptic atmospheric maps must be laboriously pieced together and are available only for limited areas, in the future it should be possible to obtain automatically a continuous series of synoptic charts covering the entire Earth.   Measurements of energy balance can help us determine the energy content of volume elements of the atmosphere (small compared with the Earth) as a function of height and geographical coordinates, the detailed schedule of input and output of various forms of energy in these elements, and their variation with time. From such measurements we can perhaps learn in detail how these functions are affected by fluctuations in solar radiation at various wavelengths, by radiation from the ground, by neighboring regions of the atmosphere, and by mechanical agencies such as Coriolis forces, convection, and horizontal pressure gradients. The decay or relaxation time of departures from equilibrium can be determined.

The atmosphere can be regarded as a gaseous shell through which radiation of differing spectral and time distributions filters from below and above, which absorbs and reemits, which is subjected to bombardment by a variety of particles with their own time, space, and velocity distributions, the whole being subjected to the forces of the gravitational and electromagnetic fields. Satellites can help us determine the resulting density, temperature, composition, the degree of molecular dissociation, the degree of ionization and excitation, all as a function of height, geographical position, and time.

There are many additional questions concerning our atmosphere which measurements from satellites might help us answer.

To what extent may we regard the Earth's atmosphere as a particular member of an infinite family of gaseous envelopes of astronomical bodies, including those of other planets and stars, whose properties differ more or less widely from those of the Earth's atmosphere, depending on differences or similarities of the governing factors such as radiation or gravity? In particular, to what extent can we refine our notions about the atmospheres of other planets, depending on our findings about our own?

Is it possible to detect any secular changes in our atmosphere? Is the atmosphere slowly accreting material from space? If so, what material and in what amounts? Is the velocity distribution of this material such that we would infer that it is part of a "solar cloud" or interstellar matter? At what rate is the atmosphere losing material by escape to space? Is it gaining material by net gains of evaporation and sublimation from the ground, or by production of gases, or release of trapped gases? To what extent is it simply a residue of a hypothetical primordial atmosphere?

Rockets and satellites can help us learn more about the boundary region in which the Earth's atmosphere blends into the near vacuum of outer space. The possibility that weather in the troposphere may in some way be affected by changes occurring in the ionosphere can be investigated. Meteors, noctilucent clouds, aurorae, and nighttime airglow can be observed.   Measurements can be made of the atmospheric density, ionization density, and chemical composition in the ionosphere. We can learn more about irregularities and dynamic motions in this region as well as about photochemical processes and radio-wave propagation.

It is amply clear from even this all-too-small sampling of future prospects that a major opportunity is presented to students of the Earth.   The availability of satellites and rockets promises to give us an accelerating accumulation of knowledge concerning our planet, its origin, and its evolution.   With that knowledge, increased understanding will inevitably follow.

5

SOME ASPECTS OF GEODESY

George P. Woollard

I. BACKGROUND

Geodesy is primarily concerned with measuring the size and shape of the Earth and deducing from these parameters some facts about the physical structure of the Earth. In principle, the aim of determining its size and shape might be achieved by measuring, with the highest possible precision, the angles and a few chosen sides ("base lines") in a closed geodetic triangulation net connecting selected points all over the Earth's surface. If this could actually be carried out, the positions of the survey points could be represented with three-dimensional coordinates in a quite arbitrary geometric system. One would thus have mapped selected points of the Earth's surface as a many-faceted polygon approximating a spheroidal figure. The points of the figure are, of course, not necessarily at the same level.

The word "level" introduces a new complication. It implies the existence of a reference figure whose surface is all "at the same level," that is, one which is everywhere orthogonal to the force field (the force in the present instance being the vector sum of gravity and the inertial force arising from the Earth's rotation). As Heiskanen and Vening Meinesz[1] suggest, the history of geodesy can be divided into periods according to

125

the figure of reference which was in use: a "spherical" era dating from the famous experiment of Eratosthenes in the third century B.C., an "ellipsoidal" era beginning with Newton and the French geodesists from Picard to Maupertuis, merging finally with the "geoidal" era of this century.

The geoid is simple in concept: It is the equipotential surface at mean sea level. It is a somewhat wavy, lumpy surface that quite closely approximates an ellipsoid, deviating from it probably not more than 50 m upward or downward. The ellipsoid in turn is very nearly the equilibrium figure of a rotating body. (The terms "spheroid" and "ellipsoid" are used quite interchangeably except in those contexts where it is necessary to distinguish the equilibrium figure from a true geometric ellipsoid: then "spheroid" is reserved for the equilibrium figure.) The location of the geoid is most often specified by its height N above or below the ellipsoid as a function of spherical coordinates (latitude φ and longitude λ). Although the ellipsoid has been superseded as a standard equipotential surface, it is still holding its own as a geometrical surface of reference or datum.

Although the geoid is simple in concept and although you can actually see it at the seashore, it is another matter to determine its actual location with respect to the ellipsoid (or some coordinate system) in mid-ocean, with no triangulation points in sight, or to trace its position under the surface of continents. In order to locate rigorously any of the equipotential surfaces, of which the geoid is a special case, it is necessary to know the value of either the potential or the vector acceleration of gravity at every point. The potential cannot be directly measured at a given point P, but is derived by evaluating the line integral $\int_0^P g\,ds$ of the gravity vector field $g(r,\varphi,\lambda)$ from some arbitrary starting point 0 to the point P. Geodesists cannot actually measure the function $g(r,\varphi,\lambda)$ everywhere, but they can sample it. The sampling is of two kinds: deflections of the vertical and gravity anomalies, which are the departure of g, respectively, in direction and magnitude from its spheroidal value.

A sufficiently dense sampling would afford the possibility of deriving unambiguous equipotential surfaces. But now two other questions arise. The first concerns the specification of the reference ellipsoid or datum. There have been quite a number of standard ellipsoids in use, some of them based on the best fit to only a limited region of the Earth's surface. If the region in question is on a hump or depression of the geoid, the datum fitted to it might be quite different from a world datum. The relation between datums in contiguous areas is not difficult to derive by overlapping triangulation, but those used on different continents can be connected only by bridging the intervening ocean by some other means.

The second question concerns the derivation of the geoid height $N(\varphi,\lambda)$ from a miscellany of deflections of the vertical and gravitational anomalies. Anomalies are measured with some sort of gravimeter (special pendulums, etc.) which can be carried almost anywhere. Deflections of the vertical require an intercomparison of station coordinates (φ,λ) determined astronomically by the direction in space of the local true vertical (geoidal coordinates) with station coordinates determined geodetically from arc lengths in a triangulation net (ellipsoidal coordinates). This latter procedure is evidently a much more laborious one, which incidentally can only be carried out on land, so it is not surprising that the gravity data are much more extensive and dense (numerous per unit area) than the deflection data. Before the gravity data can be used, however, they must be reduced to some comparable basis. For example, if an observation has been obtained at an elevated site, it must be corrected for the fact that it is farther from the center of the Earth (free-air reduction), for the mass of the elevated ground underfoot (Bouguer reduction), for the mass of the surrounding higher terrain, if any (terrain correction), and for the less-than-average attraction of the low-density roots of mountains in the immediate neighborhood, if any (isostatic reduction). In the derivation of the geoid, there is, furthermore, a slight diversity of treatment of the mass of those parts of the Earth's crust that project above the geoid.

The potential of which the geoid is an equipotential surface is the geopotential W, which is the sum of the purely gravitational potential $U(r,\theta,\lambda)$ and a rotational term:

$$W(r,\theta,\lambda) = U(r,\theta,\lambda) + \frac{(x^2 + y^2)\omega^2}{2}.$$

In this expression θ is the colatitude $90° - \varphi$, and ω is the Earth's angular velocity. The geopotential W is thus appropriate to a coordinate system rotating with the Earth and hence for geodesy; the purely gravitational potential U is appropriate to inertial coordinates and hence for satellite orbits. It is convenient to represent both of these analytically as the sum of a series of spherical-harmonic terms, which are in the most general case functions of the polar coordinates r, θ, and λ:

$$U(r,\theta,\lambda) = \frac{GM}{r} \sum_{n=0}^{\infty} r^{-n} \left[\sum_{m=0}^{n} (A_{mn} \cos m\lambda + B_{mn} \sin m\lambda) \frac{(n-m)!}{n!} P_n{}^m \cos \theta \right]$$

in which G = constant of gravitation and M = mass of the Earth; m and n non-negative integers such that $\infty \geqslant n \geqslant m \geqslant 0$; the $P_n{}^m(\cos \theta)$ are the Legendre polynomials when $m = 0$ and the associated Legendre polynomials when $m \geqslant 1$; A_{mn} and B_{mn} are numerical coefficients which are equivalent to the amplitude of the harmonics and can be evaluated in several ways. This most general expression for U is evidently a function containing (1) pure zonal harmonics when $m = 0$, which change sign n times from North to South Pole ($0 < \theta \leqslant \pi$) and (2) tesseral harmonics, which alternate sign checkerboard-fashion in spherical rectangles bounded on the north and south by the $n - m$ zeros of the (m,n)th zonal harmonics and on the east and west by meridians spaced $2\pi/m$ apart.

Since the acceleration of gravity g in inertial coordinates is ∇U and in rotating coordinates is ∇W, it can also be expressed in spherical harmonics.

In the case of a figure of revolution, the function describing it must be independent of λ, so that the tesseral harmonics vanish ($m = 0$, $A_{0n} \neq 0$, and all other coefficients $A_{mn} = B_{mn} = \dot{0}$) and only zonal harmonics remain. Furthermore, if the Earth is assumed to be in equilibrium with only gravity and centrifugal force, its figure and potential must be symmetrical about the equatorial plane, which requires the unsymmetrical odd-order zonal harmonics to vanish. Both of these simplifying assumptions have been frequently made, although without sufficiently strict justification.

The analytical expression of U in spherical harmonics has great utility in that (together with certain simplifying assumptions) it makes possible the integration of the equations of motion of a satellite in closed form (Brouwer, Sterne, Garfinkel, King-Hele, and a number of others[2-5]). The resulting orbital elements become functions of the time and of the amplitudes A_{mn}, B_{mn}, which can then be evaluated from the orbital data. These amplitudes in turn yield information on the structure of the Earth's gravitational field and hence its mass distribution.

It is evident that $W = constant$ is the form of the equation for the geoid. If enough spherical-harmonic terms are kept, it would be possible to represent analytically every bump and dent of the geoid,[6] analogously to the Fourier-series representation of function of a single variable of period 2π. The utility or applicability of this procedure is not so apparent as in the case of the potential U in satellite orbit theory, or as against a simple mapping of the geoid as an empirical function of θ and λ. On the other hand, any coefficients A_{mn} and B_{mn} evaluated by orbit perturbations or resonances are immediately available for expressing the amplitude of the undulations of the geoid, if desirable.

The lower-order harmonics have simple physical or geometrical meanings which are worth glancing at. Some of them are summarized in Table 1. The reader who wishes to pursue these questions in greater detail is referred to Jeffreys (Ref. 7, especially chap. 4) and to Heiskanen and Vening Meinesz.[1] The curves for the harmonic functions are most readily available in Jahnke and Emde.[8]

Table 1

Order n; principal period $(T = 2\pi/n)$; and type of harmonic	Significance of term
$n = 0$; period $= \infty$; zonal	Amplitude A_{00} = constant. For the geoid it corresponds to R, mean value of the Earth's radius.
$n = 1$, $m = 0$; $T = 2\pi$ in latitude φ; zonal	Amplitude $= 0$, unless the origin of coordinates does not coincide with the center of attraction. It is usually placed there by definition, in which case the presence of first-order harmonics may be said to be "forbidden."
$n > 1$, $m = 1$; $T = 2\pi$ in longitude λ; tesseral*	Amplitude $= 0$, unless the displacement of the origin from the center of attraction (if any) has a component perpendicular to the polar axis. But see last entry.
$n = 2$, $m = 0$; $T = \pi$ in latitude φ; zonal	This term corresponds to the flattening $f = (a - b)/a$, where a and b are the semimajor and semiminor axes of meridian sections of the ellipsoid. The poles are approximately $2fR/3$ below the mean sphere of radius R, and the equator is approximately $fR/3$ above it, corresponding to $P_2(\cos \theta) = +1$ at $\theta = 0°$ and $P_2(\cos \theta) = -0.5$ at $\theta = 90°$. $f \cong \frac{1}{2}_{97}$ from geodetic surveys but can be evaluated independently from orbital data.
$n = 2$, $m = 2$; $T = \pi$ in both φ and λ; tesseral*	Amplitude $= 0$, unless the Earth is triaxial, which is possible.
$n = 3$, $m = 0$; $T = 2\pi/3$ in φ; zonal†	This harmonic is the "pear-shaped" component of O'Keefe, Eckels, and Squires;[9] their results indicate that the North Pole is 15 m above and the South Pole 15 m below the ellipsoid, with the amplitude at latitudes $\pm 26°.5$ about $\mp$ 0.5 this amount.

* Tesseral harmonics with $m = n$ are sometimes called *sectorial*.

† Zonal harmonics of odd order are unsymmetrical with respect to the equatorial plane. Therefore they are usually arbitrarily excluded, on the grounds that they cannot arise from purely gravitational and centrifugal forces. Their presence or the presence of tesseral harmonics, if real, indicates the presence of other, static forces in the Earth's crust—semipermanent deformations, as it were. The analysis of such features of the geoid has definite implications for the physical strength of the crust or for the magnitude of the convection currents in the mantle which might be responsible for supporting these nonequilibrium features of the geoid.

2. GEODETIC PROBLEMS

In order to fix attention on the potentialities of artificial satellites for investigation in the field of geodesy, the Committee on Geodesy formulated in the following way what it believed to be the more immediate goals of such investigations: (1) the tying together of widely separated geodetic datums, (2) determination of the shape and size of the Earth, (3) determination of the gravity field of the Earth, both broadly and in detail, and (4) the fixing of various datums with respect to the gravitational center of the Earth. In stating these aims, the Committee did not mean to be comprehensive; no doubt other related fields for investigation will arise in the minds of the readers.

In some cases, the method of investigation of these problems will be a more or less obvious extension of the classical methods of geodesy, but in others, the artificial satellite makes possible novel procedures and opens uniquely new perspectives. Here are a few examples of both kinds:

Triangulation-trilateration is used to tie together separate geodetic nets that are geographically too remote to be connected by surface triangulation. This is a rather obvious extension of classical methods. In the simplest case we do not even need to know the trajectory of the satellite. The satellite may be regarded as a moving triangulation point whose (three-dimensional) coordinates with respect to each separate geodetic datum may be observed more or less simultaneously. Three successive point fixes, each observed simultaneously from each datum, would completely determine the transformation equations from one datum to the other. A literal synchronization of observations requires great precision in timing: since the satellite is moving with respect to the Earth with a velocity of approximately 7 km per sec, an error of 0.001 sec corresponds to an error of 7 m in the coordinates. In practice this difficulty can be avoided in several ways, of which we will mention two, the first crude and the second more refined:

1. The position of segments of satellite trajectories can be determined with respect to various datums, without highly precise timing, and the crossing of a sufficient number of such lines will yield the transformation equations connecting pairs of datums. There is no reason why *any* satellite that is high enough to be observed from widely separated stations would not serve this purpose provided that the determination of its angular coordinates were exact enough. In fact, such work has already been done with rockets.[10,11]

2. The satellite can carry a suitably instrumented flashing light (suggested by many people, including Hudson, Edgerton, Singer, Delsasso).

It would be necessary only to identify the corresponding images of the same short-duration flashes on the photographic observations from stations in the two datums. The flashing light has the additional obvious advantage that it can be observed at any time during the night. Johns and others have suggested the use of infrared radiation, which would be observable even in the daytime and probably through considerable haze and clouds.

It is also evident that the fixing of the three-dimensional position of a satellite will be greatly strengthened by some sort of precise radio-ranging system—essentially trilateration. Two currently feasible methods have suggested themselves: radar, where the signal pulse is passively reflected, and transponders, where the pulse is retransmitted. The transponder-radio beacon technique promises to be considerably more efficient than radar, which requires enormous power. In reducing distances so measured, the refractive effects of the ionosphere must be taken into account, and these are at present still inexactly known.

It is of course also possible to use range measures by themselves—without observations of angular coordinates—but since each range observation yields only one coordinate instead of two, twice as many observations are needed.

As a test of these methods, observations can easily be conducted from areas fairly well separated geographically but connected by a geodetic net. Johns has shown that the observations have the highest weight if the altitude of the satellite from each station is between 15 and 65°.

Determination of the geoid, using a continuation of the classical geometrical methods of the foregoing section, is essentially the inverse of the problem just described. Theoretically it will be possible to determine the space coordinates of a ground station X by precise observations (backsights) of a satellite whose position is known in a coordinate system defined by a minimum of three standard stations A, B, and C. If the field station X is also connected by a geodetic net and precise leveling to stations A, B, and C, its then known geodetic coordinates can be compared with its space coordinates to yield transformations from the ellipsoid to the geoid. Since the geoid height N is only a few tens of meters at most, this procedure will demand observations of high accuracy, but not beyond refined photographic tracking techniques currently under consideration.

Determination of the size and shape of the best-fitting spheroidal figure, including the case of higher harmonics, can be approached in several different ways. One is the treatment of the detailed information of the last section, i.e., geoid height as a function of longitude and latitude, either by solving it in the simplest case for the best-fitting spheroid with two parameters (the radius a, and flattening f, or meridian section eccentricity e) or by subjecting the data to a more complex harmonic analysis, which is the equivalent of specifying an ideal figure of greater complexity and hence requiring more parameters to describe it. Another more elegant treatment is the celestial-mechanical one, as opposed to the geometric, which has already been used by several investigators.[5,9] The orbit of an artificial satellite contains terms which are functions of a and f and other parameters that describe the higher harmonics.

As long as one is dealing with a small number of parameters, an orbit of only moderate precision is sufficient, although the sensitivity of the solution depends on the orbital elements themselves. For example, the accuracy with which one can determine flattening f and higher harmonics depends on orbital inclination.

The question of determining the coordinates of the center of attraction of the Earth's mass with respect to the center of the best-fitting spheroid should not arise except in the case of spheroids fitted to limited areas of the Earth's surface. In order to improve on the accuracy of existing determinations, an orbit of very high precision would be required.

Investigation of the fine structure of the Earth's gravitational field from a highly detailed and precise tracking of a satellite seems feasible. By fine structure we mean regions, from the smallest observable up to perhaps several thousand kilometers, in which the actual gravity departs from the value predicted by the model (spheroidal, with or without higher harmonics). As the satellite passes through these regions of varying gravity, slight deviations from the path predicted on the basis of the smoothed potential will result. If the magnitude and distribution of the anomalies are more or less random, their net effect should be small. The maximum deviation from a predicted orbit accumulated while passing over a strong anomaly of large effective area could hardly be greater than 100 m. In general, the wandering will be much smaller than this, and deviations will tend to cancel out in the long run.

There is an alternative approach to the problem of the gravitational fine structure. If the fine structure is represented by higher harmonics of order n, where $2\pi \bar{R}/n$ corresponds to the effective linear diameter of the anomalous region, the amplitude of the term falls off with distance r from the center as $(r/R)^{-(n+1)}$, i.e., very rapidly for the higher orders, so that the potential becomes much smoother at greater heights. O'Keefe has raised the following question: What happens if the period of the satellite is 1 day or a small integral submultiple thereof? Although admittedly the higher harmonics are very weak at heights corresponding to these periods, a 1-day period would bring the satellite over the same anomaly once per revolution, and the resulting resonance effects could be very large. Similar arguments apply to periods of $1/n$ day in combination with harmonics of period $2\pi/n$. It is possible that a deliberate attempt to bring out these resonance effects by a careful choice of orbit would yield precise results in a much more elegant way than the effort to track the detailed wanderings of the satellite— a program which, if it were carried out with the extreme precision and degree of continuity demanded, would be very laborious.

Since the detection of these anomalous perturbations may be marginal, the other sources of perturbation of a satellite orbit—for instance, those discussed in the foregoing sections, those produced by the Sun and Moon (if not negligible), and those produced by atmospheric drag—will need to be reckoned with first and eliminated from the observed perturbations. On the whole, then, it looks as if this sort of investigation will have to wait until the others are well in hand.

3. CHARACTERISTICS OF AN IDEAL GEODETIC SATELLITE, ITS ORBIT, AND TRACKING SYSTEM

If a satellite is to have enough versatility for a variety of geodetic applications, it should be bright enough to be photographed easily and it should be compact (high ratio of mass to cross section) in order that the effects of atmospheric drag be minimized. It should be spherical, or as nearly spherically symmetrical as is compatible with such external instrumentation as antennas, in order to have the same drag coefficient no matter how it is oriented with respect to its velocity vector (the "relative wind").

In order to keep the satellite compact, but at the same time ensure that it will be bright enough, it must be self-luminous, thus permitting observations throughout the night. It has been suggested that the artificial-light source might be infrared, thus making the satellite observable also by day.

The light should be bright enough to be photographed easily with equipment of moderate light-gathering power, preferably portable, at distances up to several thousand kilometers. If the satellite is not plainly *visible*, then it will be necessary to incorporate into the tracking system or plans of the tracking network some provision for training the cameras on it. The light should provide intermittent flashes of very short duration. This will attract attention, automatically provide simultaneous observations for widely separated stations, and make the best use of the available power by consuming it only a very small fraction of the time.

The satellite should carry a radio beacon and transponder to return a signal to the ground in response to a signal from the ground. This will make possible simple range measurements and will enable observers to track the satellite in bad weather.

Although there is no single orbit that will simultaneously fulfill all requirements, in general it should be high and of small eccentricity. The inclination can be anything from 0 to 90°, depending upon the purpose of the experiment, the effects to be maximized or minimized, and the geographical region from which it is to be observed.

A high orbit will maximize both the area from which the satellite can be seen at a given time and the length of time during which it can be seen from a given place. For a sunlit satellite the comparative gain is much larger, since the ratio of sunlit to dark periods is greatly increased. Such an orbit will also reduce to a minimum drag-induced perturbations. The upper limit will in general be set by the visibility of the satellite or the increase with distance of the error in the linear coordinates for a given original error of observation in the spherical coordinates. An approximately circular orbit will keep the satellite out of the denser layers of the atmosphere and will maintain a nearly constant drag. It will reduce certain other perturbations correlated with eccentricity and accordingly minimize the computational complexities. In the investigation of gravitational fine structure, if the resonance effects of the higher-order harmonics turn out to be too weak to observe in high orbits, and if as a consequence it is desired to enhance the random wanderings, the most favorable orbit would be the lowest one that still avoids prohibitive drag. This is the chief exception to the general requirement for a high orbit.

Although the required degree of precision of tracking and timing of observations varies from experiment to experiment, several investigations demand the highest degree of precision attainable. For example, a detailed investigation of the gravitational irregularities (other than by the resonance method) calls for tracking with an error of ± 10 m or less to be of any real use. The corresponding permissible error in timing is about ± 1 msec. An experiment in fundamental physics discussed in Chap. 3, namely, the comparison of gravitational and atomic time, requires that the orbital period be known with respect to an atomic clock with an even greater precision (about 1 part in 10^{11}).

The chief methods of tracking, both tried and untried, are:

1. Optical—visual (recording theodolites, Moonwatch, etc.)

2. Optical—photographic (Sattrack, Phototrack, Markowitz Moon Camera, and numerous others)

3. Infrared, detection of the thermal radiation from the sun-heated satellite shell (untried)

4. Radio—interferometer (Minitrack, Moonbeam, and their foreign counterparts)

5. Radio—Doppler shift, in which the trajectory is deduced from the line-of-sight component of the satellite's velocity relative to the observer

6. Radio—radar, which has been really successful for only the biggest antennas and power output

7. Radio beacon–transponder (untried, but promising)

There is already quite a large literature on these subjects.

The optical methods are inherently the most accurate because of their greater resolving power and their smaller liability to unpredictable refraction effects. Of all the optical methods, the most precise (angular errors of the order of 1″ or less) is the photography of a satellite against the background of reference stars. By means of reductions similar to those used in astrometrics, the known angular coordinates of the reference stars serve to define the coordinate system on the plate and the photographic distortions.

On the other hand, the use of optical methods is limited to periods of darkness and clear sky, a disadvantage that the radio methods are not subject to.

Of the various optical methods, one offering considerable promise is the adaptation of the Markowitz Moon Camera to satellite observations. The camera tracks the star field at the sidereal rate, but the image of the moving object is caught on an internal prism which rotates with respect to the camera at such a rate and orientation as to make the image of the moving object stationary with respect to the star field. The moving prism mount automatically records a time mark at known points as it rotates. Although this refined technique is unnecessary with a bright enough flashing light, its advantage for very faint satellites is obvious.

All the radio tracking methods mentioned above have been tested except the radio beacon–transponder, which appears to have great potentialities. The difficulties associated with tested radio methods and the magnitude of the errors, which arise chiefly from residual uncertainties in the corrections for ionospheric refraction, and also transmitter frequency drift in Doppler measures, are quite well known. While the errors are large compared with the smallest theoretically attainable by optical methods, radio methods are indispensable in that they are the only available ones that can be used in daylight or bad weather. Furthermore, the comparatively large quantity of radio data makes up to some extent for the lower precision. There is one obvious disadvantage of all the radio methods except radar: there must be an active transmitter in the satellite.

Several of the investigations outlined above, in particular those dealing with extensive triangulation and trilateration, call for a large number of stations scattered all over the world. The most expeditious and least costly method of meeting this requirement is probably the organization of a net of portable stations, with tough, foolproof equipment that is easy to transport and set up. A station complete enough to answer the conditions might include (1) a camera of long enough focal length to keep the errors of measurement small but not so long as to be unmanageable in the field, of sufficient light-gathering power to photograph a given satellite at the greatest operating distances, and mounted for greatest ease and flexibility in tracking; (2) radio equipment to pulse the transponder and to time the arrival of the responding pulse; (3) a command radio to activate the flashing light; (4) communications receivers and transmitters for coordination with other stations, for time signals, and so forth; and (5) portable generators.

REFERENCES

1. W. A. Heiskanen and F. A. Vening Meinesz: *The Earth and Its Gravity Field* (New York: McGraw-Hill Book Company, Inc., 1958).
2. D. Brouwer, *Astron. J.*, *63*, 433 (1958). See also Brouwer's paper continuing the development of a Delaunay-type treatment of satellite orbits, presented at the Conference on Orbits, NASA, March, 1959 (in press).
3. T. E. Sterne: *Astron. J.*, *63*, 28 (1958); *Astron. J.*, *63*, 424 (1958); *J. Appl. Phys.* *30*, 270 (1959).
4. B. Garfinkel, *Astron. J.*, *63*, 88 (1958); *Astron. J.*, *63*, 422 (1958); "On the Motion of a Satellite of an Oblate Planet," *BRL Aberdeen Rpt. 1018*, July, 1957.
5. D. G. King-Hele and R. H. Merson: *J. Brit. Interplan. Soc.*, *16*, 446 (1958). R. H. Merson and D. G. King-Hele, *Nature*, *182*, 640 (1958). R. H. Merson, D. G. King-Hele, and R. N. A. Plimmer: *Nature*, *183*, 239 (1959). D. G. King-Hele, *Proc. Roy. Soc.*, *A247*, 49 (1958); *Proc. Roy. Soc.*, *A248*, 55 (1958).
(References 2 to 5 are intended only as examples and not a comprehensive bibliography of this subject.)
6. W. M. Kaula: *J. Geophys. Res.*, *64*, 2401 (1959).
7. H. Jeffreys: *The Earth*, 3d ed. (London: Cambridge University Press, 1952).
8. E. Jahnke and F. Emde: *Funktionentafeln* [Tables of Functions], 4th rev. ed. (New York: Dover Publications, 1945).

9. J. A. O'Keefe, Ann Eckels, and R. K. Squires: *Science, 129*, 565 (1959); *J. Geophys. Res., 64*, 2389 (1959).
10. R. d'E. Atkinson: "Surveying by Astrometry of Rocket Flashes," paper presented at 5th General Assembly of IGY, Moscow, 1958. *The Annals of the IGY, 12* (London: Pergamon Press, in press).
11. *Sci. News Letter, 76*, 197 (1959).

SUPPLEMENTARY READING

H. E. Newell, Jr., and L. N. Cormier (eds.): "First Results of IGY Rocket and Satellite Research," *The Annals of the IGY, 12*, Section 3, Geodesy (London: Pergamon Press, in press). Contains results reported at the 5th Meeting of CSAGI, Moscow, August, 1958, and more recently by:

D. G. King-Hele: "The Effect of the Earth's Oblateness on the Orbit of a Near Satellite"

E. C. Cornford: "A Comparison of Orbital Theory with Observations Made in the United Kingdom of the Russian Satellites"

E. Buchar: "Determination of the Earth's Flattening by Means of the Nodal Displacement of the Second Soviet Satellite"

J. A. O'Keefe: "A Preliminary Determination of the Oblateness of the Earth"

L. G. Jacchia: "The Earth's Gravitational Potential as Derived from Satellite $1957\beta_1$"

M. Lecar, J. Sorensen, and A. Eckels: "A Determination of the Coefficient J of the Second Harmonic in $1958\beta_2$"

S. W. Henriksen: "The Hydrostatic Flattening of the Earth"

J. A. O'Keefe and A. Eckels: "Perturbation in the Eccentricity of $1958\beta_2$"

J. A. O'Keefe, A. Eckels, and R. K. Squires: "Pear-shaped Component of Earth's Figure from the Motion of Vanguard I"

R. d'E. Atkinson: "Surveying by Astrometry of Rocket Flashes"

C. A. Whitten and K. H. Drummond (eds.): *Contemporary Geodesy*, Geophysical Monograph Series, No. 4, American Geophysical Union (Baltimore: Waverly Press, 1959). Proceedings of a conference held by the Smithsonian Astrophysical Observatory and Harvard College Observatory, Cambridge, Mass., December, 1958, containing contributions by:

M. O. Schmidt: "Geodetic Fundamentals: Introduction"

A. R. Robbins: "Evolution of the Geodetic Concept"

L. G. Simmons: "Geometric Techniques in Geodesy"

M. Ewing, J. L. Worzel, and Manik Talwani: "Some Aspects of Physical Geodesy"

C. A. Whitten: "Modern Geodesy: Introduction"

R. K. C. Johns: "Some Remarks on Geodetic Astronomy"

B. K. Meade: "Geodetic Networks"

N. F. Braaten: "Orthometric, Dynamic, and Barometric Heights"

D. A. Rice: "Gravity and Gravity Reduction"

J. A. O'Keefe, Nancy G. Roman, B. S. Yaplee, and Ann Eckels: "Ellipsoid Parameters from Satellite Data"

F. L. Whipple: "Geodesy and Space: Introduction"
A. B. Mickelwait: "Rocketry"
J. A. Hynek: "Satellites"
R. H. Wilson, Jr.: "Optical and Electronic Tracking"
C. A. Lundquist: "Orbits in Contemporary Geodesy"
D. A. Lautman: "Computations"
W. Wrigley: "Space Navigation in the Solar System"

6 ≡

METEOROLOGY

Harry Wexler

1. BACKGROUND

It is only little more than a century ago that meteorological observations were first plotted on a map to obtain a synoptic picture of weather events. These first weather charts covered only an area of a few thousand square miles. With growing awareness of the usefulness of weather charts in forecasting and with the improvement in communications, the charts gradually expanded to cover many land areas, islands, and oceanic shipping routes. But these first maps were only for a small portion of the Earth's surface and also failed to depict what was happening above the surface except as could be deduced from clouds and precipitation.

With each advance in aerial observation—from manned balloons to kites to airplanes to balloon-borne radiosonde—the ceilings of the meteorologist expanded vertically, higher and higher. The advent of the large rocket succeeded in furnishing information about the important top 1 per cent of the atmospheric mass—too high to be reached by balloon. The marked upward thrust of sounding techniques, however, has not been accompanied by a similar expansion laterally of meteorological observations, especially over the vast island-free oceanic areas, except along the principal airplane and shipping routes. Less than one-fifth of the total

139

atmospheric mass is adequately probed by conventional meteorological sounding techniques today, and large storms can reside undetected for days in many desert, polar, and oceanic areas.

Now meteorologists have a vehicle and an observing platform with a global capability commensurate with the global nature of the atmosphere. By use of satellites orbiting about the Earth, man will obtain a downward look at clouds—those beautiful and ever-changing manifestations of atmospheric processes which can be used to identify and locate storms and fair-weather areas. With a proper distribution of meteorological satellites orbiting about the Earth, it will be possible to keep track of each major storm on Earth, to note the birth of new storms and the death of old ones.

No less important than the obvious practical benefits of satellites to weather forecasts will be the contribution to basic knowledge of atmospheric physics, for example, the measurement of the global distribution of the net radiant energy absorbed and emitted by the Earth-atmosphere system. Since "weather" results from winds attempting to equalize the nonuniform distribution of the net radiant energy received from the Sun, it is important to keep accurate account of the global distribution of the basic radiant energy which drives the atmospheric heat engine. This energy budget, when measured over long periods of time, will not only be useful in interpreting basic knowledge of the atmospheric processes but might also assist in formulating a new system of long-range forecasts and in anticipating climatic changes.

However, the availability of global data from meteorological satellites will not eliminate the need for knowledge of the fine-structure details of the atmosphere and important links between the top atmospheric layer and the denser layers below, made possible by balloons and rocket-borne radiosondes. The upper limit of conventional balloons is about 30 km, but the region above this height to at least 60 km is of great meteorological interest, not only for forecasting for vehicles in this upper layer but also because this layer may be a connecting link between unusual solar emissions and anomalous terrestrial weather. High-altitude sounding rockets of modest cost which can be launched daily at a number of selected locations throughout the world appear to offer the most promising means for acquiring data in this critically important region.

2. TYPES OF METEOROLOGICAL OBSERVATIONS THAT SATELLITES MAKE POSSIBLE

The various types of observations important to meteorology which can be taken from satellites include:

1. Measurement of cloud cover by photoelectric cells, television cameras, and at night by infrared measurements and photosensitive devices using reflected moonlight and starlight.

2. Radiation measurements: (a) solar radiation—direct and reflected from Earth, clouds, and atmosphere, (b) total infrared radiation from Earth and atmosphere, (c) spectral measurements in the infrared water-vapor window ($8-11\mu$) to yield terrestrial surface temperatures and nocturnal cloud cover, (d) measurements of water-vapor emission in the $6-7\mu$ band.

3. Temperature and composition: (a) approximate measurements of temperature in the stratosphere by spectral measurements in the carbon dioxide 14μ band, (b) vertical distribution of ozone amount, (c) mass of water vapor and carbon dioxide in the vertical column and perhaps a rough approximation of the vertical distribution.

4. Other more difficult measurements which are conceivable include (a) radar measurements of global precipitation and perhaps cloud stratification, (b) atmospheric turbidity, (c) mass of the atmosphere and thus the surface pressure, (d) thunderstorm distribution by lightning detection and static discharge (sferics).

Initial examples of some of the parameters listed above have already been obtained by TIROS I and Explorer VII; others should be attained within the next few years, while still others may take a decade or more. Much basic research and development, both in the laboratory and in aircraft and on balloons, must be done before instruments can be made to work successfully in satellites. With larger payloads, heavier and more complex instrumentation can be mounted on the satellite, including perhaps some preliminary data-reduction equipment to cut down the communications load.

3. OPTIMUM ORBITS AND HEIGHTS OF METEOROLOGICAL SATELLITES

To eliminate the necessity for height corrections it would appear desirable to place meteorological satellites in circular orbits about the Earth. Orbits of large eccentricity, so desirable for other types of observations (such as measurement of the Van Allen radiation belt) should be avoided in meteorological satellites.

Of the infinite variety of circular orbits of Earth satellites it appears that two offer unique advantages to meteorology: the polar orbit and the equatorial orbit. The proposed earth-oriented Nimbus satellite is scheduled for launching in a polar orbit in late 1961 or early 1962.

The polar-orbit satellite will view the entire Earth twice daily—once as it moves, say, northward during daylight, and again as it moves southward at night. If launched northward at local noon, it will cross all latitudes near local noon until it passes the North Pole; then it will move southward across all latitudes at local midnight. However, because of motion of the Earth about the Sun, the local time of passage of the satellite across each latitude circle will be earlier by 4 min each day. It would be advantageous to eliminate diurnal effects by correcting for this 4-min displacement each day. For a 500-km-high satellite, for instance, this can be done by launching the satellite not directly toward the Pole, but at an inclination of 97° with the plane of the equator (0° points to the east) so that the precession of the orbit offsets the 4-min-per-day displacement. In this way the "polar" satellite would always view the Earth at nearly the same local time moving north and at nearly the same local time 12 hr different, moving south. This is not to say that diurnal effects are not important, but only that it would simplify interpretation of satellite data if one satellite were a "noon–midnight satellite," another a "4 P.M.–4 A.M. satellite," etc.

One can conceive of an ideal system of, say, seven meteorological satellites, each 6000 km high. Six of these would move in circular, quasi-polar orbits of 4-hr period on meridians 60° of longitude apart. Of these, three would be "daylight" satellites, moving northward at 8 A.M., noon, and 4 P.M., and three would be "nighttime" satellites, moving south on the opposite side of the Earth at 8 P.M., midnight, and 4 A.M. At a given moment the daylight satellites should each be at the same latitude north, say, while the nighttime satellites should each be at the same latitude south. By such a system and taking into account the large areas seen at a given moment, no important cloud cover need remain unobserved for more than 1 hr. By selecting the Greenwich meridian as the noon or midnight satellite, the data from each of the six satellites, 60° of longitude apart, could be combined to give a nearly complete world chart for each of the four daily synoptic times.

Such a complex of "high-flying" satellites, while advantageous for global meteorology and for the identification and tracking of the large-scale weather systems, might not be the most suitable means for obtaining details of fine structure. These details are useful for identification of the smaller atmospheric systems, such as fronts, squall lines, thunderstorms, and even winds (by tracking the motion of identifiable cloud elements). It would appear that "low-flying" satellites at heights of several hundred kilometers would be more useful for furnishing information on the smaller-scale meteorological phenomena, so important for the short-range and detailed forecasting.

Although polar-orbiting satellites crossing the equator would provide useful observations to tropical nations, an equatorial-orbiting satellite would appear to offer unique advantages for these countries. As the seventh satellite moves from west to east along the equator, it could observe the weather for a certain distance north and south depending on its height and transmit its information to each station in turn. A satellite at a height of 1000 km would orbit the Earth in 105 min and could observe the Earth's surface along a belt extending from 30°N latitude to 30°S latitude. An extra dividend for the tropical countries would, of course, be the observations from the six polar-orbiting satellites as they cross the equator 60° of longitude and 4 hr apart. It is likely that satellite observations of cloud cover will be of particular value in the tropics where conventional observations and the prognostic techniques of higher latitudes have had limited success.

4. IMPLICATIONS OF SATELLITE OBSERVATIONS FOR METEOROLOGICAL OPERATIONS

As with other types of meteorological data, ways must be found to promote standardization and interpretation of satellite meteorological observations (particularly cloud cover, which will probably be the first operational observations available from satellites) and to ensure their speedy transmission to the meteorological services of the world.

4.1 Standardization

In the not-too-distant future the same cloud system will be under the surveillance of many satellites, each probably orbiting at a different height and each probably possessing different optics and sensors. It is important that the data coming from each satellite yield essentially the same major features of the cloud system so that the forecaster will not be given conflicting information. It is much too early to recommend how to obtain the desired standardization, but it is foreseeable that compatibility tests of proposed sensing equipment may be conducted by the several countries engaged in satellite meteorology.

4.2 Interpretation of Cloud Data

An objective identification and classification of clouds has long been a thorny problem in meteorology. With respect to satellite cloud observations the problem will be to combine individual clouds and cloud systems to produce a pattern which can be interpreted in terms of atmospheric motions and processes. This interpretation would be an expansion and refinement of the system of "nephanalysis" in vogue a generation ago.

Information on orbits, heights, and instrumental resolution must be disseminated so that the observations can be properly interpreted, merged with the great body of other meteorological data, and put to use in synoptic analysis and forecasting. An example of a picture which can be readily interpreted in terms of conventional meteorological systems is shown in Fig. 1. This composite of TIROS I pictures, prepared by V. J. Oliver of the U.S. Weather Bureau,[1] shows clouds produced by two cyclonic systems connected by a frontal zone, in agreement with the classical cyclone-family model. Such pictures can help locate storm systems in data-sparse areas and also reveal much information about warm and cold air masses, fronts, jet streams, convective areas, fog, etc.

4.3 Transmittal of Satellite Information

The global range of satellites also provides a unique opportunity for speedy communication of satellite information directly to those countries over which it is passing for use in local forecasting. Line-of-sight transmission with its well-known advantages can thus be used in putting the observations to use with minimum delay. However, adequate ground receivers and data-processing equipment will be needed to take advantage of this opportunity. Perhaps not all countries will establish such communication and processing facilities, and provision should be made to store data on the satellite for readout to those countries properly equipped; these countries could then process and transmit information promptly to interested countries.

Eventually it is expected that world-wide communications will be facilitated by the availability of communication satellites, a system of high-altitude (approximately 36,000 km over the Earth's surface) vehicles which will hover over a fixed point at the Earth's equator and serve as relays for line-of-sight radio transmission. Such a system will offer to the world's meteorological services speedy communication of all kinds of meteorological data so that the meteorologists' dream of drawing a truly current "world weather map" will be fulfilled. An auxiliary use of these satellites would be to keep continuous watch of clouds below them.

5. IMPLICATIONS OF SATELLITE DATA FOR METEOROLOGICAL RESEARCH

Cloud observations from satellites, once they have served their immediate forecast use, will be valuable in meteorological research. For example, they can be used to establish for the first time a truly global cloud census, to draw average charts of world cloud cover by months or other periods, and to note long-time variations in cloud amount and dis-

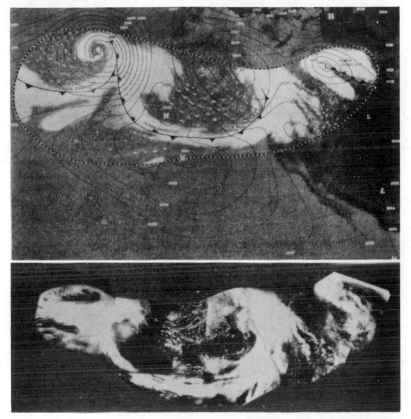

FIG. 1. A mosaic of ten TIROS cloud pictures taken starting at 2300Z May 19 and ending at 0100Z on May 20, 1960 (below), and a weather map of the North Pacific Ocean for the same time with TIROS clouds superimposed. (*After V J. Oliver.*)

tribution. However, several difficulties must be overcome in the reduction of the great mass of data from world-wide pictures to achieve a truly global cloud census. The cloud pictures are distorted, mainly because areas are inevitably foreshortened in some parts of the pictures. Secondly, if the cloud amounts are determined from photographs, the photographic process plays a role in the detection of these clouds; cirrus clouds, for example, may not be distinguishable on the photograph. Furthermore, small scattered clouds may evade detection by the television system.

Thus, after due allowance has been made for foreshortened areas, these effects may produce a smaller total cloud amount than really exists. However, there is some compensation in that fields of fairly bright scattered or broken clouds may indicate a somewhat larger cloud amount when small bright clouds fill the television raster lines.

Satellite observations of radiation—direct solar, reflected solar, and terrestrial outgoing—can be used to study weather developments and motions of atmospheric disturbances as related to the radiation balance and to compute net radiation gains and losses over the Earth. It is known that the poleward transport of excess energy from the tropics can vary considerably.[8] For example, in February, 1951, the poleward energy transport across the 30°N latitude circle varied from $+140 \cdot 10^{13}$ cal per sec to $-140 \cdot 10^{13}$ cal per sec; from mid-January to mid-February the poleward energy transport across the 15° latitude circle varied from 18 per cent to 141 per cent of the average from October, 1950, to April, 1951. When winds are blowing mostly from the west or east, the energy flow away from the tropics is inhibited. But when the energy flow pattern changes from this "high index" condition to meridional or "low index" flow pattern (typically characterized by large quasi-stationary anticyclonic and cyclonic vortices), poleward energy flow is promoted. When meridional flow persists, it gives rise to rather prolonged spells of the same general weather type, such as fair weather, droughts, floods, and storms, depending on the location of a particular geographical region with respect to the stalled-weather pattern. Thus radiation balance measurements from a satellite, by enabling meteorologists for the first time to note the space and time variations in energy storage and transport, will offer an opportunity to devise a new quantitative approach to extended-range weather prediction.

Observations of unusual solar radiations, energetic particles, and meteoric dust from space should be readily available from satellites for correlation with unusual weather behavior. The availability of world weather charts should make it possible to study contrasts and similarities in Northern and Southern Hemispheric circulation patterns and to see whether one hemisphere precedes the other in assuming anomalous patterns or whether both react simultaneously to a common external excitation such as unusual solar radiations or meteoric dust.

These are but a few examples of new horizons in meteorological research which will be opened up by the availability of global cloud, radiation, and other data. The great flow of data which will pour forth from satellites and the large number of important problems to whose solution they will contribute make it important that compilations or world charts of important elements be drawn up and made available to research groups everywhere.

6. THE FIRST METEOROLOGICAL SATELLITE EXPERIMENTS

Vanguard II. The first meteorological satellite, 1959 Alpha (Vanguard II), was launched by the United States on Feb. 17, 1959, and transmitted cloud information until Mar. 7, 1959, when the expected failure of the power supply occurred. This satellite, a 50-cm-diameter 9.8-kg sphere, carried two photocells mounted behind circular windows which look out from opposite sides of the satellite at an angle of 45° from the spin axis. The object of the experiment was to measure the distribution of cloud cover over the daylight portion of the sphere's orbit, which extended from 34°N to 34°S latitude. In order to reduce the data, this system requires that the satellite spin-rate and spin-axis orientation remain within certain narrowly prescribed limits. Unfortunately the Vanguard II meteorological satellite did not have the required motions, so that it is very difficult to derive meaningful cloud pictures from the signals.

Tiros I. The difficulties introduced by the satellite motions in Vanguard II were in part overcome with a much heavier satellite using television cameras in TIROS I.[2] The television camera takes an instantaneous picture of a large area and, provided the spin rate is not too fast, cloud pictures covering a substantial area of the earth can in general be obtained even if the satellite motions are somewhat erratic.

The characteristics of TIROS I and its orbit have been described in several places.[3,4] TIROS I, a spinning satellite launched on Apr. 1, 1960, obtained pictures successfully until mid-June, 1960. It orbited the earth in nearly a circular orbit at about 450 miles with its subsatellite point varying between latitudes 48°N and 48°S. Because of the wide-angle coverage of one of its cameras, the satellite could see appreciably poleward of these latitudes, often beyond 55°. The satellite contained two television cameras, both looking along the spin axis. The cameras were sensitive to green-red light in order to reduce the influence of scattering by the cloudless atmosphere and took "snapshots" when they were pointed at favorable angles to the illuminated Earth. The data were stored on magnetic tape for one orbit and then transmitted on command to the ground at two readout stations, one in New Jersey and the other in Hawaii. On the ground the data were received simultaneously (1) via oscillograph screen which was photographed and (2) by recording on a magnetic tape.

The wide-angle camera had a field of view when looking straight down of about 1300 by 1300 km, with a resolution of about 3 km near the subsatellite point. The resolution is determined by the number of TV raster lines and the field of view when the camera is looking straight down. The resolution will therefore be poorer than 3 km as the distance of the viewed area from the subsatellite point increases. The second TV camera had a smaller field of view, seeing about 130 by 130 km with a resolution of approximately 0.8 km.

The ability with which objects can be seen depends somewhat on the background; for dark backgrounds, the high-resolution camera was sufficient to detect most cloud features in synoptic and mesoscale systems. The narrow-angle camera took pictures which included even individual cumulus clouds.

TIROS I took more than 20,000 pictures, many of which showed interesting cloud features. Many of these have already been described and analyzed.[1,5-7] Examples of some of the large-scale vortices of diameter 500 to 1000 miles are shown in Fig. 2 (Northern Hemisphere) and in Fig. 3 (Southern Hemisphere), with locations and dates indicated in Fig. 4.

Explorer VII. Another type of meteorological experiment, the radiation-balance experiment, was launched by the United States on Oct. 13, 1959, as part of the big package aboard 1959 Iota (Explorer VII). An estimate of the total flux of radiation to and from the Earth is measured by exposing small silver hemispheres with three types of coatings and measuring their temperatures. Each hemisphere is backed with a mirror so that the system approximates a sphere. A uniformly black sphere absorbs radiation at all wavelengths from all directions. A white sphere, which has a high absorptivity in the infrared beyond 4 or 5 μ but which reflects direct and reflected sunlight, measures the long-wave radiation emitted from the Earth and its atmosphere. Another sphere with a "tabor" coating responds in just the reverse way, absorbing sunlight in the visible and near-infrared portion of the spectrum but reflecting the incident infrared radiation. Another identical sphere, shielded from direct radiation from the Sun, permits the separation of direct-beam solar radiation from the diffuse reflected rays coming from the Earth.

By measuring and recording the temperatures of these spheres, it is possible to determine various radiative fluxes and thus the radiation budget of the Earth and its atmosphere over the area under the satellite—an area which is effectively several hundred kilometers in diameter for a satellite at 500 km. The data are being reduced, and a map of the distribution of the outgoing radiation and weather fronts is shown in Fig. 5. Reception of data from this experiment terminated Oct. 13, 1960.

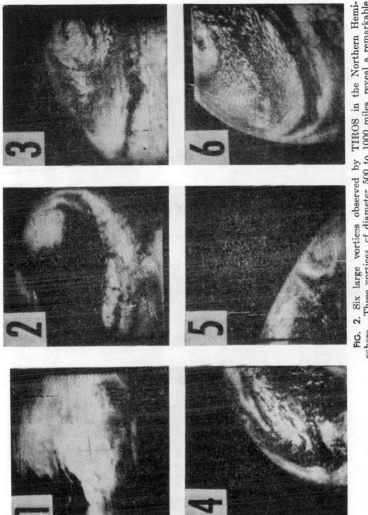

FIG. 2. Six large vortices observed by TIROS in the Northern Hemisphere. These vortices, of diameter 500 to 1000 miles, reveal a remarkable degree of cloud organization as well as great differences from one to the other. They are associated with large cyclonic storms at locations shown in Fig. 4.

149

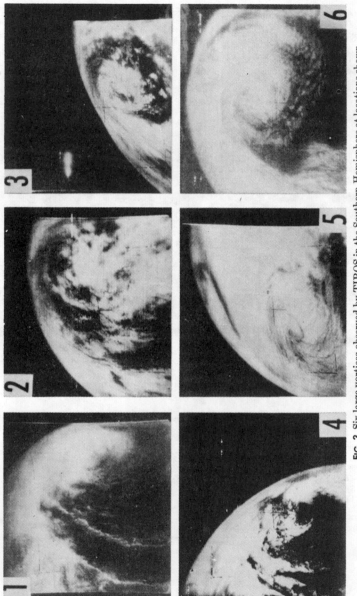

FIG. 3. Six large vortices observed by TIROS in the Southern Hemisphere at locations shown in Fig. 4. Again the remarkable degree of cloud organization and differences between vortices are apparent.

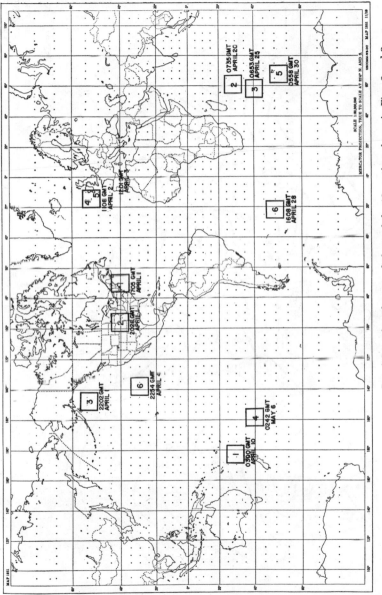

FIG. 4. Location, dates, and times of the 12 vortices shown in Figs. 2 and 3.

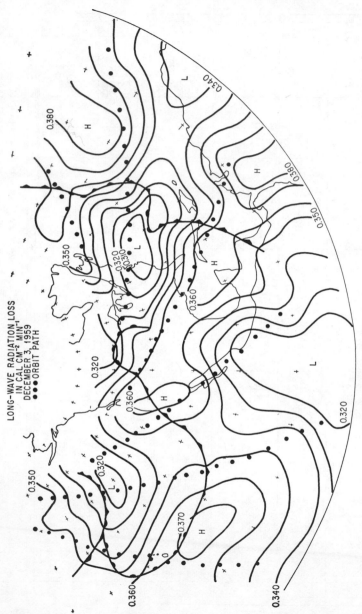

LONG-WAVE RADIATION LOSS
IN CAL CM² MIN⁻¹
DECEMBER 3, 1959
●● ORBIT PATH

FIG. 5. Geographical distribution of the terrestrial and atmospheric radiation loss to space in calories per square centimeter per minute observed by the heat-balance experiment on Explorer VII, Dec. 3, 1959. In addition to isolines of radiation loss, there are shown weather fronts and points indicating the orbital path of the satellite projected on the Earth. (*After V. E. Suomi.*)

Tiros II. Another member of the TIROS family, TIROS II, launched by the United States on Nov. 23, 1960, combined in one package a television camera and infrared sensors. The television observations were similar to those in TIROS I and were intended to measure the extent and type of cloud cover over the world. The radiation sensors were designed to measure with relatively high resolution (1) infrared radiation from the Earth, (2) albedo of the Earth, (3) emission in the 6.3-μ water-vapor band, and (4) temperature of the Earth's surface or cloud tops.

Pictures were taken at places in each orbit suitable with respect to sunlight and satellite orientation. The video information was then stored on magnetic tape and read out when the satellite passed over a ground station. On the ground the transmitted cloud pictures were reconstructed by means of a television monitor and photographed. They could then be used to locate storm areas and other meteorological phenomena after their location in space and time had been determined from the tracking data.

The data obtained from the radiation sensors were also recorded continuously and transmitted to the ground stations during each pass. The resulting magnetic tapes were then forwarded to the National Meteorological Center, U.S. Weather Bureau, Washington, for correlation with the tracking data. Although these data were intended primarily for basic atmospheric-energy studies, they may also prove to be of assistance in weather prediction.

7. INTERNATIONAL ASPECTS OF METEOROLOGICAL SATELLITES

Two international bodies, COSPAR (Committee on Space Research) and the WMO (World Meteorological Organization), are concerned with meteorological satellites.

COSPAR, a committee organized by the International Council of Scientific Unions (ICSU), has had three meetings, in London in November, 1958, in The Hague in March, 1959, and in Nice, January, 1960, with more frequent meetings of the Executive Committee.

The WMO, a specialized agency of the United Nations, consists of the meteorological services of 100 nations which are divided into six basic world regions. Its purposes are to facilitate cooperation in establishment of meteorological and allied observing stations, to promote rapid exchange of weather information, to promote standardization of meteorological observation and uniform publication of meteorological data, to further the application of meteorology to aviation, shipping, agriculture, etc., and to encourage research and training in meteorology.

It appears desirable to examine the possible roles of COSPAR and the WMO in promoting the development and use of meteorological satellites and dissemination of their data.

A natural line of division appears to lie between *research and development* and *synoptic use* of the meteorologically equipped satellites. COSPAR could encourage and coordinate a series of satellite meteorological experiments and evaluate the results of these experiments in a thorough research program. In adopting specific procedures for regular observing measures, WMO could be guided by the results. COSPAR could, because of its broad representation from the international scientific community, draw upon a wealth of knowledge to suggest new meteorological experiments and to promote the design, development and testing of new instrumentation. These instruments, based on latest developments in fields of spectroscopy, electromagnetic radiation, particle dynamics, etc., might depart widely from conventional meteorological instrumentation. Furthermore, the interplay of the various scientific disciplines engaged in research in space may lead to the unexpected development of valuable new tools and concepts for meteorologists. These might include detailed observations of energetic radiations and particles from the Sun and space, which affect the Earth's atmosphere. Also observations will some day be made of the composition and motions of atmospheres of other planets by artificial satellites and landings; comparison of the results with those on Earth should assist greatly in separating out effects common to all planets from purely terrestrial effects in the Earth's atmosphere.

The WMO, on the other hand, could keep in close touch with CO-SPAR'S activities and urge the exploitation of newly developed techniques and concepts to its member nations. The WMO could inform its members of the launchings of meteorologically equipped satellites, their orbits, heights and periods, characteristics of the sensing equipment, frequency and power of the radio transmissions, etc. It could encourage the member countries to participate in the program by launching meteorological satellites in desirable orbits, by assisting in the tracking and receipt of the transmitted data, and by taking valuable auxiliary observations, such as cloud observations. The WMO could promote the dissemination of such data and stimulate their use and interpretation by distributing literature and arranging for visits of meteorologists trained in the new techniques.

Thanks are due to my colleague Dr. S. Fritz for his careful review of the manuscript and valuable insertions and to Mr. V. J. Oliver and Professor V. Suomi for permission to use Figs. 1 and 5.

REFERENCES

1. Staff, Meteorological Satellite Lab. (U.S.W.B.): Some Meteorological Results from TIROS I, in Report on TIROS I, National Aeronautics and Space Administration (in press). (See article by V. J. Oliver.)
2. Fritz, S.: On Observing the Atmosphere from Satellites. I. Cloud Observations, *Weatherwise, 12*, 139–165 (August, 1959).
3. Stroud, W. G.: Initial Results of the TIROS I Meteorological Satellite, *J. Geop. Res., 65*, 1643–1644 (May, 1960).
4. Sternberg, S., and W. G. Stroud: TIROS I (a series of articles), *Astronautics, 5*, 32ff (June, 1960).
5. Fritz, S., and H. Wexler: Cloud Pictures from Satellite TIROS I, *Mon. Wea. Rev., 88*, 79–87 (March, 1960).
6. Wexler, H., and S. Fritz: TIROS Reveals Cloud Formation, *Science, 131*, 1708–1710 (June, 1960).
7. Anonymous: TIROS I Concludes Mission; TIROS II Readied. *Weatherwise,* 159–161, 180, August, 1960.
8. L. A. Vuorela: *Geophysica, 6*, 106 (1957).

SUPPLEMENTARY READING

J. Bjerknes: "Detailed Analysis of Synoptic Weather as Observed from Photographs Taken on Two Rocket Flights over White Sands, New Mexico, July 26, 1958," *Rand Corp. Report,* Santa Monica, Calif., April, 1951.
W. A. Dryden and N. E. Prosser: "Optimum Utilization of Satellite Observations in Weather Analysis and Forecasting," *Final Report on Contract* AF.19(604)-1754, Florida State University, Department of Meteorology, February, 1959.
Y. Fedorov: "The Satellite Studies the Earth," *Izvestiya,* Moscow, June 8, 1958.
A. H. Glaser: "Meteorological Utilization of Images of the Earth's Surface Transmitted from a Satellite Vehicle," Blue Hill Observatory, Harvard University, Oct. 31, 1957.
W. L. Godson: "Meteorological Applications of Earth Satellites," *J. Roy. Astron. Soc. of Canada, 52*:2, 49–56 (1958).
S. M. Greenfield: "Synoptic Weather Observations from Extreme Altitudes," paper presented at the AMS Meeting in New York, Jan. 23, 1956, *Rand Report* P-761, Feb. 15, 1956.
——— and W. W. Kellogg: "Satellite Weather Reconnaissance" (to be published in *Astronautics) Rand Report* P-1402, June 12, 1958.
L. F. Hubert and O. Berg: "A Rocket Portrait of a Tropical Storm," *Mon. Wea. Rev., 83*:6, 119–124 (1955).
W. W. Kellogg: "Research in Outer Space," *Science, 127*, 793–802 (1958).
A. M. Obukhov: "Sputniks as Instruments of Upper Air Research," *Nauka i Zhizn',* No. 11, 20–31 (1957). Address at All Union Society for Dissemination of Political and Scientific Knowledge, Oct. 16, 1957.
H. Wexler: "Observing the Weather from a Satellite Vehicle," *J. Brit. Interplan. Soc., 13*:5, 269–276 (1954).
———: "The Satellite and Meteorology," *J. Astronautics, 4*:1, 1–6 (1957).
W. K. Widger and C. N. Touart: "Utilization of Satellite Observations in Weather Analysis," *BAMS, 38*:9, 521–533 (1957).

7

ROCKET RESEARCH AND THE
UPPER ATMOSPHERE

William W. Kellogg

1. INTRODUCTION

A theme that runs through this book is the great advance made possible by new vehicles to carry man's instruments (and ultimately man) away from the surface of the earth. It is sometimes forgotten that sounding rockets have been used for many years to probe the earth's upper atmosphere and that a great deal is still left to be done by these relatively simple vehicles. Thus no discussion of space science can be complete without some recognition of the role which these powerful tools must continue to play, particularly in the studies of the upper atmosphere and near space.

The first sounding rocket to carry an instrument for geophysical research was a WAC Corporal, fired at White Sands Proving Ground, New Mexico, in 1945. The following year a number of captured German V-2 rockets carried scientific payloads from the same firing range into the ionosphere. Since then there have been many hundreds of such launchings, and more than half a dozen countries now have active programs of upper-atmosphere rocket research. It is fair to say that the original foundation for the space effort lies in rocket-sounding research.

There have been so many important results from the many rocket programs that no attempt will be made to summarize them here.   (The interested reader is referred to the bibliography at the end of the chapter.) Instead, an attempt will be made to look at the future and to point to some of the many promising avenues for research with sounding rockets. In a sense, this complements Chap. 8, in which the value of satellites for studying the upper atmosphere is stressed.*

2. GENERAL QUALIFICATIONS OF SOUNDING ROCKETS

In the following sections an attempt is made to review in some detail the whole range of specific experiments in the upper air and the fringe of space which need to be done with sounding rockets. This implies that the suggested observations can be done better with rockets than from the ground, from balloons, or with satellites or that at least an exploratory test with a rocket is required before trying to use a satellite.

Here are some of the kinds of tasks for which sounding rockets are indicated:

Direct measurements of atmospheric conditions below the level of satellites and above the level of balloons, which means from about 30 to 200 km.

Measurements in any altitude range of distributions *in the vertical.*

Measurements at a given time and place or simultaneous measurements at a number of places (synoptic observations).   The time can be selected to coincide with some unusual event, such as a solar flare, magnetic storm, blackout, etc.

Measurements which require very large bandwidths and correspondingly large powers for a short time.

Experiments involving recovery, which include all those involving the use of film, either photographic or stacked emulsions.

Closely related to the previous group, experiments where too long

---

* The author has drawn extensively for this material from the suggestions of an *ad hoc* Working Group of the Space Science Board.   It is thus the result of a collaboration in which well-qualified scientists with diverse interests were able to pool their ideas.   The *ad hoc* Working Group on Upper Atmosphere Rocket Research of the Space Science Board met at the National Academy of Sciences in Washington, D.C., on Oct. 19 and 20, 1959; the participating members were William W. Kellogg (Chairman), Hans J. aufm Kampe, Talbot A. Chubb, Francis S. Johnson, Leslie M. Jones, Hilde K. Kallmann, Edward Manring, Carl E. McIlwain, Herman Yagoda, and John C. Mester; invited participants included representatives from various agencies and laboratories engaged in rocket research or its support.

an exposure will be detrimental to the package, as in the case of emulsion stacks.

Exploratory measurements of upper-air conditions, where the range of parameters is uncertain.

Tests of prototype equipment to be used on space vehicles, where exposure to the launching and the space environment prior to investing in a full-scale flight may result in great savings.

The lead times (and costs) involved in preparing rocket instrumentation for a flight are usually less than those required for satellites or space probes by a factor of 2 or 3, and there is no sign that this discrepancy will decrease. Thus rocket experimentation is considerably more flexible, changes can be made as the development progresses, more sophisticated and difficult techniques can be tried, etc. Finally, the cheaper rockets, because of their relative simplicity, can be used as training grounds for new experimenters who wish to try their ideas out, thereby increasing the number of research institutions in the field and broadening the human base on which the whole research effort of a nation rests.

The typical exploratory upper-atmosphere rocket-research program can be divided into four phases, each of which costs about the same: (1) procuring the vehicles, (2) designing and building the instrumentation, (3) sending a crew out to the field to handle the firing, and (4) reducing and analyzing the data. Obviously, these may vary in relative emphasis and cost from experiment to experiment, but there is one phase which seems to be invariably underestimated: reduction and analysis of data. A large volume of significant scientific data will emerge from an upper-atmosphere rocket program, and the analysis of these data should be taken into account in program planning.

Requirements on rockets vary tremendously. For the meteorological rockets, for example, in which only a few pounds of instrumentation may be needed to determine winds and temperatures (or even just a clump of radar-reflecting "chaff" for winds alone) to 60 or 80 km, the emphasis is on simplicity and low cost. The rocket is typically a solid-propellant single-stage one and may weigh less than 20 kg. To probe the ionosphere with somewhat more elaborate payloads usually requires a rocket weighing 500 to 1000 kg, and this may be a single-stage liquid rocket or a multistage solid rocket. For still higher flights, or ones which require heavy payloads or stabilizing controls, even larger rockets are often required. These statements are necessarily general, since the state of the art of rocketry is advancing rapidly and there is now a very large assortment of available rockets in the United States and elsewhere.

3. ATMOSPHERIC DENSITY, COMPOSITION, AND WINDS

The beginning of a study of an atmosphere should be a description of its mass distribution and its motion, coupled with a knowledge of its composition. Fundamental though this knowledge is, we are able to define the mass and flow conditions above 30 km in but the most general terms, and above 150 km we have little direct knowledge of the composition as well. We are aware of variations from place to place, season to season, and day to night, and we have within the past year been able to detect significant mass (density) changes which are directly related to solar activity. However, the observations have been far too few to allow the picture to be filled in properly. Experimental programs that would help to fill these gaps are as follows.

Synoptic Meteorological Rockets. For nearly three decades meteorologists have been working with synoptic radiosonde observations obtained by simultaneous balloon flights throughout the world. In this way it is possible to draw a map showing the instantaneous picture of pressures, temperatures, and winds over an entire hemisphere. The indications are that many of the events which are seen on the high-level meteorological charts are events which are triggered from still higher altitudes. A particularly dramatic instance of this is the phenomenon known as "explosive warming," which occurs annually in the late winter or early spring in polar and subpolar regions. In this event a dramatic increase in temperature at some spot in the polar region is accompanied by a rapid change in the entire circulation pattern of the stratosphere, and in one of these events a large increase in temperature was traced to about 65 km by rockets fired from Fort Churchill.

It is proposed to extend the altitude of the present balloon network by means of meteorological sounding rockets. The Arcas rocket, developed specifically for this purpose, will carry some 2 to 5 kg to over 65 km. The smaller Loki rocket can also be used for wind determinations. A program of synoptic rocket observations in the United States is already being planned as a joint effort by the Department of Defense agencies, NASA, and the U.S. Weather Bureau. Present plans call for firings from Patrick, Eglin, White Sands, Tonopah, Point Mugu, Fort Greeley, Fort Churchill, and Wallops Island on a schedule of one rocket per day per station for one month in each of the four seasons. For special studies, as for example to observe diurnal changes, four or more per day will be fired on at least one day in each season. It is hoped eventually to extend this network in time and to add further launching sites, particularly launching sites in the polar and equatorial regions and in

Europe. Such a network will permit the upper-air analysis to be effectively extended above the level of the balloon network.

Ionospheric Densities and Winds. Above the level of the meteorological rocket it will be necessary to probe the ionosphere to obtain densities and winds as high as possible. It has been demonstrated that rocket-borne instruments can effectively measure density to 200 km or slightly higher. These direct measuring devices can also determine the composition of the atmosphere in some cases, to be referred to later.

The measurement of winds in the ionosphere has been achieved by creating various kinds of luminous trails (particularly luminous trails of alkali metals) and by tracking the motion of these trails. This technique has already been demonstrated and will be referred to in more detail under the class of photochemical experiments.

Above 200 to 250 km the direct measurement of densities from rockets becomes virtually impossible, except by certain optical techniques in which the distribution of specific constituents of the atmosphere can be determined by absorption measurements, i.e., by measuring the solar radiation in the ultraviolet which reaches a given level, from which the total depth of absorbing gas above that level can be determined. These absorption measurements can in principle be extended to very great altitudes.

The use of satellites for measuring atmospheric density is well known, and at present our knowledge of density above 250 km is based almost entirely on satellite drag measurement. While these densities are extremely useful in understanding the atmosphere, it will be necessary to refine such measurements if we are to measure short-term changes in density, for at present the density measured by satellites refers to the entire region of perigee and usually requires more than one orbit for a determination.

Composition. The measurement of the atmospheric constituents by means of rockets up to 200 km has already been demonstrated by the use of mass spectrometers and by solar-absorption techniques. Because atmospheric composition changes drastically above 100 km and because these changes must vary with solar activity and latitude, it is important to obtain such measurements at various latitudes and throughout a sun spot cycle. It is believed that optical measurements of partial pressures of atmospheric constituents can give information on the composition of the atmosphere to extreme altitudes. Measurements of density in the high atmosphere, whether by rockets or by satellites, can be of only marginal use in determining conditions in the upper atmosphere without a concurrent knowledge of the composition, since distribution of density gives only distribution of *scale height* and not *kinetic temperature*.

4. FREE ELECTRONS AND IONIZATION

Measurements need to be made of certain particular regions of the ionosphere at particular times. One such region is the F-2 over the magnetic equator, where the behavior of the free-electron density is different from its behavior in other latitudes. Another important zone of the ionosphere is the D and E region during periods of polar blackouts and sudden ionospheric disturbances: during these periods there is a marked enhancement of the ionization in these lower parts of the ionosphere, and there are practical as well as scientific reasons for wishing to observe these events by means of rockets.

The distribution of atmospheric ions is of theoretical importance for an understanding of the physics of the ionosphere. Ion distributions have already been measured at Fort Churchill during the IGY, and interesting variations from day to night have been observed. These observations should be extended to other latitudes and should be made during various seasons.

Ionospheric observations during a solar eclipse are extremely valuable for determining the rates of ionization and decay times—this type of observation, in which a rocket can be fired into the moon's shadow with some precision, is a unique use of the rocket vehicle, and it has already been demonstrated by the Naval Research Laboratory during the solar eclipse in the South Pacific in October, 1958.

The charge on a vehicle in the ionosphere is determined by the balance between the flow of free electrons and positive ions between the surrounding plasma and the skin of the vehicle. This charge is partly determined by artificial electric fields produced by radio antennas and partly due to the free-electron temperature. In the absence of radio transmissions the free-electron temperature will be the factor determining vehicle charge. Several techniques have been developed for measuring free-electron temperatures, such as the University of Michigan's bipolar probe and the Air Force Geophysics Research Directorate's ion trap, and it will be of value to extend these measurements of electron temperatures.

The theoretical understanding of the ionosphere depends on a knowledge of the rates of recombination of electrons and various ions and rates of electronic attachment. Currently, balloons carrying thermistors with special coatings have been able to measure certain recombination rates, and a possible next step is to extend these experiments above 30 km with rockets. The measurement of free-air conditions with rockets following a high-altitude atomic explosion, as has already been tried to a limited extent, would also give valuable information on reaction rates in the upper atmosphere.

5. MAGNETIC MEASUREMENTS

The measurement of the distribution of magnetic field in the vertical gives a measure of the flow of electric currents in the atmosphere. Such measurements have already revealed some surprising electric currents, such as the *double* equatorial electrojet and the complex flow of currents in the auroral zone. Since these electric currents are extremely variable from place to place and from day to night and change with magnetic activity, their measurement over a wide range of latitudes and times (preferably on a synoptic basis) would allow their patterns to be better understood. Because these electric currents are linked with the wind systems in the ionosphere, an understanding of them will also reveal something about the ionospheric circulations.

One region of the geomagnetic field shows an anomalous distribution, namely, the region over South Africa. It has been suggested that a determination of the magnetic field over this South African anomaly could be measured by a magnetometer flight to about 1000 km or more.

An exploratory flight above the F region to measure the energy spectrum of very low frequency electromagnetic or hydromagnetic waves would be of great potential value. At present the presence of such hydromagnetic waves in the range from a fraction of a cycle to 100 kc has been postulated, but no direct evidence exists. Since the range and intensity of these waves are unknown, an exploratory measurement with broad-bandwidth telemetering is indicated before more extensive measurements are attempted with satellites.

6. PHOTOCHEMICAL EXPERIMENTS

The ozone region in the stratosphere is the product of a photochemical process. The greater part of this region is accessible to balloons, and rockets would be valuable only for observations of the upper part of the ozone region. At higher levels the presence of the molecules OH and NO at 80 to 100 km is of considerable importance in determining the radiative-heat balance and the ionization of the upper atmosphere. Both of these constituents can be determined either by mass spectrographic methods or by observing their emission lines. OH in particular has a strong emission in the near infrared which could be measured from rockets.

Of prime importance in determining the composition of the ionosphere is the distribution of atomic oxygen (starting at around 80 km) and of atomic nitrogen (starting at a higher altitude). Atomic oxygen has strong emissions in the visible, and observations by rockets of the distribution of this emission would be of value in determining its role in the upper atmosphere.

A technique which has been used extensively by both the Air Force Geophysics Research Directorate and NASA has been to seed the upper atmosphere with various chemicals that either react with the atmosphere or fluoresce in sunlight. When alkaline metal vapor such as sodium or cesium is sprayed into the ionosphere at twilight, the intense glow of this trail can be easily recorded on the ground photographically. The rate of expansion of such a trail gives the diffusion rates in the ionosphere. Turbulence exists below about 105 km, but above this height the diffusion appears from past measurements to be molecular diffusion. Furthermore, by measuring the profiles of the resonant emission lines, it is possible to determine atmospheric temperature, for the alkali metal atoms quickly come to thermal equilibrium with their surroundings. Cesium, because of its low ionization potential, causes enough local ionization to permit the cloud to be observed by low-frequency radar.

The use of hydrocarbons (such as ethylene and CH_2Cl_2) instead of the metals causes an emission by photochemical reactions with the active gases in the ionosphere. At lower levels the reaction with atomic oxygen presumably dominates; at higher altitudes in the ionosphere the reaction with atomic nitrogen, producing the CN bands, will predominate. At present the cross sections of these reactions are poorly known, but in principle it should be possible to determine the relative distributions of atomic oxygen and atomic nitrogen from the intensities of these various emissions.

This technique for determining winds and diffusion rates can be used to altitudes of 300 to 400 km and perhaps can be extended to still greater altitudes. The tracking of these trails to determine winds in the ionosphere is so far the only means which has been used for wind determinations above about 90 km, and the possibility of measuring motions in the atmosphere throughout the ionosphere is extremely inviting.

7. SOLAR, AURORAL, AND TRAPPED PARTICLES

While satellites and space probes have been able to map the features of the great radiation belts surrounding the earth, there is still much to be learned about the charged particles which move in this region. In particular, the following exploratory measurements with rockets seem to be indicated.

The energy spectrum of particles in the radiation belt is not known below some tens of thousands of electron volts, and the measurement of the energy spectrum down to the order of a few electron volts would be of great value.

It would be useful to make observations in the vertical of the distribution of particles with direction and with energy over the equator. Such a measurement would require a very large bandwidth and sophisticated techniques for measuring the energies and directions simultaneously.

While a satellite can measure the large-scale variations in the outer radiation belt, its rapid motion does not permit it to discern the difference between small-scale variations and changes in time. A rocket probing through this region at relatively slow speeds would be able to observe the fine structure of the outer radiation belt. In order to do this usefully the sounding rocket would have to go out to several earth radii.

Recently the presence of energetic protons accompanying magnetic storms has been detected at balloon altitudes. These bursts of energetic particles from the sun which enter the earth's atmosphere have been cited by some as a major contributor to the phenomenon of the polar blackout. Since balloons are not high enough in the atmosphere to observe the original flux of particles, rockets are clearly indicated to measure these particles, and since the influx can be predicted to some extent, it will be possible to station these rockets in the ionosphere at the appropriate times and places.

Perhaps in no other field of upper-atmosphere research has the scientist been faced with so many surprises. Therefore this would be a good place to insert the rather obvious suggestion that upper-atmosphere research with rockets should be flexible and should be ready to exploit discoveries of unsuspected phenomena as they are uncovered.

8. COSMIC RAYS

The use of stacked emulsions to observe cosmic rays has been standard in this field for a long time, and such stacks have been flown on balloons in order to measure the heavy component of the cosmic-ray flux. However, at 30 km there is still some 6 g per cm² above the balloon, and these heavy particles with their large cross sections are seriously hampered in reaching the detector. The use of rockets to carry such emulsion stacks above the atmosphere is clearly indicated, and "pickaback" rides of emulsions in rockets have already given considerable information about the flux of heavy primaries. It is suggested that rockets devoted primarily to carrying emulsions aloft would allow optimum exposure of the emulsion pack and would greatly increase the usefulness of such an experiment. Since the trapped particles in the radiation belt cause large numbers of proton tracks in the emulsion, it is important to stay below the radiation belt in such measurements. Clearly, the recovery of these packages is required for the success of such an experiment. To give some idea of the amount of information obtained by this technique in a rocket flight, it is estimated that about 50 heavy particle tracks are observed in a 3-by 3-in. area during a rocket flight at the latitude of White Sands Proving Ground. There would be fewer at the equator and more near the poles. The ideal arrangement would be to have very large blocks weighing several hundred pounds in which an entire cascade reaction could be observed. Such blocks have been flown on balloons but never on a rocket.

9. OPTICAL OBSERVATIONS OF THE SUN AND STARS

Because of the tremendous storage capacity of photographic film, the use of rockets and the recovery of their payloads are indicated for optical observations. Recent rocket photographs of the sun in the Lyman-alpha region of the ultraviolet have emphasized the tremendous inhomogeneity of the solar disk, so observations of the sun in the ultraviolet and X-ray regions should be made with as much detail as possible.

Although many observations of the solar spectrum have been made in the ultraviolet, the region from 100 to 1000 Å needs further study. This region between the X ray and short ultraviolet is a difficult one in which to investigate because optical systems and detectors are hard to come by which can work in this region. It will be particularly important to determine how this radiation changes with solar activity.

Rocket observations of the X-ray region in the last few years have demonstrated that the sun's output of X rays changes markedly with solar activity. In fact, many of the phenomena in the upper atmosphere which accompany solar activity have been traced to these changes in X radiation. Therefore further exploratory measurements of X rays during periods of solar activity and solar quiet, particularly in the very far X-ray region where the flux is greatly reduced, are clearly indicated. Following these exploratory observations, the use of satellites for continuously monitoring the solar output would be preferable.

Rocket observations at night of ultraviolet radiation in the region of the spectrum from about 1230 to 1350 Å have shown great variations which are presumably due to intense nebulosities. Such observations of variations in the ultraviolet emphasize the need for many exploratory observations at other wavelengths in order to determine the radiation distribution from the universe. Such exploratory observations should precede the establishment of a satellite observatory.

A similar exploratory survey of radio emissions and solar noise below the ionospheric cutoff at about 10 Mc is also of great potential interest. There is also the possibility of detecting the synchrotron radiation (presumably at around 1 Mc) from the trapped particles in the radiation belts.

10. OPTICAL OBSERVATIONS OF THE EARTH

With the advent of meteorological satellites a great deal of interest will be displayed in interpreting rather low resolution television pictures for their meteorological content. In order to understand these pictures better it will be necessary to compare them with the real meteorological situation as observed from the ground, and it would also be highly desirable to compare them with high-resolution pictures obtained by conventional photography from rockets. A few such comparisons will probably aid greatly in the interpretation of cloud pictures from extreme altitudes.

Another potentially useful optical observation of the earth would be that of the visual aurorae from rockets at night. Auroral observations from the ground reveal the character of just one sector of the auroral zone at a given time: a rocket observation from several hundred miles would reveal the entire pattern of the auroral zone, showing the arrangement of the auroral rays and arcs.

REFERENCES

M. Alperin, M. Stern, and H. Wooster (eds.): *Vistas in Astronautics*, Pergamon Press, London, 1958. (Note sections by N. W. Spencer, H. K. Kallmann, H. Friedman, and H. E. Hinteregger on rocket research.)

Annals of the IGY, Vol. 12 (in press), Pergamon Press, London. (Papers presented at 5th Meeting of CSAGI, Moscow, August, 1958.)

R. L. Boyd and M. J. Seaton (with H. S. W. Massey) (eds.): *Rocket Exploration of the Upper Atmosphere*, Pergamon Press, London, 1954.

H. Jacobs (ed.): *Advances in Astronautical Sciences*, Vol. 4, Plenum Press, New York, 1958. (Note sections by J. W. Townsend and H. Friedman on rocket research.)

H. Kallmann Bijl (ed.): *Space Research* (Proceedings of the First International Space Science Symposium, Nice, January, 1960), North-Holland Publishing Co., Amsterdam, 1960.

H. E. Newell, Jr. (ed.): *Sounding Rockets*, McGraw-Hill Book Company, Inc., 1959.

————: *High Altitude Rocket Research*, Academic Press, Inc., 1953.

J. A. Ratcliffe (ed.): *Physics of the Upper Atmosphere*, Academic Press, Inc., 1960

M. Zelikoff (ed.): *The Threshold of Space* (Proceedings of the GRD-AFCRC Conference on Chemical Aeronomy, Cambridge, Mass., June, 1956), Pergamon Press, London, 1957.

8

SATELLITES AND THE UPPER ATMOSPHERE

A. H. Shapley and O. G. Villard, Jr.

1. INTRODUCTION

It is of great interest to know more about the boundary region within which the Earth's atmosphere blends into the near vacuum of outer space. At some altitude light gas molecules are no longer restrained by the Earth's gravitational field, and they diffuse or are propelled outward. On the other hand, other solid and gaseous particles are intercepted and picked up by the Earth, in the form of meteorites, micrometeorites, cosmic dust, and hydrogen gas from the Sun.

If it is possible to make a meaningful distinction between "outer" and "inner" atmosphere, a dividing line might be drawn at an altitude at which the electrical conductivity of the atmosphere becomes significant. Beginning at a height of roughly 80 km, an appreciable proportion of the atmosphere becomes ionized, with the result that the Earth's magnetic field begins to exert a powerful effect on the physical properties of the region.

Ionization is important at these altitudes because the free electrons have an appreciable lifetime between collisions. Electrical conductivity is accordingly high. Molecular collisions are so infrequent that sound waves of the conventional type can no longer propagate. Thus pro-

169

found changes in physical properties occur as altitude increases: at 250 km roughly 1 part in 10,000 of the gas is ionized; at 1000 km or so, virtually every atom is ionized.

Because of the practical importance of the state of ionization of the outer atmosphere, and because the free electrons have thus far been the easiest quantity to measure by direct experiment, this section will be concerned primarily with ionization and its behavior and the ways in which rocket and satellite experiments can increase our knowledge of the region.

2. PRACTICAL IMPORTANCE OF BETTER KNOWLEDGE OF THIS REGION

The practical benefits which may result from better understanding of the outer atmosphere may be summarized as follows:

1. The possibility exists that weather in the troposphere may in some way be affected by changes occurring in the ionosphere. By observing variations in the state of the ionosphere, it may be possible to sense changes in incident solar radiation, and physical reactions produced thereby, which are capable of producing important effects at lower altitudes where direct measurement of the radiation variations may be difficult or impossible.

2. Electric currents flowing in the ionosphere are responsible for changes in the direction and magnitude of the Earth's magnetic field as measured at the surface. The accuracy of navigation and guidance systems which depend on measurement of the Earth's magnetic field can be improved by better knowledge of the ionospheric current systems.

3. The electrons of the ionosphere are capable of bending radio waves used for accurate guidance of space vehicles and probes. Although the effect is minimized by raising the operating frequency, it is nevertheless of importance at frequencies of the order of hundreds of megacycles if very accurate control is required in situations where the line of sight passes close to the horizon.

4. Since space vehicles leave the Earth and return through the outermost layers of the atmosphere and since reliance is placed on this thin gas for vehicle-braking purposes on reentry, it is of obvious importance to know the density, the chemical composition, and the electrical state of the region. In addition to problems of heat exchange during reentry, there is the very practical problem of communication failure at certain altitudes caused by antenna mismatch and shielding resulting from an ionized shell formed around a reentering vehicle.

Bombardment by atmospheric particles can be expected to have an effect on sensitive portions of the skin of space vehicles (for example, solar cells). The extent of damage by this means will depend on the chemical state, as well as the composition, of the gas particles.

5. The possibility exists that it may be possible to utilize solar energy, stored chemically in the ionosphere, as a means of propulsion for vehicles "flying," or almost orbiting, at relatively low altitudes.

6. Better knowledge of the environment immediately outside the atmosphere may also have an effect on techniques for spaceship propulsion. For example, could any of the material of space (hydrogen, meteoric dust, etc.) be scooped up and ejected at high velocity from the "exhaust" of a nuclear-powered engine so as to provide thrust?

7. There is great room for improvement in the utilization of the ionosphere for radio-communication purposes. At the present time, serious interruptions are caused by unpredictable magnetic disturbances and fade-outs. Better understanding of these unheard, invisible "storms" should lead to better predictions and to the development of useful means for avoiding circuit outages.

8. The possibility of artificial control of the ionosphere is very real. It has already been demonstrated that only 20 kg of chemicals, released from a rocket at a height of 110 km, can create a small reflecting layer where none existed before.[1] Radio energy, beamed upward from the ground, can, in principle, accomplish the same effect:[2] in fact, in this atomic age, the power required to support a useful glow seems not at all exorbitant. It has been shown, for example, that artificial aurorae—in both Northern and Southern Hemispheres—can be caused by relatively small nuclear bursts in the ionosphere.[3]

3. THE ROLE OF SATELLITES IN IONOSPHERIC RESEARCH

To gain a better appreciation of the possibilities for ionospheric research using rockets and satellites, it is helpful to review the principle sources of experimental data obtained in the past.

1. *Nonradio techniques*

   a. Observations of absorption of the solar spectrum and of solar-excited chemicals in the ionosphere (e.g., the twilight sodium flash)

   b. Observations of meteors and noctilucent clouds

   c. Observations of the aurorae

   d. Observations of the nighttime airglow and of the gegenschein *e.* Studies over very long distances of the propagation of sound waves from blasts

    f. Measurement of daily tidal pressure variations

2. *Radio techniques*

    a. Observations on ordinary radio transmissions: fading, polarization, direction of arrival, correlation, signal loss, etc.

    b. Observations using special transmissions: pulsed or special soundings whose back-scattered echoes from the layers directly or indirectly can be observed from illuminated regions on the ground

    c. Observations in which the nonlinearity of the ionosphere is exploited (e.g., the "Luxembourg effect")

    d. Observations of signals passing through the ionosphere: cosmic noise (and the like) and echoes from the Moon; Faraday rotation of such signals

    e. Observations of thermal and other radiation from the ionosphere

The advantages and disadvantages of these various methods are more or less self-evident. The nonradio techniques are hampered by the existence of atmosphere below the region whose properties are under study, and it is not easy to separate the effects due to a particular region from those introduced by its neighbors.

Radio techniques using pulses enjoy the advantage that range resolution is ordinarily sufficient to isolate the area or layer under study. However, the radio data are not always easy to interpret since they show an *apparent* delay only, and the true height at which reflection occurs may be markedly different. It is normally necessary, for example, to use a moderately involved computational procedure in order to obtain in a reasonable estimate the true height of the ionospheric F region.

Measurements made with the aid of cosmic noise are useful for studies of refraction, absorption, and scintillation (radio star "twinkling"), but are not useful for certain types of measurements because the signal is incoherent. By observing the Faraday rotation of the plane of polarization of radar signals reflected from the Moon, a value for integrated ion density can be obtained for that portion of the path where the Earth's magnetic field is of finite strength. Beyond that point—which is fairly close to the Earth—this technique gives no data.

Pulse sounding of the radio-reflecting layers can give good information up to the height at which the maximum electron density is found. But if the wave is able to penetrate beyond this level, it will pass on through and not return. The regions above the electron density maximum can be studied by cosmic noise and radar signals reflected from the Moon, but the problem of height identification again arises.

Ground-based measurements have the advantage of low cost and relative simplicity, plus the ability in many cases to obtain data continuously. On the other hand, these techniques are for the most part limited in geographical coverage except during such special efforts as the International Geophysical Year. Much of the purely local behavior of the ionosphere has already been learned; much still remains to be found out about its global characteristics. It is now appreciated, for example, that the extent to which the outer ionosphere of the Northern and Southern Hemispheres are tied together by the Earth's magnetic field is very great.

Irrespective of the technique of investigation, study of the ionosphere is complicated by the fact that the physical conditions prevailing there cannot readily be duplicated and studied in the laboratory. For example, the pressure at 300 km is of the order of 10^{-6} mm Hg, and the molecular mean free path is in the vicinity of 10 km. In addition to the problem of providing a test chamber large compared with a mean free path, there is also the difficulty of duplicating in the laboratory the complex flux of radiant energy which is constantly present in the ionosphere.

Against this background, the advantages of rocket- and satellite-borne measurements stand out very clearly. The rocket is capable of exploring a cross section through all height regions and is extremely useful for experiments of short duration. Satellites come into their own above 300 km. Below this altitude, their lifetime becomes too short to be of practical value. For experiments requiring long durations, wide geographical coverage, and wide variations in altitude, the satellite cannot be matched.

4. PHYSICAL QUANTITIES TO BE MEASURED

At this point it may be useful to list the types of information that it would be desirable to have about the ionosphere. It would be helpful to know the following as a function of altitude:

1. The relative number per cubic centimeter of electrons, gas molecules by types, gas atoms, negative and positive ions, and radicals
2. The particulate material received from outside

3. Statistical motions of all particles (temperature, diffusion rate, collision rate, recombination rate)

4. Mass motions of particles such as winds, tides, and turbulence

5. Chemical and electronic state of particulate matter (degree of excitation, ionization, nature of the ionizing reactions, etc.)

6. Electric-current flow

7. Magnetic field strength and direction

8. Radiant energy received from outside as well as any radiation generated in the region

9. The variation of all these quantities with time and geographical position

5. THE GENERAL TYPES OF EXPERIMENTS THAT APPEAR TO BE POSSIBLE

5.1 Atmospheric Density

A measurement of the drag encountered by a satellite, especially as it reenters the atmosphere, can be used to determine total density provided the drag coefficient is known. The effect of drag shows up as a change in the speed or period of the satellite which becomes pronounced and hence readily measurable as the end of the satellite's life approaches. The order of magnitude of area–to–mass ratio of satellites launched thus far has been such that they have burned up at altitudes of the order of 100 km.[4] Reasonably good information is accordingly available about drag in the 100- to 200-km height range. To investigate drag at higher altitudes, a larger area-weight ratio is needed. Attempts have been made to launch satellites consisting of metallized balloons made of mylar plastic in two sizes—10 and 100 ft in diameter. Since it is impractical to equip such lightweight objects with radio beacons, reliance must be placed on radar or optical sightings for tracking purposes. Since the lifetime of the balloons will be short (depending on the altitude of the orbit chosen), tracking adequate for deceleration measurements presents a challenge.

There is evidence that changes in solar activity can affect the density of the upper atmosphere to an extent which can be measured as a change in the rotation period of satellites.[5]

Interpretation of drag measurements is complicated by uncertainties concerning the temperature and composition of the region and by any charge which might be acquired by the satellite. However, the answer obtained is directly usable in practical situations.

Other approaches to the problem of measuring atmospheric densities include pressure gauges, mass spectrometers, and Langmuir probes. All suffer from certain difficulties of interpretation resulting from the effect of the satellite itself on the gas in the immediate vicinity and any charge the satellite may acquire.

5.2 Ionization Density

Of the various methods for measuring ionization density as a function of height and position, three techniques seem to have found the most favor thus far: (1) probe measurements at the satellite itself, (2) measurements performed on the ground with the aid of radio signals radiated from the satellite, and (3) measurements made with an ionospheric sounder in the satellite.

Probe measurements take advantage of changes in the properties of the medium surrounding the satellite which are caused by the presence of a plasma. In a Langmuir probe, both electrons and ions can be counted. The change in impedance of an antenna immersed in a dielectric can be sensed. (An especially strong change occurs when the probe frequency coincides with a plasma resonance frequency.) Finally, the local dielectric constant can be deduced by measuring the ratio of the electric vector E and the magnetic vector H in an incident very low frequency (VLF) electric wave. The ratio of the two gives the local refractive index and hence the ambient electron density.

Probe measurements of electron density are subject to the same uncertainties which complicate other probe measurements in the vicinity of a vehicle. For example, the local situation may be complicated by the release of adsorbed gas by the vehicle, contact potentials, thermoelectric and photoelectric effects, and interference from the vehicle's own telemetering transmitters.

With the aid of beacon signals it is possible to measure refraction caused by the ionosphere, the change in polarization (Faraday rotation), and the Doppler frequency shift caused by satellite motion as a function of the time. Uncertainties exist in all three techniques because the paths followed by the two magnetoionic signal components are not precisely alike. In any event an integration of the ion density between ground and satellite is obtained—a quantity rather less informative than ion density at a particular level.

Since the level at which a satellite flies is not in general constant, it is possible to build up over a period of time a picture of integrated electron density versus height. This can be extended above the F-layer ion density maximum by subtracting out the part below the maximum which can be obtained with good accuracy by means of vertical-incidence sounders on the Earth.

An intriguing possibility is that of sounding the ionosphere from above, by means of sweep-frequency equipment in a satellite. Because of the ease with which the information could be obtained and recorded in such an experiment and because of the comparisons which would be possible with soundings from below, this experiment is regarded as one of the most potentially valuable of those which can be made in a satellite. In principle, the entire world can be surveyed in this way by one sounder in a comparatively short interval of time. Furthermore, if valleys in the electron distribution above the F-layer maximum are found, it may be possible by varying the altitude of the satellite to obtain reflections within such valleys.

5.3 Chemical Composition

Measurements of the chemical composition of the ionosphere are complicated by the extraordinarily tenuous nature of the matter in the region. The methods most suitable appear to be those using mass spectrometers and ion probes, along with measurement of solar radiation reflected or scattered by the resonant lines. This work has already yielded a new estimate of the amount of hydrogen in the upper atmosphere and its degree of excitation by the Sun.[6] Once again, the local probe measurements are subject to ambiguities, and in absorption studies there exists uncertainty as to the location of the emitting or absorbing region.

5.4 Radio-frequency Radiation and Transmission

It should be possible to study the radio-frequency radiation in and above the ionosphere with great effectiveness using satellites. The evidence now seems quite good that the source of the so-called VLF emission lies in the exosphere and is a consequence of an interaction between high-speed ionized particles falling into the outermost atmosphere in the presence of the Earth's magnetic field.[7] These signals fall for the most part in the audible frequency band. It has recently been demonstrated that detectable radio energy in the 70-Mc frequency range is generated within the ionosphere itself during certain types of disturbances,[8] possibly by bremsstrahlung associated with bombardment by extraterrestrial matter. The altitude at which radio energy of these types is generated could in all likelihood be determined by means of orbiting receivers.

The ability of satellites to remain above the ionosphere for appreciable periods of time makes it possible to study the cosmic-noise background level at those low frequencies at which the ionosphere is normally an effective shield. It is not at the moment possible to predict the intensity and type of extraterrestrial radiation which may come to light during such a search. If cosmic noise proves at least as strong at the low frequencies as it is in the frequency ranges at which it has been studied, it may be useful as a test signal with which to study the ionosphere itself. For example, the radio frequency at which such radiation is cut off by the electrons lying at an altitude higher than that at which the vehicle is flying should yield a useful value for the ion density close to the vehicle altitude.

An experiment of this type which has considerable interest is one in which a VLF receiver, tuned to a transmitter on the Earth, is carried in a satellite. The receiver output is telemetered to the ground. It has been discovered within the past few years that VLF signals can penetrate the ionosphere by what has come to be called magnetoionic duct propagation. Such signals are guided by the lines of force of the Earth's magnetic field and travel back and forth between the Northern and Southern Hemispheres. It is now known that both man-made signals and radio energy from lightning flashes can be propagated in this way with surprisingly low attenuation. What is not known is precisely how this radio energy enters the ionosphere and why it is so strongly guided by transient columns or shells of ionization. The source of these columns and their other characteristics are of very great scientific interest. During its circuits around the globe a satellite will have a good probability of intercepting one of these shells and perhaps of mapping its significant features. Whether such whistler-mode propagation actually extends between Earth and Sun (at least for latitudes north and south of the northern and southern auroral zones, respectively) as some have postulated, is a matter to be settled.

5.5 Irregularities

Satellites offer an attractive means for exploring spatial irregularities in the ionosphere such as those occurring near the auroral zone. For the most part these irregularities have a moderately long lifetime, so that it becomes possible to delineate them by noting changes in radio transmission from the satellite as the line of sight sweeps past the irregularity. Both phase path, Doppler shift, and refraction changes will serve as indications of an irregularity. Since the irregularities do not in general endure for periods of hours, the precise localization and delineation of a specific irregularity by this technique is difficult, although simultaneous measurements at more than one receiving site are of material assistance. The altitude at which irregularities of a given kind are likely to occur may, of course, be obtained with fair accuracy.

5.6 Dynamic Motions

Dynamic motions of the ionosphere can to some extent be studied with the aid of small clouds of vapor which, when released from a satellite, glow with sufficient intensity to permit motions of the cloud to be followed optically. Sodium vapor is practicable for studies of this sort, having been used successfully within the E layer of the ionosphere over New Mexico[9] and by the Russians both inside and outside the ionosphere, as in their first Moon rocket. In each instance the sodium was caused to glow by incident sunlight.

5.7 Photochemistry

It should also be possible to survey from a satellite observing platform auroral displays, zodiacal light, and the night airglow. The great advantage of this technique is the ability to survey virtually the entire atmosphere of the Earth in a limited interval of time. On the other hand, such a synoptic survey may have to be done at the expense of resolution, and attitude stabilization will be an important consideration. For measurements of dayglow, balloons or rockets appear more practicable than satellites, for a platform riding substantially above the atmosphere will see too much reflected sunlight, except possibly in the infrared.

From a satellite laboratory, it should be feasible to investigate the ultraviolet and infrared spectrum of the night airglow and the aurora as well as the bright emission lines which have been studied from the ground. Because of the absence of atmospheric scattering, twilight-zone measurements at these altitudes should be especially fruitful. It will also be possible to search for metallic resonance lines in the ultraviolet in order to establish the presence of small traces of various elements. Atmospheric calcium and lithium have recently been discovered in this way in the photographic spectrum.

The cooling of the F layer of the ionosphere could be investigated by measurement of radiation from atomic oxygen. Similarly, the oxygen red lines should be very bright in the day airglow and should give direct information on the rate of recombination in the F layer.

In the far ultraviolet region, lines from atomic oxygen should be strong and should provide a means for estimating the abundance of atomic oxygen as a function of height.

All these measurements can, of course, be performed at selected locations by rockets. World-wide measurements in satellites will probably require control of the vehicle attitude in order to be worthwhile.

5.8 Artificial Control of the Ionosphere

The effect of nuclear bursts on the ionosphere is considerable.[10] Much can be learned about the dynamics and the composition of the ionosphere from such experiments, and satellite-borne equipment is ideally suited for conducting measurements, because the duration of major ionospheric changes is of the order of hours or tens of hours.

An important drawback of the principal competing method, namely, radio echo sounding, is the fact that because of retardation, refraction, and focusing effects, the apparent height of a given reflection is often very different from the true height at which the reflection takes place. Thus satellites which travel in the affected region and which can make measurements which are free of this ambiguity will play an important role. Small detonations in the ionosphere, using both conventional and nuclear bursts, provide the first opportunity to explore the response of the gas at F-layer heights to a large impulse of short duration. Although meteors do provide this type of excitation at E layer heights, they are relatively unsatisfactory as probes because their physical and chemical properties are not known in advance.

5.9 Radio-wave Propagation

A pressing problem in radio propagation is the spatial distribution of the absorbing regions in the D layer of the ionosphere which are associated with the aurora and which are responsible for polar communication "blackouts." This extra ionization, occurring at a height level at which the collision rate, and hence radio-wave loss, are high because of the high gas pressure, is now known to be due to X rays created by particle bombardment of the outer ionosphere. Since "polar blackouts" are isolated, localized events, it may be possible to avoid them and thereby maintain communication if the characteristics of a blackout (such as its intensity and geographical extent) could be predicted. For research on polar blackouts and the way in which they are related to particles entering the atmosphere (perhaps via the outer Van Allen trapping region), satellites should provide a virtually ideal vehicle.

It seems likely that a future system of satellites carrying radiation monitors, and orbiting the Earth at very great distance, could provide early warning of an impending solar disturbance and thus substantially reduce ionospheric communication outage time.

The effect of the ionosphere on communication between orbiting vehicles is in urgent need of exploration. Under conditions where radiation from a vehicle falls upon an ionized layer at nearly grazing incidence, the bending power of the layer becomes very high. (The effect is analogous to the optical mirage.) For communication via the F layer between two points located on the Earth, the highest normally usable radio frequency is approximately 30 Mc. It is not known how high this figure may be extended when the source and the receiver are located underneath or within the layer. It seems likely that the maximum usable frequency will then be essentially limited by the spatial inhomogeneities within the layer and that the familiar "secant law" for computing maximum usable frequencies from vertical incidence measurements no longer has application.

In some situations this bending power may be useful, for example, in VHF communication between satellites; in others, for example, guidance and control, it may prove quite detrimental.

6. THE FUTURE

Studies of the ionosphere and the exosphere with the aid of rockets and satellites can be expected eventually to make this region as familiar to us as the lower atmosphere. Progress can be expected to speed up considerably as experience is gained and as technology improves, because of the way in which measurements interlock: for example, once temperature is known, drag can be interpreted with greater accuracy. When some form of control over satellite attitude and relative position with respect to other satellites becomes practicable, it will be possible to do a variety of very important studies with the aid of two cooperating satellites. Two vehicles, traveling at the same altitude within line of sight of each other, would permit a wide variety of electromagnetic radiation experiments wherein a source at one vehicle would transmit to a receiver at the other. Such experiments, if properly designed, offer the possibility of minimizing uncertainties arising from contamination or disturbance of the air in the immediate vicinity of the satellites themselves. Furthermore, altitude uncertainty is eliminated. The range of wavelengths of the radiation useful for such experiments would be very great. An interim version of the same experimental approach would call for the automatic ejection, from a given satellite, of small expendable instrument-carrying packages which could provide transmission data during the brief interval after ejection.

REFERENCES

1. J. Pressman, F. F. Marmo, et al.: *Pl. Sp. Sci.*, *1*, *227* (1959).
2. V. A. Bailey: "Method of Producing and Utilizing Certain Electrical Conditions

in the Ionosphere," Commonwealth of Australia Patent No. 102,635, Nov. 25, 1936.

3. A. L. Cullington: *Nature, 182,* 1365 (1958).
4. D. G. King-Hele and D. M. C. Walker: *Nature, 182,* 426 (1958).
5. W. Priester: *Naturwissenschaffen, 46,* 197 (1959).
6. H. Friedman: *Proc. Inst. Radio Engrs., 47,* 272 (1959).
7. R. M. Gallet: *Proc. Inst. Radio Engrs., 47,* 211 (1959).
8. H. J. A. Chivers and H. W. Wells: *Nature, 183,* 1178 (1959).
9. J. Pressman, L. M. Aschenbrand, et al.: *J. Chem. Phys., 27,* 187 (1956).
10. S. Matsushita: *J. Geophys. Res., 64, No. 9,* 1149 (1959).

SUPPLEMENTARY READING

G. Kuiper (ed.): *The Atmospheres of the Earth and Planets,* rev. ed. (Chicago: University of Chicago Press, 1952).

R. L. Boyd and M. J. Seaton (with H. S. W. Massey) (eds.): *Rocket Exploration of the Upper Atmosphere* (London: Pergamon Press, 1954).

H. E. Newell, Jr. (ed.): *High Altitude Rocket Research* (New York: Academic Press, 1953).

M. Zelikoff (ed.): *The Threshold of Space,* Proceedings of the GRD-AFCRC Conference on Chemical Aeronomy, Cambridge, Mass., June, 1956 (London: Pergamon Press, 1957).

PART **4** ≡

THE MOON AND THE PLANETS

9

THE MOON

Harold C. Urey

1. INTRODUCTION

The Moon is an old object, according to our present ideas, and has
undergone less modification during the course of geological history than
have the Earth, Mars, and Venus, in all probability. Violent processes
of a peculiar kind have left their marks on its face, namely, shallow craters
which today we believe were mostly produced by the collisions of objects
on its surface. At the turn of the century, the idea of Sir George Darwin
that the Moon separated from the Earth was generally accepted. But in
the first decade of this century, Moulton of Chicago showed that this
theory was most improbable. This view was later accepted by Jeffreys,
and since the thirties all students of the subject have abandoned Darwin's
hypothesis.

The Moon appears to be one object which was not accumulated by the
Earth during its own formation from solid objects. It appears that
objects similar to the Moon contributed, in part, to the formation of the
Earth—together, in all probability, with other objects containing considerably larger amounts of the element iron than is characteristic of the
Moon. There has been no erosion by running water on the Moon; in
this way it is quite different from the Earth, and if Mars and Venus had

oceans at some time in the past, it is quite different from these planets as well. We therefore can expect that it has retained more of the history of the last 4.5 billions of years than is characteristic generally of the planets. From this point of view the Moon is a much more important object of investigation than are the planets.

The density of the Moon is 3.34 as determined merely by its mass and its observed radius. By estimating the density of the material of the Moon at ordinary temperatures and pressures (making reasonable assumptions of the coefficient of expansion and compressibility), it is possible to get some idea of its composition. The result of such studies indicates that the Moon probably has considerably less iron than the Earth and, in fact, may have considerably less than is recorded in the usual abundance tables of the elements. This would seem to indicate that the Moon may have the same composition as the Sun with respect to the nonvolatile fraction of the elements. Astronomical observations on the abundances of elements in the Sun favor lower concentrations of iron at the present time, and to find an object in the solar system which would agree with the composition of the Sun would be very interesting indeed. Conclusions of this kind are uncertain, but then there is very little reason to send instruments to the Moon if we are sure that we know all about the Moon beforehand.

The surface of the Moon has been studied intensively during the last century. A very noteworthy paper by G. K. Gilbert[1] in 1893 made enormous progress in understanding the surface of the Moon. He concluded that the surface was fashioned mostly by the collision of objects with it and that the smooth gray areas of the Moon are the direct result of the collisions of great objects with the surface of the Moon. He also maintained that most of the craters of the Moon were due to such collisions and, incidentally, had the view that there were no volcanoes on the Moon that he could find. Many authors have disagreed with this point of view, but it is doubtful that we shall be able to decide this question without much more detailed investigation of the Moon than can be done from the Earth.

The great smooth gray areas of the Moon have been generally assumed to be due to lava flows. Some believe that they came from the interior of the Moon, and some believe that they were produced through the mechanism of great collisions. Among those favoring the mechanism of the great collision are some who think that these collisions merely released lava from below the surface of the Moon while others believe that the lava was at least partially, and probably mostly, produced as a result of the collisions.

FIG. 1. The full Moon (north at bottom as seen through a telescope). Maria are the dark, smooth regions. Some of the
craters are the center of ray systems. Among the features are
the following, located by polar coordinates with center as origin
(clock dial for position angle, fractions of radius for distance
from center): Mare Tranquillitatis (8:30, 0.6); Mare Imbrium
(5:30, 0.7); Ptolemaeus, walled plain (12:00, 0.1); ray craters—
for example, Tycho (12:30, 0.7); Copernicus (4:30, 0.4); black
mountains, the very dark patches to left of Copernicus (just
below center); polar regions (top and bottom edges). (*Courtesy of Mt. Wilson and Palomar Observatories.*)

The Moon's surface shows very great irregularities. Recently, Watts has found differences in elevation on the eastern limb amounting to 9.7 km, which would be very high even for the Earth. These great differences in altitude on the Earth are supported by isostatic equilibrium, that is, essentially by the floating of low-density material in high-density material. In order to support such large differences in elevation, some 50 km of the low-density basalt or granite is required. That such quantities of material differentiated in the surface of the Moon is difficult to understand. The assumption of great masses of metal below the surface of the low regions (which also would account for these observations) can hardly be accepted with confidence without some direct evidence for them. What seems likely is that the outer parts of the Moon have very great physical strength and are able to support very considerable differences in elevation in the surface. This was a point of view put forward by Gilbert in 1893.

In connection with these considerations, it would be of very great interest to determine the age of the surface of the Moon by the potassium-argon dating method. This method dates the time since materials were last heated sufficiently to cause the loss of argon-40, and it is thus a sensitive indicator of the time when the last plutonic processes occurred. It would also be of interest to investigate the date by the lead-lead method, which measures the time since the iron meteorites last were separated from uranium and thorium, on the assumption that the second sample of material—the Moon in this case—has had a constant ratio of uranium to lead from the time at which the two samples became separated, an assumption that cannot always be justified for given samples of matter.

The surface of the Moon probably retains an integrated record of cosmic-ray activity during the time since the surface was last heated. This will be retained only in the outer 30 cm mostly, and since the equatorial regions are warmed by the Sun, it will be necessary to obtain samples near the poles for this study. In meteorites this record is studied through the concentrations of the inert-gas nuclides.

The Moon has no atmosphere, or rather a very small atmosphere, perhaps as low as 10^{-9} (or less) of the Earth's atmosphere. Because of its low gravitational field, the lighter of the elements would escape completely from the Moon, and one can hardly expect that anything remains except perhaps the heavier inert gases. Most chemical substances would react with the surface of the Moon, and not many gaseous materials can be expected to be there in any important quantities in any case.

The dark color of the Moon may be due to the effects of light and high-speed particles on its surface, but the recent reports of carbonaceous gases escaping from the Moon may be consistent with a coloration due to carbon on its surface. Chapter 3, The Nature of Gravitation, of this volume suggests a moderately high temperature for the Moon during its past history. This is in disagreement with other suggestions. If the surface materials of the Moon have a K^{40}–A^{40} age of 4 or 4.5 $\times$ 10^9 years, then they have not been at higher temperatures than 200 to 230°K for times of the order of 10^9 years. This conclusion is based on estimates of the rate of loss of argon from meteorites as a function of temperature. Thus K^{40}–A^{40} dating of the surface may contribute a decisive answer to some of the questions raised in that chapter.

Life would not be supported on the surface of the Moon in any important way. It would be very difficult to be sure that terrestrial organisms would not find some way to support themselves at least temporarily in the subsurface regions of the Moon where there may be carbon compounds of an inorganic type, that is, produced by inorganic processes. It is very doubtful that there is any indigenous life on the Moon—so doubtful, in fact, that it can be considered as a certainty within the usual definition of that term.

2. CHEMICAL COMPOSITION

In order to understand the composition of the Moon, it is necessary to consider the composition of the Earth's surface and the composition of the meteorites, the two sources of information from which we might be able to draw some conclusions. Table 1 is a collection of data for the achondrites and chondrites, and there are two groups under each classification as listed. The data are taken from Urey and Craig[2] for the meteorites. These are to be compared with the data on granites and basalts which are taken from Rankama's book on geochemistry.[3] The data in column 3, the high-calcium achondrites, are similar in some ways to the data under the basalts. In fact, there is greater similarity here between these two groups than between any other groups of stone meteorites and terrestrial rocks. It should be noted that granite and basalt show a very considerable increase in their silica content compared with the chondrites, and this similarity follows along comparatively well for other elements until we come to the alkali metals, where there is a marked discrepancy. This is also true of the concentration of uranium and thorium as well as potassium, as shown in Table 2. And there are many other elements for which a similar discrepancy occurs. What we seem to see is this: First, the chondritic meteorites are very low in potassium and the alkalies generally and in uranium and thorium. Second, the achondrites are higher in uranium and thorium, low in potassium, and the terrestrial rocks are high in the alkalies and in uranium and thorium. We wonder very much whether the Moon follows any of these groups of

Table 1. Granites, Basalts, Chondritic, and Achondritic Meteorites: Typical Analyses[2,3]

	Achondrites		Chondrites		Granite	Basalts
	Low calcium	High calcium	Low iron	High iron		
SiO_2	52.56	48.65	39.49 (46.00)	36.17 (48.53)	70.18	49.06
MgO	30.47	9.87	24.55 (28.60)	22.93 (30.76)	0.88	6.17
FeO	11.45	16.31	14.97 (17.44)	9.26 (12.42)	1.78	6.37
Fe_2O_3					1.57	5.38
Al_2O_3	1.09	11.71	2.61 (3.04)	2.36 (3.17)	14.47	15.70
CaO	1.20	10.39	1.96 (2.28)	1.95 (2.62)	1.99	8.95
Na_2O	0.36	0.83	1.04 (1.21)	0.91 (1.22)	3.48	3.11
K_2O	0.11	0.27	0.18 (0.21)	0.17 (0.23)	4.11	1.52
Cr_2O_3	0.83	0.40	0.43 (0.50)	0.27 (0.36)		
MnO	0.39	0.47	0.27 (0.31)	0.23 (0.31)	0.12	0.31
TiO_2	0.12	0.50	0.11 (0.13)	0.11 (0.15)	0.39	1.05
P_2O_5	0.10	0.10	0.24 (0.28)	0.17 (0.23)	0.19	0.30
Fe	2.68		7.04	17.76		
Ni	0.17		1.06	1.68		
Co			0.07	0.10		
FeS	0.96	0.57	5.77	5.69	(0.14)	(0.14)
H_2O	0.89	(0.40)	0.04	0.05	0.84	1.62

NOTE: Within the parentheses are given analyses on the basis of the silicate fraction only.

Table 2. Uranium, Thorium, and Potassium in Igneous Rocks and Stony Meteorites,[3,4,5] in PPm

	Igneous rocks	Chondrites	Achondrites
U	1–4	0.0114	0.126
Th	3.9–13.45	0.0396	.0055 and 0.54
K	See Table 1	863	10–500

materials. The terrestrial rocks have undergone a long fractionation in the crust of the Earth, apparently due to partial melting processes which have caused the flow of material from the deep interior to the surface. This sort of differentiation seems not to have been present on the Moon: it could hardly be expected because of the much greater ratio of surface to mass and hence much greater cooling of the Moon compared with the Earth. But the question still remains as to whether the Moon may not have been highly melted in its early history and whether great fractionation into granites and basalts might not have occurred at this time. In order to test this, it would be well to be able to analyze many samples from the surface of the Moon. This seems to be difficult to do, but a very good indication of the differentiations can be secured by investigating the naturally radioactive elements (uranium, thorium, and potassium) in order to find out what differences may exist between terrestrial rocks and those of the Moon and how the Moon compares in composition with the meteorites.

3. THE IRREGULAR SHAPE OF THE MOON

Astronomical data indicate that the Moon has a triaxial configuration with the ellipticities quite different from those expected from the effects of the tides. This is particularly true of the ellipticity involving the difference in the moments of inertia (about its polar axis and about the axis pointing toward the Earth) divided by the mean moment of inertia. This difference can be calculated from the dynamical motions of the Moon, and all quantities appear to be very well established. Hence we may conclude that the Moon has, indeed, an irregular shape. This ellipticity is some seventeen times as great as would be calculated from the present tidal forces. This must be due either to great strength in the interior of the Moon (amounting to an ability to support some 20 atm of stress at the center of the Moon), or else it must be due to a variation in density with angle in the outer parts of the Moon. It is difficult to believe that the interior of the Moon can support such stresses for geological periods of time; hence the idea that there are variations in density with latitude and perhaps longitude at the Moon is an attractive idea which has been put forward only recently. A satellite of the Moon would be able to detect these irregularities of the Moon's structure with much higher precision than we have been able to calculate them from past observations. The satellite must be close to the Moon in order to be stable, for otherwise the perturbing effects of the Earth will always distort its orbit.

4. THE SURFACE CHARACTERISTICS OF THE MOON

There has long been a controversial argument about the composition of the surface layer of the Moon. The measurements of Pettit and

Nicholson many years ago indicated that the surface of the Moon is covered by a thin layer of fine dust in vacuum and that below this some insulating material, with about the properties of pumice, will satisfy the thermal observation. This conclusion rests, in turn, on the data of Smoluchowski, who measured thermal conductivity of particulate solids down to pressures of air of 0.05 mm. The vacuum on the Moon is much lower, and probably the surface is more nearly like fine sand rather than dust. In recent years, other suggestions have been made as to the character of the Moon's surface. There is the traditional one that the maria consist of great lava flows and that these underlie the surface features of the Moon at least, with only a thin layer over them. More recently the suggestion has been made that fine dust, produced by light erosion, covers the surface of the Moon,[6] and speculation has appeared in the literature that perhaps the surface region of the Moon is covered with chondritic material such as is found in the stone meteorites. This is a gravelly sort of material mixed with fine iron-nickel metal particles of the body-centered cubic and face-centered cubic iron-nickel phases.

Radio observations of the Moon indicate that we receive reflections only from the center of the Moon's disk, and this indicates that the surface is remarkably smooth from the standpoint of radio waves. It appears to be almost perfectly rough from the standpoint of light waves, so that they are reflected from the surface with a comparatively small limb effect. The radio waves appear to come back as though the Moon were nearly a perfect reflector. This indicates that both the mountainous regions in the center of the Moon as well as the maria regions (Sinus Vaporum being the one directly involved) are nearly smooth in spite of the rather rugged appearance of the Moon's surface.

5. THE INTERIOR OF THE MOON

The Moon has such a low density that it seems improbable that the amount of metallic iron-nickel could be very large in the body of the Moon as a whole. Calculations indicate, however, that some few per cent of the mass of the Moon might be iron-nickel metal. The question arises as to whether this iron-nickel is at present accumulated into a core in the Moon. It seems most likely that this is indeed a possible structure since the interior of the Moon, because of radioactive heating, should be at a fairly high temperature and possibly above the melting point of metallic iron. On the other hand, the meteorites have structures which indicate that the irons have not been part of a core of a large planet but have been imbedded in a silicate material and their

FIG. 2. Northern region of the Moon (north at bottom as seen through a telescope). Features shown include maria or "seas" (darker, smoother areas), circular mountain chain (rim of mare), and crack-like structure near the south edge of Mare Vaporum (top, center). (*Courtesy of Mt. Wilson and Palomar Observatories.*)

masses have been not much larger than the masses of the iron meteorites that we observe to fall on the Earth. If the Moon is an object of the type that has supplied the meteorites, and arguments have been put forward to this effect, then we must expect that masses of iron-nickel may be scattered throughout the body of the Moon in a "raisin-bread" type of structure. Seismic studies on the Moon might be able to answer questions of this sort, establish whether there is an iron core, and give us information about the composition of the Moon.

A theory for the origin of the solar system, pointing out that objects of approximately the size of the Moon must have been involved in the formation of the materials of the meteorites, has been proposed. A considerable number of the satellites of the solar system have approximately the mass of our Moon, and the existence of such objects may have been an important part of the evolution of the system. Such a suggestion as this makes the problem of investigating the character of our Moon even more important than it would be otherwise. If, indeed, it is a primitive type of object that appeared in large quantities early in the history of the system, then it is obvious that a study of such an object would be of very great interest in considering the entire problem of the origin of the solar system and of stars generally. At least it may be possible to prove or disprove this suggestion as a result of the studies being proposed.

6. MOONQUAKES AND TIDAL EFFECTS

The Moon's orbit is fairly elliptical, with an eccentricity of 0.0549, and since the distance from the Earth varies from $a/(1 + \epsilon)$ to $a/(1 - \epsilon)$, a total variation of distance of 11.5 per cent occurs. This would raise a variable tide in a liquid moon of 16 m. Such an effect may cause only elastic distortion, or it may cause breaks in the Moon's surface and hence lead to damping of the radial motion. Cracks have been reported in the Moon's surface, and these may be due to such tidal effects. There is evidence that dissipation of tidal energy occurs in the Moon, for only in this way can the Moon's face remain oriented toward the Earth as any tidal effects occur such as movement away from the Earth. If dissipation of energy in radial tides could be observed, this would constitute evidence for an origin of the Moon by capture, that is, by a process just opposite to that proposed by Darwin. Also, if gases are escaping from the Moon because of any type of plutonic effects, seismic disturbances of small size might be observed.

Heating of the deep interior by radioactivity and cooling by conduction will produce a considerable amount of seismic activity, according to recent calculations. These effects can be tested by seismometers placed on the Moon's surface.

7. EXPERIMENTAL INVESTIGATIONS

A brief summary of some specific proposals for further experimental study of the Moon is given below. The relative importance of the projects, in our opinion, is indicated by the arrangement; however, this does not refer to the order in which the observations can be made, for this depends upon the development of apparatus and the availability of vehicles. Here we attempt to state what is of interest from the standpoint of scientific knowledge.

7.1 A Satellite of the Moon

(1) Counting systems should be devised for the detection of potassium, uranium, and thorium. A satellite flying some 100 km above the surface would be able to determine the relative abundances of these elements and be able to determine whether the surface is granitic, basaltic, or meteoritic in composition and whether the compositions of the maria and land areas are different. This bears on the question of complete or partial melting of the Moon. The apparatus could be used also for investigations from a soft landing. (2) Television of the back and front areas should be made if high resolution can be secured. The purpose is to add to our knowledge of the relationships of maria and land areas (terrae) and to enable us to know locations on the surface in addition to those known telescopically. (3) The mass and mass distribution can be secured from orbital constants of a satellite. This bears on the question of complete melting. Are there irregular distributions of high-density materials within the body of the Moon or near its surface? (4) The density and composition of its atmosphere could be secured by use of suitable mass spectrometers. (5) The determination of reflectivity of the surface as a function of wavelength should be made. (6) Exploration of the lunar magnetic field with high-sensitivity magnetometers and tests for trapped low-energy particles should be made, i.e., a lunar Van Allen effect.

7.2 A Hard-landing Lunar Probe

(1) A wide-open ion chamber could be used to determine the atmospheric density by radioing the results as the vehicle approached the

Moon.   (2) It should be possible to test the hardness of the surface by a probe at the end of the vehicle.

7.3 A Soft-landing Lunar Probe

(1) The surface should be televised with and without magnification and with the aid of a microscope. This should enable us to decide whether the material was produced by solidification of a melt or by consolidation of conglomerates. Also minerals could be detected, and this would indicate whether the Moon was granitic or basaltic in composition, particularly if broken surfaces were available. (2) The surface should be tested for magnetic substances (both on the immediate surface and some meters down) to determine how extensive the arrival of meteoritic material has been. This should be done at a number of locations. (3) Hardness tests and probes of considerable depth should be used to test whether the maria and interiors of craters are conglomerates or solidified lava. (4) Seismic observations should be made at various points to detect internal irregularities of density and composition. Such studies may determine whether the dissipation of tidal energy is occurring at the present time and whether heating in the interior is causing seismic activity. (5) Counters for the detection of uranium, potassium, and thorium would provide an analytical tool to distinguish granite, basalt, etc. This follows the suggestion discussed above in connection with a lunar satellite. (6) A spark-type mass spectrometer would make possible detailed chemical analysis. (7) The temperature as a function of depth, latitude, time of lunar day, and type of lunar surface should be measured. The temperature gradient and loss of heat from the interior should be measured. (8) X-ray fluorescence spectra could be secured by intense radioactive sources which are now available. X-ray diffraction analysis should be considered as well. (9) Spectroscopic analysis of the surface rocks should be possible. (10) Surface materials might be heated to detect volatiles. (11) Measurement of the Moon's gravity might be attempted, but because of varying and unknown altitudes, interpretation would be difficult. A gravimeter will measure the lunar monthly tides and determine the rigidity of the Moon, and hence its physical state in the deep interior.

7.4 The Return of Samples

Samples (both surface and subsurface), if they can be returned from the Moon, should be obtained from many locations. Some particular ones are Mare Tranquillitatis, because of its very black color and its irregular shape, which indicate that it is a lava flow; Mare Imbrium, because of its gray color and its obvious origin as a collision mare; the interior of a walled plane, such as Ptolemaeus; mountainous regions; a region that is an outstanding example of a ray from one of the ray craters; the black mountains west of Copernicus; and the polar regions for the study of cosmogenic nuclides of the rare gases. Samples of lunar dust should also be collected under sterile conditions for the use of biologists in making cultures.

The terrestrial tests needed are ordinary chemical analysis, X-ray fluorescence analysis, analysis for the content of ordinary gases and for the inert gases which may be produced by cosmic rays, potassium-argon dating and dating by other methods, microscopic examination, and mineral analysis.

Apparatus for the collection and return of lunar and planetary samples should be developed.

7.5 Manned Landing

The scientific qualifications of the first man to go to the Moon are important. He should have a considerable knowledge of several fields of science, but he should be particularly a hard-rock geologist with some acquaintance with meteorites. All plans in this respect, however, should be made with the realization that the Moon is very different from the Earth and that naive analogies are useless. The surface of the Moon will not be like that of the Earth. The surface origin is quite different and, in particular, there will be no sedimentary rocks.

REFERENCES

1. G. K. Gilbert: *Bull. Phil. Soc., Wash., 12,* 241 (1893).
2. H. C. Urey and H. Craig: *Geochimica et Cosmochimica Acta, 4,* 36 (1953).
3. K. Rankama: *Geochemistry,* University of Chicago Press.
4. H. Hamaguchi, G. W. Reid, and A. Turkevich: *Geochimica et Cosmochimica Acta, 12,* 337 (1957).
5. G. L. Bate, J. R. Huizenga, and H. A. Potraz: *Geochimica et Cosmochimica Acta,* in press.
6. T. Gold: *Monthly Notices of the R.A.S., 115,* 585 (1955).

SUPPLEMENTARY READING

Dinsmore Alter: *Publications of Astronom. Soc. of Pacific, 67,* No. 397 (1955); *68,* No. 400 (1956); *68,* No. 404 (1956); *69,* No. 407 (1957); *69,* No. 408 (1957); *69,* No. 411 (1957); *70,* No. 416 (1958). Descriptive of lunar features.
R. B. Baldwin: *The Face of the Moon,* Chicago University Press, 1949. An excellent survey of many lunar features with many references.

R. S. Dietz: *J. Geol.*, *54*, 359 (1946). A geologist's point of view.

Gilbert Fielder: *J. Brit. Astr. Assn.*, *66*, 1 (1955); *66*, 6 (1956); *Bull. Lunar Sec. of B.A.A.*, *5*, 4 (1957); *J. Brit. Astr. Assn.*, *67*, 8 (1957); *J. Internatl. Lunar Soc.*, *1*, 2 (1957); *J. Brit. Interplanetary Soc.*, *17* (1959); *Space Flight, 1,* 9 (1958). Descriptive of lunar features.

G. P. Kuiper: *Vistas in Astronautics*, vol. 2, pp. 273–311, 1959. Excellent photographs. Conclusions based on purely surface observational details. The interior is assumed to have been largely molten, with solid silicates floating unstably on their liquids.

H. C. Urey: *The Planets*, chap. 2, Yale University Press, 1952. This chapter attempted to bring together some more physical and mathematical discussions of a subject which is largely treated descriptively. Many details are out of date.

————: *Sky & Telescope, 15,* 108 (1956). Descriptive of a few critical features of the Moon.

————: *Vistas in Astronomy*, vol. 2, Cambridge University Press. A review mostly of older work.

10

THE PLANETS

Harold C. Urey

1. INTRODUCTION

It may seem unnecessary to justify an intense interest in the study and exploration of the planets by means of satellites and space probes on any grounds other than simple curiosity. Nevertheless, there exist also compelling scientific reasons for such investigations.

Just as in the case of the Moon, there is at present a great deal of uncertainty concerning the mechanism of the origin of the planets and the evolutionary history of the solar system generally. There can be no guarantee of final success, but it is almost certain that many of the existing uncertainties will be resolved when it becomes possible to study the nature and composition of the planets more intimately. The problem of the mechanism of the solar and planetary origin is of interest not only in itself, but also as an example of the origin of the stars.

Although it may be construed as a special topic in the evolution of the solar system, the possibility of the existence of life on Mars or Venus is of profound significance to biology (see Chap. 20). In spite of the fact that a considerable body of observational evidence supports the contention that some living organisms exist on Mars, it will require close inspection before it is possible to verify the hypothesis and to determine the relationship between such living organisms as may be found and terrestrial forms. The possibility of discovering evidence of the preexistence of organisms now extinct is certainly of equal significance.

In the sections which follow, some of the more immediately evident matters of general interest are discussed, together with problems connected with individual planets. This discussion must, of necessity, be superficial, for in spite of the considerable amount of diligent observation of the planets already made, we have firsthand knowledge of only one of them, and even in the case of the Earth this knowledge is confined to a relatively thin shell (see Chaps. 4-8).

The bulk of our knowledge of the other planets is based on astronomical observations (though some inferences can be drawn from study of meteorites). The distortions and obscurations introduced by the atmosphere are serious handicaps to the acquisition of more information than now exists, and it may be expected that observations from very high altitudes in the Earth's atmosphere and from satellites of the Earth will yield significant results. It will probably be several years before a useful astronomical telescope can be established outside the Earth's atmosphere; in the meantime, it is likely that several packages of instruments will have been sent to the vicinities of Mars and Venus. Limitations on the scope of experiments due to the state of rocket, instrumentation, and communications technology can be expected to recede, and it is to be hoped that the embodiment of meaningful experiments in suitable equipment will keep pace.

2. ATMOSPHERES

The atmospheres of the planets have been studied over many years of astronomical observation. The results of these studies are given in Table 1, which lists those constituents of the atmospheres which are well established, or upon which rather careful measurements have been made, and those which can be inferred to be present from the conditions that we know to obtain on the planets. It is quite evident that the compositions of none of the atmospheres and none of the planets are reliable in a quantitative sense. Infrared pictures and spectroscopy from balloons at high altitude might very well improve our knowledge of the atmospheres (as in the case of recent work on Venus), and this may be the best approach to this problem short of actual landing on the planets, analyzing by chemical methods, and transmitting the information back to the Earth.

Table 1. Composition of Planetary Atmospheres[1]

Planet	Substance	Detected	Amount, cm atm (NTP)	Basis of estimate	Remarks
Mercury					Probably fluorescing free radicals and ions produce haze.
Venus	CO_2	Yes	10^5	Spectroscopic	Much below the cloud layer.
	H_2O	Yes	Oceans	Polarization of clouds	Vast oceans are assumed to exist below the cloud: spectroscopic evidence of H_2O in the atmosphere has recently been obtained.
	N_2†	Yes	?	Spectroscopic	N_2 and N_2^+ bands in the night sky.
	CO†	Yes	<100	Spectroscopic	CO^+ bands in night sky and absorption bands in day sky. Limit fixed by near-infrared bands.
Earth				Many constituents	
Mars	CO_2	Yes	3,600	Spectroscopic	
	H_2O	Yes	?	Polarization of clouds	Polar caps consist of ice. Some clouds have the polarization of ice crystals.
	N_2	No	1.8×10^5	Total pressure measurement	N_2 is accepted as the most likely noncondensable constituent.
Jupiter	CH_4	Yes	1.5×10^4	Spectroscopic	Above cloud layer.
	NH_3	Yes	700	Spectroscopic	Above cloud layer.
	H_2	No	2.7×10^7		Assumed to be present in solar proportions relative to methane on the basis of the Marcus calculations.*
	He	No	5.6×10^8	Density of the planet	
	N_2	No	4×10^5		
	Ne	No	1.7×10^4		
Saturn	CH_4	Yes	35,000	Spectroscopic	Above cloud layer.
	NH_3	Yes	200	Spectroscopic	Above cloud layer.
	H_2	No	6.3×10^7		Assumed to be present in solar proportions relative to methane.*
	He	No	1.3×10^7	Density of the planet	
	N_2	No	9.5×10^5		
	Ne	No	2.7×10^4		
Uranus	CH_4‡	Yes	2.2×10^5	Spectroscopic	He and H_2 are assumed to be effective molecules in producing transitions of H_2.
	H_2	Yes	9×10^6	Calculated on Herzberg's assumption	
	He	No	2.7×10^7		
	H_2	Yes	4.2×10^6		N_2 and H_2 are assumed to be effective molecules in producing transitions of H_2. Solar proportions of He and H_2 are assumed.
	He	No	8.6×10^5	Calculated	
	N_2	No	4.2×10^6		
Neptune	CH_4‡	Yes	3.7×10^5	Spectroscopic	
	H_2	Yes	Larger than in Uranus	Spectroscopic	Assumed to be effective molecules in producing transitions of H_2. Solar proportions of H_2 and He assumed.
	N_2	No			
	He	No			
Titan	CH_4	Yes	2×10^4	Spectroscopic	
	He	No			Assumed high-diffusion layer for the preservation of H_2.

Kuiper (1952) has been unable to detect N_2O, CH_4, C_2H_4, C_2H_6, and NH_3 on Venus; SO_2, O_3, N_2O, CH_4, C_2H_4, C_2H_6, and NH_3 on Mars; O_3 and SO_2 on Saturn and Uranus; CH_4 and NH_3 on the satellites of Jupiter; and NH_3 on Titan. In most cases, the substances could not be expected to be present because of thermodynamic instability under the known conditions of the planet involved.

* Recent work indicates that the proportions of H_2 to CH_4 on Jupiter are much less than that assumed here. It is probable that this is also true for Saturn.

† More recent studies have not confirmed the observations on the bands of these molecules, and their presence is not proved.

‡ Methane has not been considered as the molecule inducing the hydrogen transitions, but it should contribute to this effect.

It is obvious that the atmospheres of the terrestrial planets—Venus, Earth, and Mars—are very highly oxidized. This oxidation is well known to originate from the escape of hydrogen from these planets. It is presumed that the planets once had a much more reduced atmosphere than is now characteristic of them. It should be remembered that carbon dioxide is a highly oxidized substance, as is also nitrogen gas. So far as we know, only the Earth's atmosphere contains appreciable amounts of oxygen, though it can be stated with confidence that small amounts of oxygen must be present on both Venus and Mars because of our knowledge of the photochemistry of carbon dioxide, which is present in the atmospheres of both of these planets.

The general evolutionary progress of the atmosphere of the planet could be outlined approximately as follows. The escape of hydrogen from the planet results in the production of carbon compounds which are more oxidized than methane, the loss of the hydrogen being equivalent to an oxidation process. At the same time the loss of hydrogen will result in the production of compounds containing larger amounts of oxygen, which again is an oxidation process. The immediate result of this should be to produce complicated carbon compounds containing carbon, oxygen, hydrogen, probably nitrogen, and sulfur as well. As the process continues, one of two things may occur. If water is present in excess, as on Earth, all the carbon compounds, or at least most of them, may be oxidized to carbon dioxide, with excess water remaining. On the other hand, if the carbon compounds were present in excess, it can be expected that the water would eventually be completely used up and the carbon compounds only partially oxidized to carbon dioxide: the result would be a dry planet with very little water and with carbon compounds of high boiling point (Hoyle's petroleum on Venus). The rate of escape of hydrogen from Mars is undoubtedly very high—so high in fact that the small amount of water in its atmosphere should be destroyed in a very short time if it is not replenished from the interior of the planet. Hence it is of interest in connection with this planet to discover, if possible, whether there are substantial sources of water beneath the surface. In the case of Venus we have far less information about the lower atmosphere than in the case of Mars. Present indications are that it may have a fairly high temperature, and perhaps there are no water sources on this planet at the present time.

As the oxidation process continues, carbon dioxide will react with the silicate rocks of the surface of the planet if adequate contact between the gas and the solid can be secured. This is promoted on the Earth by the erosional effects of water; if such effects occur on the planets, one must expect that the carbon dioxide will be removed from the atmosphere. Venus has very large quantities of carbon dioxide, and for some reason this has not been lost (see Sec. 6 below).

It is also to be expected that oxygen will react with the silicate rocks, if opportunity is presented, to produce more oxidized forms of iron than are to be expected in cosmic material. The meteorites, it should be remembered, are very highly reduced and would absorb oxygen as they do after they arrive on the Earth. If other planets started with material of this state of reduction, which seems most reasonable, then we must expect that the oxygen will be absorbed by the rocks if adequate opportunity for such processes is available.

The objectives of space investigation should be, so far as the atmospheres are concerned, to elucidate the problems outlined above and to investigate such things as the very high atmosphere, as we have done on Earth. Such investigations will follow the line of continued spectroscopic investigation both from the high-flying balloons of the Earth and, if they can be established, from space observatories, by the flight of probes in the neighborhood of the planet, and by landing on the planet. Most interesting pictures have been taken of Venus as it approaches conjunction with the Sun. This enables us to investigate the high atmosphere of the planet when light passes through large thicknesses of the atmosphere. It is probable that much useful work could yet be done on this type of problem from the surface of the Earth, but in recent years interest in astronomy has gone so largely to the stars that such mundane (or, let us say, cytherean) investigations have not been of interest.

Mercury probably has a very limited atmosphere because of its low gravitational field and the high temperature of the hemisphere which is exposed to sunlight. It does present most interesting problems, however, because of the possibility of an equilibrium atmosphere due to an increased concentration of gas as compared with interplanetary gases and because of the special conditions on its dark hemisphere. The atmosphere of the Moon, too, may be an equilibrium one.

If landings can be made and analysis of the atmospheres becomes possible, we shall have for the first time much more precise information than we can get by any other methods that so far have been attempted.

3. SURFACES

The surface of the Earth presents a most complicated problem for study, one which has been pursued by geologists for over a century. The general features of the development of the Earth's surface are well understood.   We observe that there have been extensive lava flows and great volcanic activity.   Such activity is particularly to be expected on a large planet because of the very effective heating of the interior of the planet as compared with the rate of heat loss.   Such activity is not to be expected on small planets.   It would hardly be reasonable to look for extensive volcanism on the Moon at the present time.   Even on Mars it seems likely that there is less volcanic activity than on Earth.

In addition, water erosion has shaped the general features of the Earth. Large energetic processes, probably accompanied by convection currents within the Earth, which cause buckling of the surface, have produced enormous mountains.   These have then been eroded by water and cut into very rugged and sharp peaks.   We cannot expect that this sort of thing happens on a planet unless running water is present.   So far as we know at the present time, Mars has no such features, but if water has been present on that planet in the past, then we can expect that similar mountains have been carved from its surface.   Our knowledge of Venus of course is much less because of the dense cloud cover.

Life exists on Earth and has produced its own characteristic features on the surface.   In particular, it is probably responsible for the production of oxygen in the atmosphere of the Earth.   Living organisms have produced a distinctly reduced character to the sediments of the Earth as this oxygen atmosphere was produced.   We have no evidence that the escape of hydrogen by itself would produce oxygen at such a rate that free oxygen would exist in the atmosphere of the Earth.   It should be remembered that oxygen is absorbed by the rocks of the Earth: if the rate of absorption is equal to the rate of loss of hydrogen, no free oxygen could be expected.   If living organisms of any complexity were ever present on other planets, we should expect to find their fossils in the rocks.   Not only should we look for present life on these planets, which would be one of the most fascinating discoveries of all modern science, but also we should look for the evidence for the existence of past life on the planets. It would indeed be a keen disappointment to find a planet on which life had once existed but was now extinct.   Nevertheless, such a discovery would be of tremendous interest.   Chapter 20 discusses this subject further.

4. STRUCTURES IN THE INTERIOR OF THE PLANETS

During the past century, and especially in recent years, a great deal of evidence about the interior structure of the Earth has been secured, predominantly by means of seismic studies though also from very intense chemical studies of the Earth's surface. This evidence shows the Earth to have a large core with a radius greater than one-half the radius of the Earth and, on the outside, a crust of varying thickness. The dimensions of these regions of the Earth have been established by means of seismic studies. In the same way, it is to be expected that similar studies on the planets would enable us to understand their structures. However, no seismic studies can be made except by landing apparatus on the surface. It seems impossible to investigate these questions adequately in any other way, and in general it can be expected that very extensive efforts will be required in order to gain any clear picture of the structure of these objects. Though it is unknown whether the planets have cores like that of the Earth, it seems most likely that Venus has such a core and possibly also Mars. Mercury is a planet of very high density, and most ideas indicate that Mercury would also have a core of large volume relative to the volume of the planet.

We are also interested in the composition of the planets. In Chap. 9, on the Moon, it was noted that its density is very low. It follows that either the iron content alone is very low as compared even with the meteorites—and especially low as compared with the Earth—or that it contains some very low density material. The latter possibility would permit a higher concentration of iron to exist without exceeding the observed density. On the other hand, Mercury has a very high density, one that cannot be accounted for except by the presence of very high density materials. If differentiation of the surface has occurred to the same extent as it has on Earth, studies of the surface compositions of the planets are likely to be disappointing as means of learning about their internal compositions. It is quite impossible to deduce the mean composition of the Earth, even at the present time and with the benefit of all the extensive studies that have been made both of the Earth's surface and of the interior. Only in recent years have there appeared papers which attempt to do this in any reasonable way. It is to be expected that both Mars and Venus will give us trouble with respect to this problem.

5. MAGNETIC FIELDS

The Earth is well known to have a dipole field of a somewhat unsymmetrical kind, with the magnetic poles not coinciding at the present time with the geographic poles. The origin of this dipole field is still uncertain but is believed to be due to conduction in the liquid core of the Earth. At least this theory has gained more acceptance in recent years than any other. Questions naturally arise as to the possibility that other planets have magnetic dipole fields and, if so, whether they are related to liquid cores or to some past magnetic field in the solar system. The existence of magnetic fields in the past has been suggested as a means for accounting for certain features of the origin of the Earth and planets. Evidence for such a field would be a most interesting confirmation of this past history of the solar system, and it would have wide implications for the origin of stars generally. Investigation of such magnetic fields can probably be made more effectively from space probes flying in the neighborhood of the planets than by the use of apparatus on the surface because of the very large number of surface readings which would be necessary in order to establish the general character of the planet's dipole field and its possible change with time. Recent observations indicate that the meteorites are magnetized. The origin of this magnetized condition is unknown. According to reports from the U.S.S.R., the Moon does not have a surface magnetic field larger than approximately 0,001 that of the Earth.

6. FEATURES OF PARTICULAR PLANETS

6.1 Mercury

Mercury, because of its nearness to the Sun, is at a very high temperature on the sunward side. The planet rotates once in its year and hence keeps the same side to the Sun. This side is at a very high temperature—so high that, if instruments were landed on it, it is doubtful that the electrical equipment necessary for the transmission of information back to Earth could be made to function properly. On the other hand, the side away from the Sun is at a very low temperature; if equipment could be landed on this side, there seems to be no reason why it should not operate successfully and transmit information to the Earth.

Mercury has a very high density, approximately 5, and hence must contain a very considerably increased concentration of metallic iron or, as has been recently suggested, iron silicide. If the first assumption is correct, one must postulate the loss of very considerable amounts of silicate materials during the formation of this planet in order to account for a residue of metallic iron. If the second one is correct, preliminary calculations indicate that again very substantial amounts of material must have been lost from the planet, though the materials would have been of a different chemical composition and the method of loss might have been quite different. Various suggestions have been made in regard to this problem. This bears again on the question of the processes occurring during the origin of the solar system. Information giving us a decision in regard to some of these questions would make it possible to narrow the range of hypothetical processes which might have occurred during the origin of the system, and again this would be of importance in connection with the evolution of our system and the evolution of the stars.   Efforts should be made to fly instruments into the neighborhood of Mercury and perhaps land them on the cold side of the planet.   Instruments of particular interest would be both chemical analytical apparatus (although it is very difficult to devise such equipment to operate under conditions which are very badly known) and seismic apparatus, which would enable us to determine something of the structure of the inside of the planet.

6.2 Venus

Venus has thick cloud cover, and many speculations on the structure of this atmosphere have been made.   It has been suggested that there are extensive oceans on the surface of the planet, then again that there is no water at all and that it is completely arid and dry.   It has further been suggested that the clouds are filled with hydrocarbons which have not become quite completely oxidized, as they have in the case of the Earth. It has also been suggested that the suboxide C_3O_2 and its polymers are responsible for these clouds.   Carbon suboxide is a very unstable compound, and hence its occurrence in any but trace amounts can hardly be expected.   Carbon dioxide, if suitable contact with silicate materials is

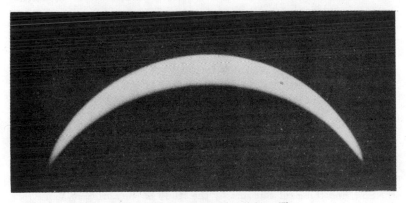

FIG. 1. Venus near inferior conjunction, in blue light.   The twilit edge of the atmosphere inside the crescent is distinctly fuzzier than the limb or horizon.   (*Courtesy of Mt. Wilson and Palomar Observatories.*)

available, would react to give limestones and sand, and eventually the partial pressure of carbon dioxide would become less than that existing at the surface of the Earth. The relatively high concentration of carbon dioxide in the Earth's atmosphere must exist because of the slowness of the reactions taking place to produce limestone, dolomite, and a residue of sand from the silicate material. This takes place on the surface of the Earth because of the excellent contact provided by erosion and running water.

Carbon dioxide exists in large quantities in the atmosphere of Venus. For some reason the absorption of carbon dioxide in silicate rocks does not seem to have occurred on Venus. It has been suggested that this is due to the presence of extensive oceans covering the entire surface of the planet, which would then prevent or limit contact between carbon dioxide and silicate materials. It has also been suggested that this is due to the completely arid character of the planet, which means very poor contact between carbon dioxide and solid materials. An arid planet might have some carbon-hydrogen compounds which have not been completely oxidized. It may also be due to the presence of such an overwhelming abundance of carbon dioxide in the atmosphere that even after complete reaction with all the superficial silicate rocks, there still remains the observed excess. Also, if the high surface temperatures reported are indeed correct, the high pressure of carbon dioxide may be an equilibrium one, for the low pressure mentioned above is that expected at about terrestrial surface temperatures. It will be interesting to see how the situation accounts for the observed facts.

Apparently, clearing of the atmosphere occurs, as has been observed by the French astronomers particularly, and one wonders what sort of material could exist in these clouds that would permit such a clearing of the atmosphere. It is still not known at what frequency the planet rotates. The French astronomers have maintained for years that Venus rotates only once in its year, while American astronomers generally have favored a rotation time of a few weeks.

An aurora on Venus has been reported by the Russian astronomer Kozyrev. This has been confirmed only doubtfully, if at all, by American astronomers. Efforts should be made to decide whether the aurora is real or not, and it may be that we shall learn a great deal about the origin of the aurora, its relationship to the interplanetary particle streams from the Sun, and things of this sort by the study of the aurora of Venus.

Life on Venus is a question of interest, but if the high temperatures reported recently by the Naval Research Laboratory (of the order of 300°C, on the basis of measurements at radio frequencies) prove to be

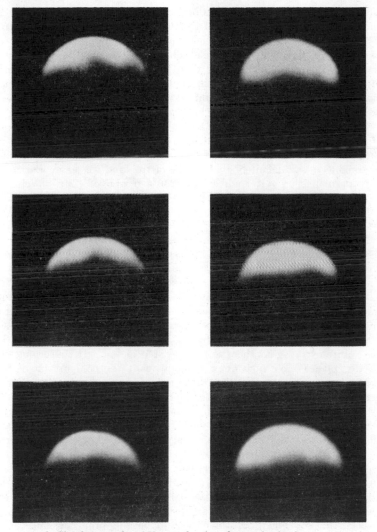

FIG. 2. Six photographs of Venus, showing changes in cloud pattern. (*Courtesy of Mt. Wilson and Palomar Observatories.*)

correct, it is doubtful if there can be any liquid water on the planet. If such high temperatures prevail at the surface of the planet, it is doubtful if any of the reactions that are characteristic of living organisms that we see on the Earth could be possible at all. Furthermore, all protein materials would be coagulated; hence this type of material, so characteristic of living organisms in the Earth, could hardly exist there. It is not entirely certain that such high temperatures exist on the planet's surface; hence it is possible that life may be present.

In asking whether life exists on a planet many people suggest that a life of a completely different sort from that on Earth would be possible. On the basis of our knowledge of the behavior of carbon compounds, it seems reasonable to say definitely that no life of the kind we see on Earth, or any approximation to it, could exist at 250°C or above. Life on Venus is hardly to be expected unless there is now liquid water on its surface.

6.3 Mars

Mars is a planet which has been studied by astronomers more extensively than any other because its atmosphere is very thin and it has been possible to see the solid surface. This surface has dark markings on it which many observers regard as greenish in hue whereas others insist are only gray in color. Because of the seasonal color changes which occur in these dark areas—greenish or grayish in the Martian spring and reddish or brownish in the fall—and periodic changes in the size of the dark areas, it has been supposed that plant life of some kind exists on this planet. In fact, quite extravagant theories have existed in the past concerning life on this planet. We now know enough about the composition of the atmosphere to believe that life of the active forms found on the Earth is most improbable. These depend upon the high, free energy supplied by an oxidizing atmosphere which is not present on Mars. However, the planet's atmosphere does contain very small amounts of water and carbon dioxide. A great deal of living material exists on the Earth under anaerobic conditions, and it seems probable that life evolved on the Earth under such conditions. Therefore there is no particular reason to believe that life could not exist on Mars. Vast dust storms are observed to occur on this planet; such dust could settle over the dark areas and eventually cover them up completely. This has not occurred, and for this reason it seems that some material which has rejuvenating properties must exist on the dark areas. This has been pointed out by Öpik and is one of the important reasons for believing that life exists. Interestingly enough, the dust storms never seem quite able to cover the dark areas completely at all; hence if they are due to plants, the plants must have a "rough-

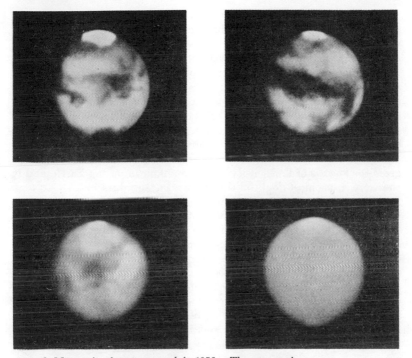

FIG. 3. Mars at its closest approach in 1956. The upper pair, taken 12 days apart, show the seasonal shrinkage of the polar cap during the Martian summer. The two pictures on the left show approximately the same hemisphere taken with an orange filter; in the lower picture the presence of patchy, yellow haze is attributed to dust clouds. The lower right picture, taken in blue light, shows Mars almost completely obscured by blue haze. (*Courtesy of Mt. Wilson and Palomar Observatories.*)

ness" sufficient to stand above the surface of the dust layer. Recently Sinton[2,3] has found that infrared bands characteristic of the carbon-hydrogen bond resonance in large organic molecules can be observed in the dark areas of Mars and not in the light areas. This, perhaps, is the most positive evidence we have that life exists on Mars. It can be considered a reasonable expectation that life does exist on Mars and that an investigation of this question is of first importance in the space program.

The oblateness of Mars has been, and is, one of the great puzzles of this planet.   From the motion of the moons, it can be deduced that a bulge of uniform density, 0.52 per cent of the radius, exists in the equatorial region. On the other hand, direct observations over many years by many very careful and competent astronomical observers lead to agreement that the visual (and photographic) height of the bulge is approximately 1.2 per cent.   Taking these figures as they stand and assuming that they are both reliable requires that some low-density material is piled in great depths on the equatorial regions of Mars.   If the bulge is composed of granite differing, say, by 20 per cent in density from the other materials of the planet, the depth of the granite layer would have to be about 100 km in order to account for the observations described above.   Such great thicknesses of low-density rock are unknown on the Earth, and it therefore seems most doubtful that they occur on Mars.

If life now exists on Mars, we probably must assume that liquid water existed on this planet in the past, for it is difficult indeed to imagine how life, at least of the variety known on Earth, could evolve in the absence of water.   We know of no other complicated chemistry of the carbon compounds or those of any other element which would seem likely to imitate the very complex chemical processes which constitute living organisms.   We thus conclude that if life is present, there must have been oceans or seas in the past.   If oceans existed in the past, undoubtedly glaciers would cover both poles continuously so long as water was present on the planet.   It would be difficult to say whether any liquid water

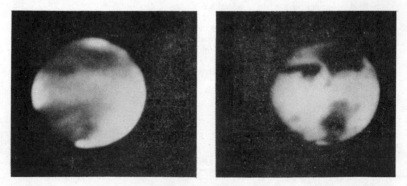

FIG. 4. Mars in blue (left) and red (right) light.   The picture on the left shows thick patches of blue haze in some regions, comparatively clear sky in others (see Fig. 3, lower right). (*Courtesy of Mt. Wilson and Palomar Observatories.*)

would exist in the equatorial regions of this planet if vast amounts of water were present, but as mentioned above, it is doubtful if life approximating anything we know would have evolved unless liquid water were present. Such glaciers, if they existed in the past, may have piled up a great deal of rubble in the equatorial regions. This would be another source of low-density material. Ice could not remain in the equatorial regions because it would flow to the polar regions under the gravitation of this planet. On the other hand, glacial rubble and gravel with water constituting a part of this might well have such high viscosity, let us say, that it would not flow toward the poles. We might ask the question: do the equatorial regions contain vast amounts of water locked up as ice beneath the surface which only slowly escapes to the surface of the planet? Such an explanation, or indeed an acceptance of the observational data at all, requires that the atmosphere be much more dense at the poles than at the equator. No such atmospheric effect has been reported.

But either life or water of this kind requires that oxygen must escape, for no oceans are now observed on this planet. In fact, it is an exceedingly arid planet, with only small amounts of water. Hydrogen should escape from this planet in a very short period of time and leave no observable water at all. It thus would appear that both oxygen and hydrogen must escape from the high atmosphere of this planet if we are to be consistent in our postulate that life may occur on this planet. An investigation of the high atmosphere of the planet should be made in order to determine whether oxygen can escape and whether it is possible that water existed in large quantities in the past.

The radius and mass of Mars are such that the planet may not have a core. If this is the case, it would indicate generally low temperature conditions for the origin of the planets. However, the radius of Mars is uncertain. Determinations of the radius have ranged from approximately 0.52 to 0.535 of the radius of the Earth. The lower radii indicate that there is little core in this planet. The higher radii would indicate a moderate one. The question of the magnetic field of this planet is of great interest, especially in connection with the theory of the origin of magnetic fields generally, namely, due to circulation in the core of the planet.

A blue haze exists in the high atmosphere of Mars, which disappears from time to time and whose origin is most uncertain. It has been ascribed to solid carbon dioxide, ice, fluorescence of free radicals, and carbon smoke. At the present time no agreement in regard to this phenomenon has been secured. It is to be hoped that observations in the future will lead to more definitive understanding both of the appearance of the Martian upper atmosphere and the chemical composition of the atmosphere as a whole—now presumed to be mostly nitrogen, with demonstrated quantities of carbon dioxide and perhaps a small amount of argon.

6.4 Asteroids

The asteroids are small objects lying between Mars and Jupiter, and the problem of reaching them by space vehicles is considerably more difficult than reaching the other planets. We do not know the structure of these asteroids, the largest of which is 400 km in radius, but it is presumed that the meteorites generally come from these objects as a result of collisions between them. This theory seems to be the most usual one that has been accepted in the past. Whether it would be possible to land instruments on an asteroid is difficult to say. The object is very small. It exists in a vast region of space. The orbits generally are inclined at rather large angles to the plane of the ecliptic, and the problem of guiding a space vehicle to an asteroid appears to be a difficult one. Samples of material from these objects would be most interesting from the point of view of meteorite studies and the abundances of the elements.

6.5 Jupiter

There are certain features of Jupiter which have been puzzling for many years. The weather bands are possibly qualitatively understood as merely the circulation on a rapidly rotating planet under the heating action of the Sun, but the great red spot which appears to be floating in some way on the surface is a very great puzzle. We do not know its composition, what holds it together, or why its movements are as they are. Also, the occurrence of bursts of radio emissions from somewhere deep below the visible surface of the planet has been a most interesting observation in recent years. Observations of the radio emissions from Jupiter suggest that the planet has an ionosphere, a magnetic field of at least 2 gauss, and that the sources of the radio bursts rotate with the surface of an invisible solid body. Further study of these phenomena is of considerable interest and may yield information bearing on the composition and physical state of the solid body of Jupiter. In this connection, although direct approach to the planet may not be feasible, use of one of Jupiter's satellites as an observation point would avoid the extremes of gravity, if such a feat should become possible. The other major planets are probably beyond our most optimistic plans for the immediate future and will not be discussed.

FIG. 5. Jupiter, taken in blue light, shows the belts (which have been interpreted as analogous to weather or prevailing wind zones set up by heating and circulation), the Great Red Spot, and satellite Ganymede and its shadow. (*Courtesy of Mt. Wilson and Palomar Observatories.*)

6.6 Comets

The comets are believed to be very loosely constructed, low-density objects from 1 to 100 km in diameter. The icy conglomerate model is generally accepted as most reasonable. It is suggested that they consist of cosmic matter, except for the absence of hydrogen, helium, and probably neon, and that they contain chemical compounds of considerable energy content. They arrive from all directions with about equal probability, become visible at about 5 A.U., and greatly increase in brightness as they approach the Sun.

These objects probably contain most of the elements in some primitive cosmic proportions, and samples would be most interesting from the point of view of elemental abundances. They are generally regarded as parts of the solar system. In this case, the isotopic abundances should be the same as those of terrestrial matter.

Whether it will be possible to send a space probe to the immediate vicinity of a comet is difficult to estimate at the present time. The aiming and guiding problems will be very great. However, because of the great interest of astronomers in these great distances from the Sun, consideration should be given to this problem.

7. GENERAL CONSIDERATIONS IN THE STUDY OF THE PLANETS

Special projects which can be undertaken or considered in the immediate future may well be summarized.

1. *Television observations* of many features of the solar system at points either near the planets or on their surfaces are advisable. Such television observation should be made in light of varying wavelengths. Television from outside the planet could have a resolving power of perhaps 10 km or thereabouts. If soft landings can be made, television of the landscape and the immediate neighborhood, and even through magnifying apparatus, would be important in order to detect life, minerals, erosional and tectonic processes, and general topography. The temperatures might be determined from outside the atmosphere by using infrared radiation.

2. *Magnetic fields* should be studied as mentioned previously. These can best be done from satellites of the planets because of the very large number of observational points that would be required on the surface.

3. *Temperatures* should be determined. These can be done partly by infrared studies. With soft landings it may be possible to determine the temperature, pressure, and depth of atmosphere by suitable apparatus as a balloon descends. The *ionic effects* in the high atmosphere are of very great interest. The *chemical composition* of the atmosphere might be secured from spectra, mass spectrometers, or even from simple chemical analytical apparatus. In the case of Venus it would be interesting to detect oceans if they are present.

4. By the use of satellites it should be possible to secure the *mass and shape* of Venus. Satellites would enable us to investigate the *lightning flashes*, if there are any, in the atmospheres of Mars and Venus. Also this should be a way of investigating the very interesting *radiation of Jupiter*. The planet radiates in the 14- and 27-Mc region and seems to have a rather sharp cutoff in the neighborhood of 30 Mc per sec, but the low-cutoff region is unknown.

5. *Seismic apparatus.* The landing of seismic apparatus on the planets should be attempted in order to secure information about their internal structure.

6. *Biological tests.* These are most important from the standpoint of detecting extraterrestrial life. Experiments which might feasibly be made with planetary probes and which might yield useful information can be categorized as follows: (a) Measurement of the physical and chemical characteristics of the environment. (b) Detection of spectra characteristic of known organic matter, e.g., chlorophyll. (c) Detection by pulsed radar inspection of returns similar to those of terrestrial vegetation. (d) Detection of the growth of microorganisms by observation of the products of metabolism: this to be done with a suitably instrumented container designed to enclose a sample of the environment after a "soft landing." (e) Photography and, in the case of soft landings, listening for noises. See also Chaps. 19-20, concerned with the biological sciences and space research.

In general, every opportunity should be taken for testing the validity of experimental techniques on the Earth by means of balloons, sounding rockets, and Earth satellites.

Information of biological significance may need considerable simplification before transmission; information theory may be helpful; and simple, low-power, slow computers may be required. In the case of some kinds of photography, it would be advantageous to be able to reduce the redundancy in successive pictures before transmission.

7. *Balloon flights* in the Earth's atmosphere should be encouraged and financed because nearly all that can be learned from the observation of light can be observed as well from the Earth as from near the planets, provided we can eliminate the effects of our own atmosphere. This cannot be done entirely by high-flying balloons, but very much better work can be done in this way than has been done in the past. Also, the expense of such balloon flights will prove to be much less than any interplanetary flights.

REFERENCES

1. *Handbuch der Physik*, vol. 52, rev. ed. (Berlin: Springer Verlag, 1959).
2. W. M. Sinton: *Astrophysical Journal, 126*, 231 (1957).
3. W. M. Sinton: *Science, 130*, 1234 (1959).

SUPPLEMENTARY READING

G. P. Kuiper: *The Atmospheres of the Earth and Planets* (University of Chicago Press, 1952).

H. C. Urey: *The Planets* (Yale University Press, 1952).

G. de Vaucouleurs: *Physics of the Planet Mars* (London: Faber & Faber, 1954).

PART 5

FIELDS AND PARTICLES
IN SPACE

11

PHYSICS OF FIELDS AND ENERGETIC
PARTICLES IN SPACE*

J. A. Simpson

There exist processes within the solar system and elsewhere in the Galaxy whereby particles attain high energies through acceleration by large-scale electromagnetic processes, and not from nuclear or particle decay. The outstanding and historic example of this fundamental acceleration mode is the cosmic radiation, most of which comes from our Galaxy. The spectrum of particles includes the nuclei of the elements covering a vast range of energies extending up to at least 10^{19} ev. At present we believe the energy density of the galactic cosmic rays is approximately equal to the energy density of galactic magnetic fields which interact with them. In turn, it appears that the turbulent energy density of the Galaxy is approximately equal to the magnetic field energy density. Thus energetic particles in the Galaxy are important for an understanding of the Galaxy. More recently, observations in the Crab

* The content of this chapter and of Chaps. 13 and 14 are based upon the paper by J. A. Simpson in *Astrophysical Journal*, Suppl., Ser. IV, No. 44, p. 378 (1960). Since the preparation of this part late in 1959, some new results have been obtained with space probes: some chapters have been edited to account for these; e.g., references to such recent results have been noted briefly wherever possible; Chap. 16 on auroral theory was prepared late in 1960.

Nebulae indicate that there is synchrotron radiation from accelerated electrons to account for the observed polarization of its light.[1] Nonthermal radio noise from sources within and beyond the Galaxy also point to the existence of energetic particles throughout the Universe. Within the solar system nature has provided several sources of accelerated particles. The most dramatic example is the acceleration of particles to energies extending into the cosmic-ray range on the occasion of unusually large solar flares. Indeed, these solar flares represent the only direct observation of the birth of cosmic-ray particles.[2] Flares also appear to release lower-energy particles in great abundance.[3] Nonrelativistic protons from the Sun enter the polar regions following solar flares;[4] auroral particles in the range of 50 to over 100 kev energy for electrons and protons are well established; much of the trapped radiation recently found[5] to exist in the terrestrial magnetic field is of high energy and partly may arise from local acceleration. Thus we find within the solar system the acceleration of particles covering a vast range of energies—a range of over 10 decades of energy. Figure 1 gives an indication of the energy spectra of particles from different sources as they are known at the present time. Spectrum a of the cosmic radiation, mostly from the Galaxy, has been derived from a series of measurements extending over 15 years.[6] The first spectrum derived from acceleration within the solar system is shown as spectrum b for protons from a large solar flare in 1956.[2] Spectrum c is also from a solar flare, which produced much lower energy protons.[3] Spectrum d represents the very recent measurement of the Van Allen trapped radiation close to the Earth.[7]

Particle acceleration by electromagnetic mechanisms within the solar system and Galaxy presents one of the major problems in physics at the present time. In many cases, even the location of the source is unknown to us. By an intensive study of particle acceleration, processes such as the solar flare may lead to our understanding the basic problems of acceleration and may open the possibility for extending this knowledge to the more energetic events in the Galaxy and beyond. Thus the primary discussion in what follows focuses upon solar-system physics.

Although the basic mechanism for particle acceleration has not so far been uniquely determined and in many cases even the location for acceleration of particles in the solar system is unknown, it is certain that the mechanism and the region of acceleration are occupied by magnetic fields capable of transferring some of their stored magnetic field energy, and motions, to ions. Thus intimately related to the energetic particles are the magnetic fields in the solar system—especially at the Sun and in the interplanetary space nearby.

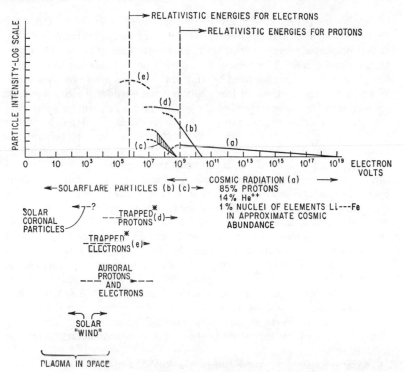

FIG. 1. The spectra of energetic particles observed in the solar system. Dash lines indicate unknown extension of the spectrum; asterisk denotes trapping in the geomagnetic field (some of these particles are from neutron decay). All particle distributions except the cosmic radiation *a* arise from acceleration mechanisms within the inner solar system. The spectrum of the galactic cosmic radiation observed at Earth is controlled by solar-system electrodynamics.

Stellar energy is the fundamental energy source for the generation of magnetic fields and acceleration of particles. Energy from the Sun's interior is transferred, by mechanisms as yet not understood, to the overlying ionized high-temperature gaseous atmosphere—the chromosphere and corona. Motions are imparted to magnetic fields rooted in the photosphere, but extending into the chromosphere and corona, so that the manipulation of these fields from within the Sun results in energy transfers to the chromosphere and corona. A small fraction of stellar energy is stored in these magnetic fields under conditions which frequently lead to instabilities and the sudden release of a substantial fraction of the stored magnetic energy in the form of kinetic energy imparted to the highly ionized gas.   The solar-flare event is an outstanding example of this process.   The intense local heating of the corona above active regions as a result of energy transfer leads to the rapid outflow of ionized gas, or plasma, into the outer fringes of the corona and interplanetary space.

Close to the Sun near sunspots, the magnetic field energy density is generally such as to impart motions to the plasma and to control the plasma motions; but in the interplanetary medium the situation is reversed, and plasmas impart motions to the magnetic fields *in situ* and carry magnetic fields within the plasmas into space.   Thus the interplanetary medium near the Sun is in reality an extension of the solar atmosphere, composed of a quiescent outflow of gas upon which are superimposed transient magnetic fields and plasma flows.   Clearly, the whole interplanetary medium is pervaded by magnetic fields, partially ordered at some times and locations by solar plasma emission and disordered at other times and locations.   Energetic particles coming from outside the Galaxy or from the Sun move along paths in these magnetic fields, whereby they eventually have access to all portions of the nearby interplanetary medium.   Whether particles from a given source direction have access to the Earth at any given time, for example, is determined by their energy and by the configuration of the interplanetary magnetic fields of solar origin.

The interactions of these magnetic fields, plasmas, and energetic particles with the Earth's permanent magnetic field, ionosphere, and atmosphere constitute the study of terrestrial phenomena of solar origin such as geomagnetic storms, the aurorae, ionospheric absorption effects, and the behavior of trapped particles in the geomagnetic field.   In early years, most of these phenomena were studied by correlations between solar events and terrestrial consequences and constituted the subject of solar-terrestrial relationships.   These correlations shaped some of our present ideas concerning the form of ionic streams from the Sun and the structures of interplanetary magnetic fields.

Near the photosphere the existence of magnetic fields is shown by optical techniques such as the Zeeman effect.   At greater distances the description of magnetic fields rests upon indirect evidence.   In the region 10 to 20 solar radii, solar eclipses help to suggest the configuration of magnetic fields near the Sun at various times of the solar cycle.   Radio observations, where distant stars transit the outer fringes of the solar corona, permit studies of the variations in electron densities as a function of position.[8] They suggest a considerable irregularity and disordering of the field regions. For the main volume of interplanetary space beyond this, deductions are based in large measure upon the way charged particles coming to the Earth behave in the medium. Some of our prime evidence rests, first, on cosmic-ray particles which reach the Earth from the Galaxy and, second, on cosmic-ray particles released at the time of solar flares from the Sun. They behave as probes. The temporary storage of solar cosmic-radiation bursts provides the principal experimental evidence that magnetic fields are present, even though their detailed structure is open to debate.

It has been proved within the last decade that the primary cosmic radiation coming to us from outside the solar system undergoes drastic changes in energy spectrum and intensity with time and that these changes are all of solar origin. It is the low-energy portion of the cosmic-ray spectrum that is profoundly influenced—the region below approximately 50 Bev. This modulation of preexisting cosmic radiation has led to the development of models for the interplanetary magnetic fields of solar origin at different times in the solar cycle and has resulted in some tentative descriptions of the interaction of the interplanetary fields with the Earth's fields and the plasma conditions in space around the Sun at special times of solar activity. Thus the cosmic radiation—both galactic and solar—are tools to probe further these fundamental questions, and the possibilities for direct observations of the cosmic radiation opened by satellites and space probes should lead to unique experiments. Because both acceleration of particles to high energies and the modulation of particles take place within the solar system by electromagnetic phenomena of solar origin, the investigation of the low-energy end of the primary cosmic-ray spectrum, and of even lower-energy particles, is of intense interest to investigators at the present time. Indeed, it is clear from Fig. 1 that the best-known spectra of energetic particles are those near relativistic energies and higher and that over the low-energy range of 0 to 10^7 ev very little information is available. Satellite and space-probe experiments will drastically change this situation. The inner solar system has become one vast laboratory for the investigation of dilute plasmas, magnetic fields, hydromagnetic waves, and shock phenomena that cannot be scaled down properly for laboratory study. For example, the question of the validity of the three adiabatic invariants for the trapping of charged particles in the geomagnetic field is of special interest to those concerned with the general problem of energetic particle containment by magnetic fields. It will not be surprising, therefore, if out of these studies there also unfold new ideas regarding the behavior of dilute plasmas and shocks in magnetic fields which may have application to laboratory experiments such as thermonuclear reactions.

From the above introductory remarks, it is clear that one must cut across fundamental fields in both physics and astrophysics to approach the basic questions of particle acceleration, the generation of magnetic fields in stars and space, and the motions of matter and fields in space. This rapidly developing area of research may appropriately be called "high-energy astrophysics." From a humble beginning with studies in the solar system, a better understanding may come of broad cosmological questions such as the development of galaxies, origin of the high-energy cosmic radiations, origins of magnetic fields associated with the planets and stars, etc.

The prime purpose of this chapter is to set forth some current fundamental problems in this field which may be open to attack through investigations outside our atmosphere. Thus we outline briefly what we are learning about the interplanetary medium, the solar atmosphere, and the interaction of these regions with the geomagnetic field. Our attention is devoted to atomic matter in space, its charge and mass, to magnetic and electric fields in space, to energetic particles, and to their origins and acceleration processes. Thus this chapter briefly outlines only a limited selection of topics. Other than for questions concerned with the geomagnetic storm and the trapping and motion of particles in the geomagnetic field, no discussion has been included on the immediate region about the Earth such as the ionosphere, the permanent magnetic field of the Earth,* or the recent findings on ring currents in the geomagnetic field.† We have excluded discussion of such larger particles as molecules, dust, and micrometeorites, all of which contribute to our knowledge but which are discussed elsewhere in this volume.

Several experiments and observations are discussed that take advantage of the recent technical advances in rocketry, satellites, and space probes. These vehicles, when combined with recent developments in balloon

---

* On recent measurements of the geomagnetic field relatively close to the Earth, see, for example, J. P. Heppner, J. D. Stolarik, I. R. Shapiro, and J. C. Cain, in "Space Research," p. 982 (North-Holland Publishing Co., Amsterdam, 1960).

† Magnetometer measurements on USSR space probes I and II indicate the existence of current systems within the outer radiation belt; see S. S. Dolginov, E. G. Eroshenko, L. N. Zhuzgov, N. V. Pushkov, and L. O. Tyurmina, in "Space Research," p. 863 (North-Holland Publishing Co., Amsterdam, 1960). Current systems beyond the range of 6 earth radii have been deduced from magnetometer data obtained on Explorer VI and Pioneer V; see E. J. Smith, P. J. Coleman, D. L. Judge, and C. P. Sonett, *Jour. Geophys. Res.*, *65*, 1858 (1960).

techniques, miniature instrumentation, and advances in information theory and computer research, open new experimental fields in physics.

REFERENCES

1. J. H. Oort and T. Walraven: *Bull. Netherlands Astron. Inst.*, *12*, 285 (1956).
2. P. Meyer, E. N. Parker, and J. A. Simpson: *Phys. Rev.*, *104*, 768 (1956). J. Simpson, *Nuovo Cimento* X, Suppl. 8, No. 2 (1958).
3. K. A. Anderson, R. Arnoldy, R. Hoffman, L. Peterson, and J. R. Winckler: *J. Geophys. Research*, *64*, No. 9, 1133 (1959).
4. H. Leinbach and G. C. Reid: *Phys. Rev. Letters*, *2*, 61 (1959)
5. J. A. Van Allen, C. E. McIlwain, and G. II. Ludwig: *J. Geophys. Research*, *64*, 271 (1959).
6 For surveys on topics related to cosmic radiation, see J. G. Wilson and S. A. Wouthuysen (eds.): "Progress in Elementary Particle and Cosmic Ray Physics," Vols. I to V (Interscience Publishers, Inc.)
7. S. C. Freden and R. S. White: *Phys. Rev. Letters*, *3*, 9 (1959).
8. A. Hewish: *Monthly Not. Roy. Astron. Soc.*, *118*, No. 6, 534 (1958).

12

THE INTERPLANETARY GAS AND MAGNETIC FIELDS

E. N. Parker

1. CONDITIONS AT THE SUN

The Sun is a spherical mass of gas forming the energy source for essentially all the dynamical processes occurring in the solar system.[1] The central temperature of the Sun is of order of 15×10^{6}°K. The total mass is 2×10^{33} g, most of which is in the central core: the mean density is 1.4 g per cm³; the density at the center is about 100 g per cm³; the density at the photosphere is 10^{-8} g per cm³. Energy production in the Sun is at the rate of 2 ergs per g sec, largely as a consequence of the proton-proton chain, forming helium. It is interesting to note that the extreme brightness of the Sun is more a consequence of its large mass than a high metabolic rate, for a comparable mass of living, breathing humans would generate 5000 times as much heat as the Sun.

The visible surface of the Sun, the photosphere, has a diameter of 1.4×10^{6} km. On the other hand, the visible surface is an imponderable thing, being the result of a tenuous distribution of negative hydrogen ions, rather than any substantial surface. Thus it might be better to give a much smaller diameter, such as 0.8×10^{6} km, for the Sun itself, referring to everything outside the core as the solar atmosphere. For it is outside the core that the convective churning takes place, resembling somewhat the meteorological effects that occur on Earth as a result of the daytime surface heating. The convective zone in the Sun begins about 0.5×10^6 km from the center of the Sun and ends near the top of the negative hydrogen-ion clouds that form the visible surface.

The churning motions in the convective zone are as fast as 1 km per sec in the upper regions and evidently lead to the small (1000-km) convective cells, called granules, which are observed to cover the photosphere. In some way the convective motions may also be responsible for the spicules, which appear to be 30 km per sec jets of gas spurting up continually over the entire surface of the Sun.

Above the 6000°K photosphere the temperature of the gas decreases slightly and then rises rapidly to form the solar corona, which is a region of hot (10^{6}°K), tenuous, ionized gas extending far out from the Sun into interplanetary space. Apparently the corona is heated by the dissipation of sound waves and hydromagnetic waves generated in the convective zone.[2] During an eclipse of the Sun by the Moon the corona can be observed as far as 20 solar radii (14×10^6 km) into space. The corona is visible largely because white light from the photosphere is scattered by the free electrons of the corona.

The Sun is observed to have a general dipole magnetic field of about 1 gauss extending up through the negative hydrogen-ion clouds; at present the lines of force extend outward from the south polar region and in at the north polar region. The field is observed to reverse in periods of years.[3] In the equatorial regions the magnetic field is constantly shifting and is too disordered to be assigned any general topological character. It appears to have an average strength of the order of 1 gauss, though there is recent indication that over the dimensions of one granule the local field intensity may be as large as ± 5 gauss.

Into this picture of the quiescent Sun there regularly intrudes, on a 22-year cycle, regions of disturbance collectively called *solar activity*. The most obvious disturbance is the sunspot, often visible to the naked eye at sunrise or sunset. The sunspot is a cool (4500°K) region visible as a dark spot in the negative hydrogen-ion clouds. The sunspots have associated with them magnetic fields up to 3000 gauss and characteristic dimensions of the order of 10^4 km. If the lower temperature of the sunspot observed in the photospheric clouds should extend to a depth as great as the observed width of the spot, then the magnetic field of the sunspot is probably nothing more than a sweeping up of the general 1-gauss field by the anticyclonic motions of the gas in the spot. Because of their conspicuous nature, the occurrence of sunspots is often used as

an index of solar activity.   It should be noted, however, that the sunspot
may be only one symptom of the progress of much deeper lying processes.
Therefore the number of visible sunspots must not be interpreted too
literally as "solar activity."

Sunspots usually form in the broad, active regions which appear at the
photosphere during the years of solar activity.   The active regions
exhibit enhanced emission in calcium and generally enhanced magnetic
fields (up to several gauss over extended regions of the photosphere).
What lies in the murk beneath an active region we do not know.   Above
them, we find cool, bright clouds of gas, called quiescent prominences,
apparently suspended in the solar magnetic fields.   One also finds active
prominences which surge out from the photosphere, usually draining
back but sometimes disappearing 10^5 or more kilometers above the solar
surface.   The corona associated with or lying above an active region
is hotter than the 1 to 2 $\times$ 10^6°K corona of the quiescent Sun, being 2 to
3 $\times$ 10^6°K, or even 4 $\times$ 10^6°K following particularly active occasions.

The solar flare is, so far as interplanetary and terrestrial effects are
concerned, perhaps the most important aspect of the visible solar activity.
Ultraviolet and X rays may be absorbed at Earth within minutes of the
flare onset.   The large flares herald a sudden outburst of solar activity, the
results of which may be observed at Earth one or two days later as aurorae,
magnetic storms, cosmic-ray decreases, etc.   A solar flare is a bright
cloud materializing above the photosphere in a period of a few minutes
and lasting perhaps half an hour.   Flares are associated with sunspots
and particularly with sunspot groups.   They range in size and brightness
from the barely visible class 1 flare, which may appear every 30 min or so
in an active region, to the giant class 3+ flare, which may be brighter
than the neighboring photosphere and occur but a few times a year.   A
large flare, with dimensions of the order of 4 $\times$ 10^4 km, may radiate
10^{32} to 10^{33} ergs of energy during its life of 10^3 sec.   This is so much
energy that its only plausible source is the annihilation of magnetic
fields of 500 gauss or more.   The large flare is an indication that the coronal temperature over the active region may increase by 1 to 2 $\times$ 10^6°K.

The individual active regions in the Sun often maintain their identity
for several solar rotations ($\sim$27 days per rotation) so that the terrestrial
effects for which they are responsible show a 27-day recurrence tendency.

2. INTERPLANETARY SPACE

Consider the extension of the Sun into interplanetary space.   The
solar corona, with its 10^6°K temperature, is obviously entirely ionized.

Its composition is undoubtedly comparable with that of the bulk of the Sun, i.e., mainly hydrogen, with perhaps 1 in 10 or 20 atoms being helium, and a trace of the heavier elements. At a height of 3×10^5 km above the photosphere, the density is approximately $n = 3 \times 10^7$ atoms per cm³. For all practical purposes this may be regarded as 3×10^7 protons and 3×10^7 free electrons per cm³. The corona is visible largely as the result of the scattering of sunlight by the free electrons. Quantitative measurement of the intensity of scattered light has shown that the coronal electron density is continuous from the Sun out at least as far as the orbit of Earth, where the density has fallen to the order of 100 electrons per cm³. We may infer from this that the proton density is also $\sim 10^2$ per cubic centimeter at the orbit of Earth because the interplanetary medium must be electrically neutral. Chapman[5] has pointed out that this interplanetary gas may be nothing more than the hydrostatic extension of the normal $2 \times 10^{6\circ}$K solar corona in the solar gravitational field.

The original suggestion of Lindemann, that streams of ionized gas from the Sun are responsible for the geomagnetic storm and the aurora, is now generally accepted, largely because of the work of Chapman and Ferraro.[6,7] Observations show that, one or two days following a violent flare and solar eruption, the aurorae and the geomagnetic fluctuations greatly increase for a day or so. This is attributed to the effects of ionized gas ejected from the Sun with velocities of one or two thousand kilometers per second (so that the transit time to Earth at a distance of 1.5×10^{13} cm is a day or two).

The *direct* evidence supporting the view that ionized gas moves outward from the Sun is rather meager. It is based principally on the Biermann's[8] analysis of the motion of Type 1 comet tails. These comet tails consist largely of ions (such as CO and CN_2 molecular ions) and accelerate straight away from the Sun. Biermann pointed out that ionization and excitation of such tails, as well as the large observed acceleration away from the Sun, can be accounted for only as a consequence of solar corpuscular emission. He pointed out that while comets are a relatively rare occurrence, the indications are that material is always streaming out from the Sun in all directions. For the quiescent Sun Biermann suggested corpuscular streams with velocities of the order of 500 km per sec and densities of the order of 100 particles per cm³. This density is substantiated by the observed electron scattering of sunlight from interplanetary space. When the Sun is active, the comet tails suggest that the stream velocities may for brief periods reach 1500 km per sec and the densities may approach 10^4 per cubic centimeter. Biermann cautions that comet tails show evidence of magnetic fields, with their fine striations and helical motions, so that a simple interpretation of their motion may at best be only qualitatively correct. Thus, while we accept the comet analysis as a working hypothesis, it is nonetheless important that the corpuscular streams be observed directly from space vehicles in order to establish their nature in a more quantitative fashion.

Some of the strongest arguments for the existence and structure of magnetic fields in interplanetary space, and their solar origin, have come from cosmic-ray experiments over the past decade. This evidence is discussed in Chaps. 13 and 14.

To go beyond these few basic observations it becomes necessary to build a theoretical model, based on inference and indirect argument. The validity of any such model can be judged only by careful calculation, so that the quantitative results which a model produces can be compared with the number of *ad hoc* assumptions. Until direct observations are made in the geomagnetic field and in interplanetary space, any such models as one may construct must be regarded as a working hypothesis at best. It will be our purpose to outline a working model of the dynamical effects at the Sun and the way in which it appears that they may affect Earth.

3. SOLAR WIND

Let us begin with Biermann's comet analysis,[8] suggesting that corpuscular streams are more or less continuously issuing from the Sun with 500 km per sec velocities. Instead of the usual assumption that the solar corona is in hydrostatic equilibrium, we admit of the possibility that it may be expanding hydrodynamically. With a simple spherically symmetric coronal model it is easily shown[9] that if the observed $2 \times 10^{6°}$K temperature is maintained to 5 solar radii, then a 500 km per sec expansion with a density of 100 ions per cm^3 at the orbit of Earth is the result. The coronal temperature can be observed as far out as 3 solar radii, and there is no sign of the temperature decreasing. Thus it is tempting to assume that Biermann's corpuscular streams may be the result of a simple hydrodynamic expansion of the solar corona. Accordingly, we should prefer a hydrodynamic terminology. We shall refer to the 500 km per sec efflux of gas from the Sun as the *solar wind*. And we shall construct our model of the dynamical conditions in interplanetary space with no other solar emission than this hydrodynamic solar wind, which of course may vary with solar activity within the range already indicated.

4. MAGNETIC FIELDS IN INTERPLANETARY SPACE

To progress further with our understanding of the extension of the Sun into interplanetary space, we must discuss some of the dynamical properties of the interplanetary gas. For instance, the mean free path of a thermal proton in interplanetary space (where the density is 100 ions per cm) is of the order of 10^5 km if the gas is $10^{4}°$K, and 10^7 km if $10^{5}°$K. The electrical conductivity is approximately $10^7 T^{3/2}$ esu, or 10^{13} to 10^{15} esu, depending upon the temperature. Such a high electrical conductivity means that the gas will tend to carry with it any magnetic fields that are present. It can be shown (using the skin-depth formula) that the rate at which a material medium of electrical conductivity σ can drift across the lines of force of a magnetic field B of scale l is $c^2/l\sigma$ cm per sec. Thus if $lv\sigma/c^2 \gg 1$, where v is the velocity of the medium, the magnetic field is dragged along by the gas; the lines of force are "frozen" into the medium. As a consequence of the large scales associated with nearly all astrophysical phenomena, the magnetic Reynolds number[10] $lv\sigma/c^2$ is large. For instance, above a sunspot ($l \sim 10^4$ km) a temperature of $10^{4}°$K yields a magnetic Reynolds number of 10^6 with velocities of only 1 km per sec. The same velocity in the solar corona at $10^{6}°$K, and a scale of 10^5 km, yields 10^{10}. At the orbit of Earth, $10^{4}°$K and 1 km per sec yields 10^{10} because the scale is so large ($l = 10^{13}$ cm). We conclude that the coronal gas and the solar magnetic fields are inseparable. Where one goes, there also must go the other. This point was first emphasized by Alfvén.

Magnetic lines of force do not have ends. Each line is infinitely long, circling incommensurably round and round through the region occupied by the field. With such high magnetic Reynolds numbers, a given line of force must be regarded as a permanently connected topological entity. It may be pulled and stretched and twisted without limit, but its topology cannot be altered.[11] Thus it is convenient to think of the lines of force as infinitely extensible rubber bands. In this way the deformation by a given fluid motion is easily visualized.

Of course, a conducting fluid may flow freely *along* the magnetic lines of force, but if it flows in a direction perpendicular to the lines of force, it must carry the lines with it. The energy density or stress in a magnetic field is essentially $B^2/8\pi$. The energy density or stress in an ionized gas of N atoms per cm^3 and temperature T is essentially $2NkT$. If $B^2/8\pi > 2NkT$, then the magnetic field stress dominates, and the gas is effectively limited to flow along the lines of force. The field may have nearly a static-equilibrium configuration unless the gas has such large macroscopic velocity that the kinetic energy density $1/2NMv^2$ exceeds $B^2/8\pi$; i.e., only if the velocity v is highly supersonic will the field be distorted significantly by the gas motions.   On the other hand, if $B^2/8\pi < 2NkT$, then it is the fluid pressure which dominates and determines the magnetic configuration.   If the fluid has significant mass motion, it will carry the field with it.

To apply these principles to the Sun, consider the solar corona 3×10^5 km above the photosphere where $N = 3 \times 10^7$ and $T = 2 \times 10^{6\circ}$K. Then the gas pressure is 1.7×10^{-2} dyne per cm². The general solar field of 1 gauss carries a stress of 4×10^{-2} dyne per cm² so that the gas and field have comparable strengths.   Thus each may be expected to influence the motion and configuration of the other.   On the other hand, suppose we make the assumption that the solar dipole field extends to the orbit of Earth, which is at a distance of some 210 solar radii.   Then the 1 gauss observed in the photosphere yields 10^{-7} gauss at Earth.   The magnetic stress is accordingly 4×10^{-16} dyne per cm², whereas 100 atoms per cm³ at $10^{4\circ}$K yields 3×10^{-10} dyne per cm⁰.   Thus a hypothetical solar dipole field would be completely overwhelmed in interplanetary space and would be twisted and contorted out of recognition by the slightest interplanetary-gas motions.

In particular, the solar wind extends the lines of force of the general solar field into a radial configuration.   Each line of force is drawn out radially through interplanetary space for as far as the solar wind blows, and we have no way of estimating how far that might be except that it is beyond the orbit of Earth.   Somewhere far out in interplanetary space the lines of force issuing from one solar hemisphere cross the equatorial plane and return to the opposite hemisphere.   It is easily shown from geometrical considerations that if the lines of force of a 1-gauss field are extended radially from the Sun, the field density at the orbit of Earth will be close to 2×10^{-5} gauss.   Of course, the lines of force are really only approximately radial, so that 2×10^{-5} gauss is only an approximate density.   In the first place, the Sun rotates about once each 27 days so that the lines of force spiral somewhat, being inclined perhaps 20 to 30° to the radial direction at the orbit of Earth.   In the second place, within about one or two solar radii of the Sun, the magnetic field is sufficiently strong that it partially guides the coronal expansion, tending somewhat to concentrate the outward flow toward the equatorial plane.   Thus, though we shall speak of the "radial" solar field, it must be remembered that the concept is only a rough working model.

If one investigates the stability of the radial solar field, he finds that there are two mechanisms which may cause disorder beyond the orbit of Earth.[12]   As already noted, the mean free path of an ion in the solar wind has become rather long, 10^5 to 10^7 km, by the time the orbit of Earth is reached so that the expansion of the outward-flowing gas perpendicular to the radial direction will decrease the thermal motions in that direction without a corresponding decrease in the radial direction.   Near the orbit of Earth, where the magnetic field is still principally radial, this anisotropy in the thermal motions may lead to "hose instability," in which the dominant thermal motions along the lines of force increase any kink in the field with their centrifugal force.   Far beyond the orbit of Earth, where the increased spiraling makes the field more nearly azimuthal, the anisotropy leads to a clumping of the field with particles accumulating in the regions of weak field.   The scale of such disorders would appear to be of the order of 10^6 km.

The development of many of our theoretical ideas, such as both the radial field inside the orbit of Earth and the disordered field outside, have come as a result of the cosmic-ray evidence to be discussed in a later section.

5. INTERPLANETARY DYNAMICAL EFFECTS PRODUCED BY THE ACTIVE SUN

Large solar flares usually herald an increase in the local coronal temperature, which sometimes rises to $4 \times 10^{6°}$K.   It is readily shown from the hydrodynamic equations that such a sudden increase of temperature and gas pressure will lead to an enormous outburst of solar gas, rushing out into interplanetary space.   Since the conducting gas carries with it its central magnetic field and since no field-free regions are observed on the Sun, it follows that there can be no field-free plasma cloud from the Sun in interplanetary space.   The outward expanding gas forms a shock wave of considerable strength.   The shock will have a sharp front ($\leq 10^4$ km) in spite of the very long mean free paths, for in the absence of collisions there is the radial solar field, which may produce a shock interaction via the hose instability.

The high velocity behind the front will draw out the lines of force from the Sun in a more nearly radial direction than had the slower-moving gas ahead, so that a jog in the lines of force at the front must result.   In the jog the field density may be increased by as much as a factor of 10, and it will be shown later that this may have important cosmic-ray effects.

Gold and Morrison suggested some years ago that the outburst of gas associated with a solar flare may inflate portions of the magnetic field associated with the sunspot group containing the flare.   In this way a long tongue of reentrant field would be pushed out from the Sun, sweeping across the orbit of Earth a day or two after the flare.[13] They have argued that such a magnetic tongue is necessary to account for certain observed cosmic-ray phenomena, which will be discussed later. Piddington has recently suggested a somewhat similar model.[14] Whether such tongues, rooted in the Sun, must be added to the solar wind and radial field model is a question which will probably have to be decided by direct observation of solar wind density and velocity, along with simultaneous magnetometer and cosmic-ray intensity measurements.

Now consider the terrestrial effects of the solar wind. The solar wind blowing against the geomagnetic field can push tongues of gas in between the lines of force to a depth where the magnetic stress density becomes comparable with the pressure of the wind. The solar wind of 500 km per sec and 100 ions per cm^3, produced by the quiet Sun, can in the equatorial plane intrude into the geomagnetic field to within about 5 Earth's radii of the center of Earth, where the field is $\sim 3 \times 10^{-3}$ gauss. The geomagnetic lines of force crossing the equatorial plane at 5 Earth's radii come down to the surface of Earth about 25° from the geomagnetic poles. All lines of force reaching the surface nearer to the poles than 25° must be seriously disturbed by the solar wind.[15] And in fact, one observes perpetual geomagnetic agitation at polar geomagnetic stations. Further, in the auroral zone, normally lying 20 to 25° from the geomagnetic poles, one observes an aurora every clear night, so that the aurora does indeed occur at the base of those lines of force which go out to the solar wind and thereby communicate with material from the Sun. When the solar wind is high, as a consequence of solar activity, the wind may intrude to within about 1½ or 2 Earth's radii, which is in agreement with the observation that the aurora may then be observed at 30 to 50° geomagnetic latitude. Such high solar winds may be able to account in a simple way for the observed primary auroral proton spectrum.[15]

It has been believed for a long time that the shock wave from a solar outburst was responsible for the sudden commencement of the geomagnetic storm,[6] and it has been shown[16] recently that field free plasma injected into the geomagnetic field, by intrusive tongues of solar wind, can account for the main phase of the geomagnetic storm, in which the horizontal component at the surface of Earth decreases by perhaps 10^{-3} gauss for a day or two.

Thus there is substantiating geophysical evidence for both the quiet day and the enhanced solar wind. In a later section we shall discuss the cosmic-ray evidence.

REFERENCES

1. G. P. Kuiper: *The Sun* (University of Chicago Press, 1953).
2. L. Biermann: *Z. Astrophys.*, *25*, 161 (1949).
   M. Schwarzschild: *Astrophys. J.*, *107*, 1 (1948).
   H. Alfvén: *Monthly Not. Roy. Astron. Soc.*, *107*, 211 (1947).
   T. G. Cowling: *Monthly Not. Roy. Astron. Soc.*, *116*, 114 (1956).
   J. H. Piddington: *Monthly Not. Roy. Astron. Soc.*, *116*, 314 (1956).
   E. N. Parker: *Astrophys. J.*, *128*, 677 (1958).
3. H. D. Babcock, *Astrophys. J.*, *130*, 364 (1959).
4. A. Behr and H. Siedentopf: *Z. Astrophys.*, *32*, 19 (1953).
5. S. Chapman: *Smithsonian Contr. Astrophys.*, *2*, 1 (1957); in M. Zelikoff (ed.),
   Threshold of Space (Pergamon Press, London, 1958).
6. S. Chapman and V. C. A. Ferraro: *Terr. Mag. and Atm. Elec.*, *36*, *77*, 171 (1936);
   37, 147, 421 (1932); *38*, 79 (1933); *45*, 245 (1950).
7. V. C. A. Ferraro: *J. Geophys. Research*, *57*, 15 (1952).
8. L. Biermann: *Z. Astrophys.*, *29*, 274 (1951); *Z. Naturforsch.*, *7a*, 127 (1952);
   Observatory, *77*, 109 (1957).
9. E. N. Parker: *Astrophys. J.*, *128*, 664 (1958).
10. W. M. Elsasser: *Phys. Rev.*, *95*, 1 (1954).
11. E. N. Parker and M. Krook: *Astrophys. J.*, *124*, 214 (1956).
12. E. N. Parker: *Phys. Rev.*, *109*, 1874 (1958).
13. G. Cocconi, T. Gold, K. Greisen, S. Hayakawa, and P. Morrison: *Nuovo Cimento*
    X, Suppl. 8, 161 (1958).
14. J. H. Piddington: *Phys. Rev.*, *112*, 599 (1958).
15. E. N. Parker: *Phys. Fluids*, *1*, 171 (1958).
16. A. J. Dessler and E. N. Parker: *J. Geophys. Research* (in publication, 1959).

13

THE ACCELERATION AND PROPAGATION OF PARTICLES WITHIN THE SOLAR SYSTEM

J. A. Simpson

1. THE EXPERIMENTAL DATA

Of the various phenomena leading to the acceleration of charged particles in the solar system, the most energetic is the solar-flare production of cosmic-ray particles. This is the only process for which the birth of cosmic rays has so far been observed. Since their first detection in 1942 there have been five events[*] which clearly fulfill the condition of a particle-intensity increase following closely a solar flare; however, only the last of the five events—the flare of Feb. 23, 1956—provided undisputed evidence for particle acceleration to relativistic energies in the vicinity of the solar flare and for particle storage in magnetic fields in the interplanetary medium.[1] Therefore we discuss this event in detail as an example of the type of phenomenon leading to the production of relativistic particles and to their use for probing magnetic fields in the

[*] A short-lived burst of relativistic particles appeared on May 4, 1960, along with nonrelativistic protons which escaped from the inner solar system gradually over a period of 3 to 4 days following the solar flare.

interplanetary medium.   Recently, measurements at very high altitude
have revealed intense fluxes of nonrelativistic particles occurring much
more frequently from large solar flares, and these events will also be
reviewed.   These phenomena and their interpretation provide a basis
for future experiments in rockets and space probes to extend our knowledge of the acceleration mechanism and composition of the radiations
at even lower energies, where, as shown in Fig. 1 of Chap. 11, very little
is known about energetic particles in nature between 0 to 10^7 ev.

Within the chromosphere and between a pair of sunspots there often
occurs a sudden increase in the optical and radio emission of much greater
intensity than the chromospheric and coronal background emissions.

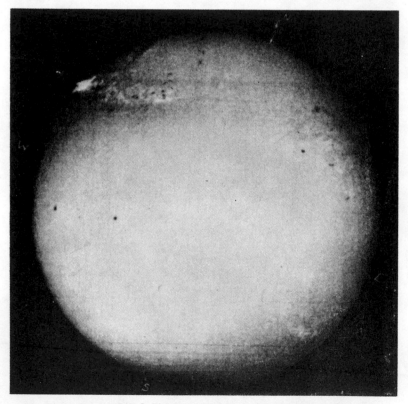

FIG 1. The great solar flare of Feb 23, 1956, recorded in the
light of H_α (see Ref. 2).

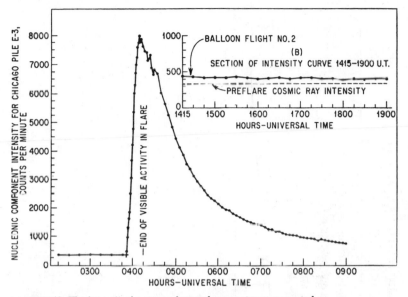

FIG. 2. The intensity increase of secondary neutrons generated in the atmosphere from primary solar-flare protons. These observations were obtained with a neutron monitor pile at Chicago.

The intensity may rise to a maximum value within minutes and continue at a high level for times of an hour or more. From the emission in H_α and from the cosmic-ray evidence, the total energy expended in solar flares extends over a range of 10^{30} to 10^{33} ergs, released in solar volumes $\leq 10^{29}$ cm³. Since the total energy content of the entire solar corona and chromosphere is less than the flare energy, the energy required for immediate release in a flare event must have been stored in the vicinity of the flare prior to the onset of the event and could not have been drained from the surrounding regions. This implies that the energy was stored within the local magnetic fields between the sunspots. If the magnetic fields are not stable and release some of their energy as kinetic energy, then in the motion of the magnetic fields interacting with the surrounding plasma, it is not unreasonable to expect the appearance of both electromagnetic radiation and charged-particle acceleration. Thus the large solar flare is a readily distinguished process in solar physics which occurs at unpredicted times and is statistically related with special

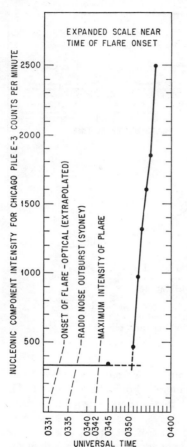

FIG. 3. The time sequence of phenomena related to the solar flare and solar protons.

electromagnetically active regions on the Sun. Figure 1 shows the H_α recording of the flare for Feb. 23, 1956.[2] White-light emission was also observed. From the fact that the radio-emission frequencies rapidly descended downward in time to approximately 19 Mc, it appears that the location for the source of energy release extended rapidly outward to at least a solar radius beyond the photosphere.

We emphasize here the energetic-particle observations. By 0341 UT, the solar particles began to arrive within special regions of the geomagnetic field. The general form of a cosmic-ray increase resulting from the solar flare is shown in Figs. 2 and 3. Continuous measurements are obtained by detecting the secondary nucleonic (neutron) or meson components generated by the primary radiation. The initial time of intensity increase following the preflare level of intensity is defined as the onset time. One of the characteristics discovered regarding the arrival of the first particles from the flare is that the highest-energy particles appear to arrive ahead of the low-energy particles, the spread in time being the order of 10 to 15 min for an energy range of 10 Bev for protons.[3] This has been defined as a dispersion effect and is shown in Figs. 4 and 5 for the Feb. 23, 1956, flare. Examples of prompt and delayed onset times are shown in Fig. 4 taken from a world-wide distribution of cosmic-ray-intensity recorders. From the dependence of intensity with time at late times, the primary flare particle spectrum in Fig. 6 has been constructed taking advantage of the geomagnetic field analysis possible for a world-wide distribution of neutron intensity monitors. From these data theoretical models may be constructed for the production,

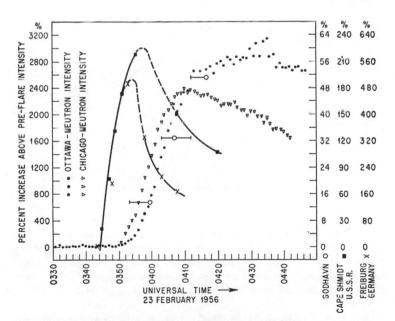

FIG. 4. Detectors located in different parts of the geomagnetic field respond to different energies of solar protons provided they come from a point source—the impact-zone effect.

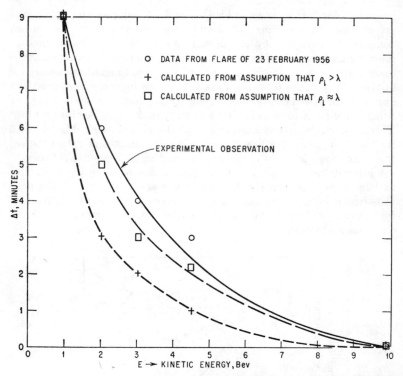

FIG. 5. The spread in time of the first arriving particles as a function of energy. This is called the dispersion effect and probably results from particle diffusion through relatively intense but irregular magnetic fields at the Sun. ρi is the Larmor radius of the charged particle inside the magnetic irregularity of scale size λ.

propagation, and escape of solar cosmic rays from the solar system. Since deductions on the likely acceleration process and release of energy at the source depend upon the consequences of the analysis of experimental data regarding their propagation and storage, especially relative to the total energies involved, the problem of production is deferred until later.

The progress of the Feb. 23, 1956, event may be described as follows: The first arriving particles come to the earth from a limited-source direction in the sky. This apparent source is a relatively large area which includes the Sun. Initially the particles are of the highest energies in the flare spectrum; subsequently the whole sky becomes "illuminated" with particles extending to lower energies; for these low-energy particles, and late-arriving high-energy particles, there appears to be remarkable isotropy. Following the onset of isotropy, the particle intensity gradually diminishes with the flare particle spectrum essentially unchanged as shown in Fig. 6, while the particles escape from the magnetic fields which store them in the solar system. The intensity at the Earth is observed to diminish to its preflare level within a period of 15 to 20 hr.

The time sequence of events immediately suggests three intervals in the development of the cosmic-ray flare:

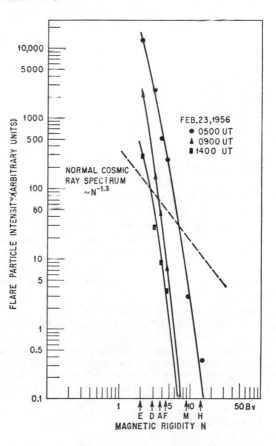

FIG. 6. The differential magnetic rigidity spectrum for the solar protons after particle storage or trapping in the solar system had taken over. Here the particle magnetic rigidity $N = pc/Ze$, where p is momentum, c is velocity of light, Ze is the particle charge, N is measured in volts. The scale is given in Bv = billion volts.

1. Beginning with the initial release of high-energy particles to the time when the cosmic-ray intensity reaches a maximum at the Earth, the particles come from a limited source direction. This period of time is of the order 10 min to $\frac{1}{2}$ hr, depending upon the solar-flare event.

2. A brief period of transition sets in when particles begin to arrive from directions other than the source. This suggests that particles arrive late following scattering or passage through preferred magnetic channels in the magnetic fields connecting the Earth and the Sun region.

3. At late times, when isotropy has been established, all evidence for the release of energy in the solar-flare region has vanished, but the influx of cosmic-ray particles at the Earth continues for many hours. This fact and the fact that no source direction persists for even the highest-energy particles strongly support the view that the Sun accelerates particles only during a short interval of time and that the particles are trapped and stored in interplanetary magnetic fields subsequently to be lost from the solar system or to arrive at the Earth. The decay mode of the particles from the vicinity of the Earth opens the possibility for determining the characteristics of the storage magnetic fields. This kind of evidence for the storage of charged particles is at present the strongest evidence for the existence of interplanetary magnetic fields.*

It is known from the arrival of solar protons at the equator from the vertical over Huancayo, Peru, that particles in excess of 24 Bev must have been present in the flare spectrum. The lowest energies detected were of the order of 1 to 2 Bev measured at high latitudes by balloon flights. The absorption mean free path was consistent with the assumption that the radiation was mainly, or entirely, protons. At even lower energies, one must turn to indirect evidence regarding the spectrum below 100 Mev. From the analysis of ionospheric forward-scatter radio measurements by Bailey[4] and from the interpretation of certain types of cosmic-noise absorption from more recent events by Little, Reid, and Leinbach,[5] it seems clear that at the time of the Feb. 23, 1956, flare, there was production of very low energy particles, probably extending below ~10 Mev for protons with a relatively flat spectrum. Indeed,

---

* Space probe Pioneer V, launched Mar. 11, 1960, carried a magnetometer and charged-particle detectors. The magnetometer shows directly the existence of weak fields in interplanetary space; see P. J. Coleman, Jr., L. Davis, and C. P. Sonett, *Phys. Rev. Letters*, *5*, 43 (1960). The charged-particle observations following the solar flare of Mar. 30, 1960, show that these fields must be of large scale and are manipulated by solar plasma; see C. Y. Fan, P. Meyer, and J. A. Simpson, *Phys. Rev. Letters*, *5*, 269 (1960).

as we discuss later, there is strong evidence that many large flares produce these nonrelativistic particles which have access to the Earth.

The spectrum shown in Fig. 6 is the spectrum of stored particles. The spectrum at time of production is unknown, but presumably is less energy-dependent since high-energy particles in a storage field tend to escape more readily than low-energy particles to form a steeper spectrum than originally existed. The composition of the radiation from the flare is consistent, the bulk of the radiation being protons, although a large component of singly and doubly ionized helium nuclei is by no means excluded. The existence of these nuclei and heavier elements for this flare was not determined. This constitutes one of the most important problems for study with satellites and space probes. From evidence obtained at low energies during at least one other flare, it seems that alpha particles may be accelerated by the Sun.[6]

2. MAGNETIC FIELDS TO ACCOUNT FOR THE PROPAGATION, STORAGE, AND ESCAPE OF SOLAR COSMIC RADIATION

An explanation for the foregoing evidence requires the existence of storage or trapping magnetic fields. At present we are only at the threshold of understanding solar electrodynamic phenomena and dilute plasmas, and therefore proposals for the origin and structure of interplanetary magnetic fields are numerous and in dispute. However, the requirements imposed by the dispersion, anisotropy, and subsequent isotropic storage of solar cosmic rays considerably limit these possibilities and, in fact, provide the most direct evidence for the existence of interplanetary magnetic fields within the inner solar system. This fact has stimulated investigations on the origins of these fields, from which some fairly clear, but still controversial, ideas are beginning to emerge. Some of the main lines of thought at the present time have been summarized in Chap. 12 and are largely based upon our increasing knowledge of the propagation of charged particles in the solar system. The solar origin of the major magnetic fields in the interplanetary medium seems clear, and as a result, the interplanetary magnetic fields must be assumed to change with time, especially throughout the progress of the solar activity cycle. Thus one of the basic difficulties in attempting to obtain a general picture of the particle motions in magnetic fields is that the field configurations may change from time to time and from event to event. The main problem at present is therefore to understand the principal features of the field structure, leaving the details to be filled in for the individual events under study.

We begin by considering what the requirements are for the storage of cosmic-ray particles once the radiation arriving at the Earth appears isotropic. We note that the first arriving particles appeared to come from a definite source direction, including the Sun. From the details of this evidence, the intervening magnetic fields could not have been highly disordered and strong so as to produce large scattering of the high-energy particles between the Sun and the Earth. This leaves two possibilities: (1) either there was a negligible field between the coronal fields of the Sun and the Earth, or (2) there was an approximately radial field connecting the Sun and the Earth which would not destroy the approximately plane-wave character of the advancing front of radiation in the initial stages of propagation.

Now a generally smooth field between the Sun and the Earth may either be an over-all solar radial field such as suggested in Chap. 12, or it might be a much more local channellike field such as suggested by Cocconi, Gold, et al.[7]—a field whose lines ålmost return directly to the Sun and occupy only a small tonguelike region of space. Because of the rotation of the Earth, it is clear that any fields which have existed for appreciable periods of time tend to spiral because of the angular momentum imparted to the interplanetary gas by solar rotation. At present there is serious doubt that the radial field itself could store the particles, so they decay away with a period of order 1 hr over the 10- or 15-hour increase of intensity in the manner observed. Another possibility is to assume that the storage is accomplished mainly by requiring that the solar particles, although readily moving outward from the Sun to at least 1 A.U., encounter at greater radial distances disordered magnetic fields which prevent their immediate free escape into the Galaxy.[1] The particles at these distances and beyond therefore undergo scattering and diffusion through disordered magnetic field regions before escape. The problem then becomes one of describing the parameters of this diffusion and deciding from a simple model whether the time constants are consistent with the observation. An idealized model based upon these thoughts has been worked out.

It should be pointed out that there are two extreme ways of treating the motion of charged particles in magnetic fields. On the one hand, for fields that are sufficiently smooth and only slowly changing in direction and intensity with time, the particle trajectories can be considered as spiral motions either described point by point in detail, or if the particles have small Larmor radii, a guiding-center approximation may be invoked. If, however, the field varies rapidly in intensity from one point to another and there are interspersed regions of high field intensity and low field intensity, and if, in addition, the scale size of the intense-field regions are not greatly different from the Larmor radii of the particles, we may describe the particle motion as a diffusionlike process in which the charged particles "collide" with the high-intensity-field regions and scatter, but propagate in approximately straight lines while in the low-field regions. We define this as the "diffusion" of charged particles through magnetic fields. Clearly, the coefficient of diffusion for high-energy particles is a function of particle energy and the diffusion coefficient

$$K(E) = \left(\frac{c}{3}\right) L(E)$$

where $L(E)$ is the energy-dependent mean free path.

As an example of the application of the diffusion concept, consider a simplified cross section of the inner solar system as shown in Fig. 7. For simplicity we make this heliocentric system entirely symmetrical and assume that either radial fields or negligibly small fields are dominant between the vicinity of the Sun and a distance ≥ 1 A.U. Beyond this region there is the question of the behavior of radial fields or, indeed, the

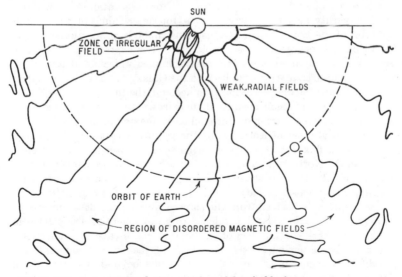

SUN

ZONE OF IRREGULAR FIELD

WEAK RADIAL FIELDS

E

ORBIT OF EARTH

REGION OF DISORDERED MAGNETIC FIELDS

FIG. 7. This is a simplified theoretical model suitable for calculating the consequences of storage and escape by particle diffusion in magnetic fields.

fields carried by any cloudlike plasma. It seems likely that disordered magnetic fields develop: one mechanism for producing disordered fields has been discussed in Chap. 12 to account for the model proposed here. It can be shown that a value of $B_{rms} \approx 10^{-5}$ gauss in the disordered region is sufficient to provide the right-order holdup for the particles within the inner region. The general idea, then, is that in the inner solar system the burst of radiation is stored; gradually the particles leak out of this region by diffusion through the disordered magnetic field barrier into the Galaxy. If $J(E)$ represents the density of cosmic-ray particles with energies in the range E and $E + dE$, then for this model $J(E)$ varies according to the diffusion equation

$$\frac{\partial J(E)}{\partial t} = K(E)\nabla^2 J(E)$$

The equation

$$J(E) = \frac{C}{(\pi k t)^{3/2}} \exp \frac{-r^2}{\pi k t}$$

is a special solution of the above differential equation under the assumption that a burst of particle radiation occurs at $t = 0$ and at the origin, $r = 0$, of an infinitely diffusing medium. For observations of changes in particle density near the source, that is, for small values of r (including the orbit of the Earth), then $J(E)$ is approximately proportional to $1/t^{3/2}$ for all particle energies. The simple power-law expression, however, is overtaken by the onset of an exponential intensity decline at late times, arising from the escape of particles into the Galaxy at the outer boundary of the diffusing barrier. Taking into account the finite diffusing depth, noting that the diffusion coefficient increases with particle energy, and observing that the interior region is filled to maximum density at about 0358 UT (beginning of isotropy for the radiation reaching the Earth), the incoming flux $J(E,t)$ has been fitted to the low-energy data from a station in the Northern and a station in the Southern Hemisphere for the flare of Feb. 23, 1956, as shown in Fig. 8. The data indicate that if the diffusing region exists in nature, it has a depth of approximately 5 A.U.

This depth was derived from the elapsed time for the decay process to go over from a power-law dependence to an exponential decay (that is, conditions where the number of particles which escape is proportional to the number of particles present). To fulfill these requirements, B_{rms} in the diffusing region must be $\sim 2 \times 10^{-5}$ gauss beyond the orbit of the Earth. One of the remarkable features of the observed flare spectrum at late times is the constancy of the spectral shape with time. This is predicted for observations made inside an enclosed diffusing region.

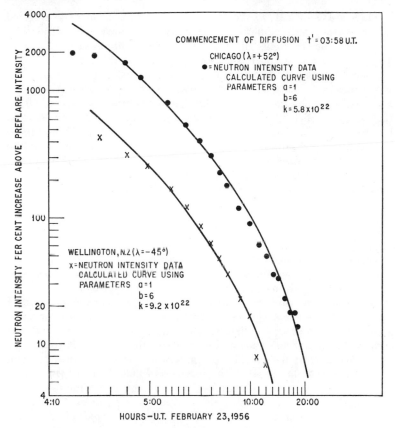

FIG. 8. Comparison of calculated results of diffusion with experimental observations in both hemispheres for solar-flare particles.

It is interesting to note that an earlier large flare producing solar cosmic rays on Nov. 19, 1949, also leads to the conclusion that interplanetary magnetic fields are required for storage but that the decay process was almost entirely exponential. This implies for the diffusion storage model that the magnetic field diffusion barrier between the Earth and the Galaxy was relatively "thin" at that time. The storage in radial or smooth magnetic fields does not lead to the prediction of exponential solutions for the escape of particles from the storage regions.

There are valid criticisms to be leveled against all the models suggested above. Also, the modulation of primary cosmic-ray flux of nonsolar origin and the recurrence of modulation effects, discussed in Chap. 14, as well as terrestrial effects such as the geomagnetic storm, place additional conditions on theoretical models for plasmas and fields in space. Experiments to study directly the magnetic fields, plasmas, and energetic particles may determine the dominant structure of the interplanetary magnetic fields.* The foregoing arguments may be summarized by the statement that the storage of solar-cosmic-ray particles can be accomplished by suitable interplanetary magnetic fields and that the cosmic-ray evidence is the strongest argument for these fields. Beyond this, our knowledge at present does not allow a decision as to which model is correct for the structure of the field. Presumably, a mixture of these possibilities represents the physical situation at any given time, and an identification of a dominant structural form may be difficult to achieve.

One of the interesting observations first noted for the flare of February, 1956, was the dispersion effect shown in Figs. 4 and 5. This effect does not occur in the geomagnetic field,† but rather is most likely a phenomenon associated with magnetic fields close to the solar source. The explanation may be that irregularities in the general solar magnetic field extending far out into the weak corona require that particles initially accelerated at or near the flare site undergo random walk through the coronal magnetic field region and escape into the weaker interplanetary field structure. If the irregularities in the magnetic fields near the Sun are of suitable scale size, then the particles of higher energy are able to escape more rapidly than particles of lower energy—with the result that an observer at Earth detecting the first arriving particles outside this diffusing region around the Sun would find high-energy particles to which are added at later times lower- and lower-energy particles in the beam. The parameters available at the present time for the description of the magnetic fields and the particle motions indicate that the diffusion times are of the right order of magnitude to account for the approximately 10-min delay between the first arrival of 10-Bev protons and 1-Bev protons in the flare of February, 1956, as shown in Fig. 5. This dispersion effect was also a characteristic of the Nov. 19, 1949, flare. Alternatively,

---

* See note on page 246.

† Recent direct measurements of solar-flare protons outside the storage region of the geomagnetic field show that the storage is not connected with the geomagnetic field; see, for example, the results from Pioneer V, C. Y. Fan, P. Meyer, and J. A. Simpson, *J. Geophys. Res.*, 65, 1862 (1960), and R. L. Arnoldy, R. A. Hoffman, and J. R. Winckler, *J. Geophys. Res.*, 65, 3004 (1960).

it may be that the dispersion effect arises almost at the flare site as a consequence of the relatively intense but disordered magnetic fields which follow the sudden release of energy through magnetic field instabilities.

3. THE FLARE ENERGY AND ITS SOURCE

Almost any of the models provides an estimate for the total kinetic energy imparted to the solar-flare cosmic-ray particles; for the flare of February, 1956, energy of the order of 10^{30} ergs was carried away from the source by solar cosmic rays. It is difficult to reduce this energy estimate an order of magnitude by describing special models having smaller storage volumes since they generally open up other propagation channels by which particles may rapidly escape from the source to the Galaxy, thereby posing an increased power load upon the source. Various calculations suggest that the total energy of the flare was well in excess of 10^{32} ergs, and it follows that less than 1 per cent of this energy was required for injecting relativistic particles. From the estimates of the visible flare volume, the average energy density available for the flare phenomena was greater than 2×10^3 ergs per cm^3. Since the average thermal energy density of the corona and the chromosphere is many orders of magnitude below this, it seems clear that the energy required for the solar flare was stored at the site of the flare prior to the energy release.

Considerable attention has been focused recently upon the magnetic fields which are known to exist in sunspot groups at the site of the flares between sunspot groups. It seems likely that the energy is stored at the flare site in magnetic fields which have received their energy from below the photosphere. Severny has recently provided observational evidence to indicate that these general lines of thinking are correct.[8] Since magnetic fields are observed to be present in the flare site after the flare has ceased, one must assign sufficiently large magnetic field intensities so that only a portion of the preflare field need be destroyed to provide the energy for the flare effect. This implies that magnetic fields must attain values of approximately 400 to 1000 gauss, or more, so that the energy release represents a reasonably small fraction of the total magnetic energy. To store such large amounts of energy, there have been several suggestions for a field-free configuration in order that there be no appreciable pressure exerted by the magnetic field upon the chromospheric gases in which they are imbedded. It has been shown[9] that

$$\frac{1}{c} (J \times \bar{B}) = (\nabla \times \bar{B}) \times \bar{B} = 0$$

or that electric currents flow only along lines of magnetic force so that $\nabla \times \bar{B} = \alpha\bar{B}$, α being a scalar function of space coordinates in a restricted volume.

For the acceleration of charged particles to cosmic-ray energies in the Galaxy, Fermi[10] proposed a mechanism based upon charged-particle collisions with advancing magnetic inhomogeneities in interstellar space. This mechanism, reduced in scale size with inhomogeneities established by unstable magnetic fields at the solar-flare site, is extremely attractive as the basic mechanism for the acceleration of ions in the flare volume. Times for acceleration to relativistic energy appear to be approximately 2 to 5 min, for this process.[11] The calculated-power-law spectrum for this mode of acceleration is not in disagreement with present experimental observations. Acceleration by the Fermi mechanism requires that the ions of all kinds of atoms present in the flare site also be accelerated. This prediction, along with the requirement that the particles in a Fermi mechanism are accelerated to approximately the same velocity (electrons would be accelerated to only $\frac{1}{1840}$ of the proton energy), suggests several direct experiments which might be carried out in space away from the Earth to test this hypothesis.

Because the magnetic fields in the region are intense, there have been suggestions that the only way that particles could escape from the solar region is to lose their charge temporarily through charge exchange. If this were so, only the decay products of neutrons and the neutrons themselves should be observed at considerable distances from the Sun following solar flares and no appreciable numbers of alpha particles should be detected.

4. NONRELATIVISTIC SOLAR PARTICLES ASSOCIATED WITH LARGE SOLAR FLARES

In addition to the relatively rare, large-scale events leading to the generation of relativistic particles discussed in the preceding section, there is now proof that other giant solar flares produce intense bursts of particles more frequently that do *not* attain relativistic energies. The evidence for these events during the past two or three years has partially come about because of improved techniques and increase of the total amount of time available to observers at very high altitudes, since particles below relativistic energy do not penetrate deep in the atmosphere even through their secondary production and hence are not observable at fixed stations on the Earth. We earlier noted for the flare of Feb. 23, 1956, that there was strong evidence for continuing the particle spectrum below 2-Bv magnetic rigidity and that most of this evidence came from ionospheric effects.[4]   Another technique for observing the ionospheric effects due to ionization by energetic, but nonrelativistic charged particles, has been developed recently by Little, Leinbach, and Reid based upon earlier ideas by Mitra and Shain.[5]   The absorption of cosmic radio noise passing through the ionosphere at approximately 27 Mc is observed, and the changes of this absorption due to increases of ionization in the 50- to 90-km level has been interpreted as the arrival of protons in the energy range 10 Mev and upward.   This has been called Type III absorption— a polar-cap absorption—and has been observed over a wide range of longitudes in the polar regions.   More than 30 of these events have been definitely identified within the last three years; and, within the last two years, the direct arrival of protons has been detected by high-altitude balloon observations.*

The magnetic rigidity spectrum of these protons has already been measured on two occasions by Ney et al. and is shown in Fig. 9 in comparison with the cosmic-ray spectrum.[12]

The data obtained from the onset time for cosmic-noise absorption after the solar flares provide convincing evidence that the particles are of solar origin.   From the published data[13] we have prepared a histogram in Fig. 10 showing the number of events versus time of transit to the Earth.   The actual times are less than shown because of uncertainties in determining the onset of absorption at Earth.

From the data obtained both by radio techniques and from direct particle detection, the sequence of events following the solar flare is as follows.   The first high-energy particles (order 10^2 Mev) arrive within 1 to 5 hr following the solar flare.   On only a few occasions has the first arrival of high-energy radiation been delayed more than 4 or 5 hr.   The flare producing the particles is generally accompanied by a strong, low-frequency solar-noise storm.†   The particles are observed to arrive over

* These protons have now been directly detected by instruments carried on space vehicles: (1) The presence of the radiation was first observed in the course of Explorer IV observations; see P. Rothwell and C. McIlwain, Nature, 184, 138 (1959).   (2) The first determination of a proton event and its time dependence, free from geomagnetic trapping fields, occurred Sept. 3, 1959, on Explorer VI; see C. Y. Fan, P. Meyer, and J. A. Simpson, in "Space Research," p. 963 (North-Holland Publishing Co., Amsterdam, 1960).   (3) The first observations of a series of solar proton bursts were obtained on Pioneer V at distances greater than 5×10^6 km from Earth; see footnotes on pp. 246 and 252.

† See, for example, H. R. Thompson and A. Maxwell, Planet. Space Sci., 2, 104 (1960); J. F. Denisse, A. Boischot, and M. Pick-Gutmann, in "Space Research," p. 637 (North-Holland Publishing Co., Amsterdam, 1960); A. N. Charakhchian, V. F. Tulinov, and T. N. Charakhchian, in ibid., p. 649.

the entire polar cap and down to latitudes limited only by the prevailing geomagnetic cutoff. Particles continue to arrive for a period of many hours to several days following a solar flare. In a manner typical for large solar flares, a low-energy beam or plasma region independently reaches the Earth within about a day following the flare to produce a

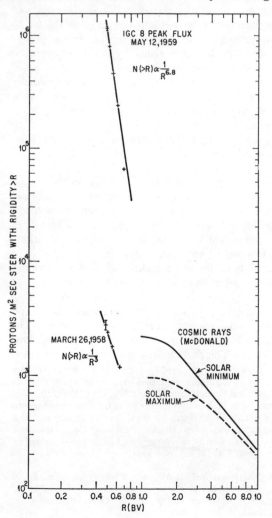

FIG. 9. The spectrum of nonrelativistic protons from the Sun measured in photonuclear emulsions by Ney et al.[36] $R = pc/Ze$ magnetic rigidity in Bv.

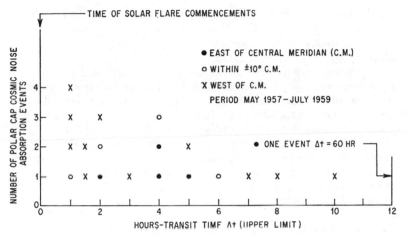

FIG. 10. Using published data by Reid and Leinbach,[13] the upper limit for the transit time Δt of solar protons to the Earth have been determined. The location of the initiating flare on the solar disk is indicated.

geomagnetic storm. The low-energy particles continue to arrive throughout the geomagnetic storm effect and, in addition, are observed at geomagnetic latitudes which normally forbid their arrival. These low-energy particles, in the range of a few hundred million electric volts, arrive only at low, forbidden latitudes during the intense periods of geomagnetic storms. An outstanding feature of these low-energy bursts is the very high flux values attained on some occasions. (Since preparation of this chapter, there have been four very large solar flares leading to enormous bursts of low-energy particles. The maximum fluxes attained have been of the order of 10^4 to 10^5 protons per cm^2 per sec)*.

Because of their prompt arrival at the Earth as shown in Fig. 10, it is certain that these particles are not initially released from the trapped Van Allen radiation belts, but rather come directly from regions of the Sun.†

Their existence, along with the small relativistic-flare-particle effect observed by Firor, and more recently observed by others using neutron

---

* J. Winckler et al., to be published; K. B. Fenton and J. A. Simpson, to be published; for a recent review see, for example, T. Obayashi and Y. Hakura, in "Space Research," p. 665 (North-Holland Publishing Co., Amsterdam, 1960).

† See also note † on page 252.

intensity monitors, indicates that all solar flares may produce particles, but that for most of the flares the particles are accelerated in a region below relativistic energies, and that from a position on the Earth, not all particle bursts can be detected.

All the evidence taken together points to the fact that the Sun is a prolific generator of particles covering over a 10-decade range of energies. And it would be indeed surprising if a solar flare were the only mechanism by which particles are accelerated in the vicinity of the Sun. In Fig. 1 of Chap. 11 we note that there is a range of over 10^8 where very little is known about the nature of accelerated particles. The distinct possibility exists that the Sun on the average is almost a continuous generator of energetic particles. However, at present, these conclusions still leave the Sun as only a small contributor to the general cosmic radiation of the Galaxy, as we shall now see.

5. SOLAR PARTICLES AND THE GALACTIC SPECTRUM

The importance of cosmic-ray solar flares for the origin of the cosmic radiation can be estimated from presently available data. If we first ask the question, what does the Sun contribute to the cosmic radiation without requiring further acceleration, we may take the relativistic-flare-particle spectrum given in Fig. 6 and assume that such a flare occurs on the Sun once every 10^7 sec. The main contribution will be relativistic particles of approximately 1 to 2 Bev for protons. Now the emission of 2-Bev protons to be maintained by stellar sources in the Galaxy is 5×10^{33} particles per sec based upon the assumption that each star in the Galaxy contributes equally to the mean flux observed at the Earth. Thus the ratio of average stellar production to average solar production is $(5 \times 10^{33})/(3 \times 10^{24}) = 10^9$. Estimates may be obtained from the point of view of energy. Estimates of the total cosmic-ray energy in the Galaxy give roughly 10^{54} to 10^{55} ergs, excluding possible storage of cosmic rays in the galactic halo. Taking into account the lifetime of the stored galactic cosmic rays, the energy input from all stellar sources is approximately 10^{44} ergs per sec, or 5×10^{28} ergs per sec for an "average" star. On this basis, the solar output power is too small by a factor of 10^6. Thus we see that the direct injection of *relativistic* particles by the Sun cannot be the "average" star process by which relativistic particles are contributed to the cosmic radiation.

On the other hand, it might be argued that processes like solar flares on the Sun merely provide the injection for further acceleration in the Galaxy. As an injector, the solar-flare process contributes particles over a wide range of *nonrelativistic* energies, and here the flux may be sufficiently high to provide a significant contribution for future galactic acceleration. There is increasing observational evidence that other classes of stars undergo flarelike phenomena that may provide more adequate stellar injection. Qualitatively, therefore, the Sun is being studied through the solar-flare process as an illustration of a basic mechanism in nature for the injection of particles extending up to and into the relativistic energy range.

REFERENCES

1. P. Meyer, E. N. Parker, and J. A. Simpson: *Phys. Rev.*, *104*, 768 (1956). J. Simpson: *Nuovo Cimento* X, Suppl. 10, 133 (1958).
2. Photograph in light of H_α by Kodiakanal Observatory, India.
3. R. Lust and J. A. Simpson: *Phys. Rev.*, *108*, 1563 (1957).
4. D. K. Bailey: *Proc. Inst. Radio Engrs.*, *47*, No. 2, 255 (1959).
5. C. G. Little and H. Leinbach: *Proc. Inst. Radio Engrs*, *46*, 334 (1958); *ibid.*, *47*, 315 (1959); H. Leinbach and G. C. Reid: *Phys. Rev. Letters*, *2*, 61 (1959).
6. E. P. Ney et al. (unpublished).
7. G. Cocconi, T. Gold, K. Greisen, S. Hayakawa, and P. Morrison: *Nuovo Cimento*, X, Suppl. 8, 161 (1958).
8. A. B. Severnyi: *Report of Joint Comm. Solar Terr. Relationships*, I.A.U., Moscow, U.S.S.R., 1958.
9. S. Lundquist: *Arkiv Fysik*, *2*, 361 (1950); R. Lust and A. Schluter: *Z. Astrophys.*, *34*, 265 (1954).
10. E. Fermi: *Phys. Rev.*, *81*, 683 (1951); *Progr. Theoret. Phys.*, *5*, 570 (1950).
11. E. N. Parker: *Phys. Rev*, *107*, 830 (1957).
12. E. P. Ney, J. R. Winckler, and P. S. Freier: *Phys. Rev. Letters*, *3*, 183 (1959).
13. G. C. Reid and H. Leinbach: *J. Geophys. Research*, *64*, 1801 (1959).

14 ≡

SOLAR MODULATION OF COSMIC RADIA-
TION AND OTHER ENERGETIC PARTICLES
REACHING THE EARTH

J. A. Simpson

1. THE EVIDENCE FOR MODULATION

The changes of secondary-cosmic-ray intensity as a function of time have been observed for over thirty years by detectors located deep in the atmosphere.[1] The radiations detected are the secondary particles generated by nuclear collisions of the primary cosmic radiation in the atmosphere of the Earth (Fig. 1). Only within the last decade has it been proved that the most important of these variations are a property of the primary beam of cosmic radiation arriving at the top of the atmosphere and not due, for example, to the atmospheric effects of the secondaries.[2] Using the measurements of the nucleonic component (neutrons and protons) as an indicator of the primary-cosmic-ray intensity, the effective range of magnetic rigidities has been greatly extended over which the geomagnetic field may be used as an analyzer of primary charged particles. This reveals that the variations are energy- or magnetic-rigidity-dependent and that the energy spectrum of the primary radiations changes with time. By analysis of the changes of intensity, it could also

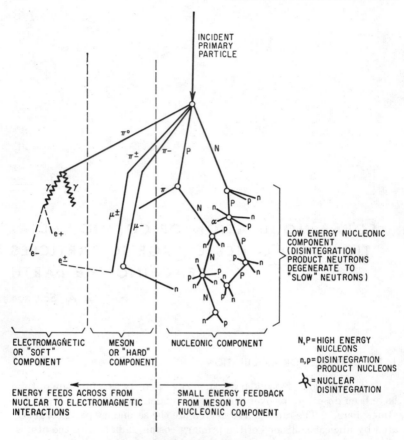

FIG. 1. The development of secondary components of the cosmic radiation in the atmosphere from primary-cosmic-ray particles. These secondaries are also generated in space vehicles.

be shown, for example, that the variations in the geomagnetic field arising from the geomagnetic storms were not the origin of the major changes with time, but that intensity variations were characteristic of the primary cosmic radiation approaching the earth.[3]   The major changes of intensity display close correlations with solar magnetic activity and, for some types of variations, with discrete solar events.   Thus it has been shown that the changes in the primary cosmic radiations have a solar origin.[3] The behavior of the variations with magnetic rigidity suggests that magnetic fields of solar origin are the seat of the mechanism for producing the observed variations with time. This process is called the *modulation* of primary-cosmic-ray intensity.

The average cosmic-ray spectrum appears to consist mainly of particles of nonsolar origin, except possibly for the rarely observed nonrelativistic portion of the primary spectrum. Hence we have here the modulation of a particle flux from outside the solar system by electromagnetic processes within the solar system. In addition to the convincing evidence of correlations with solar activity, the time scale of galactic phenomena is too long for the observed cosmic-ray phenomena to be of galactic origin.

Following these developments, it has been shown recently that the different charged components in the primary spectrum—$Z = 1$ and $Z = 2$ particles, $A/Z = 1$ and $A/Z = 2$ particles—undergo changes in such a way as to suggest that they experience common modulation.[4,5] Current research is now directed to the nature of the solar modulation mechanisms and to whether they have the scale size of the solar system or are operative in more restrictive regions such as near the Earth. Also, there is the question of how many basic mechanisms are required to account for the different kinds of variations. Clearly, an understanding of the solar modulation of energetic particles in the interplanetary medium and near the Earth is fundamental to our understanding of interplanetary magnetic fields and plasmas.

Of astrophysical interest is the question: What is the true primary spectrum of cosmic radiation outside the solar system and at low energies? Hence the modulation also bears on problems of particle acceleration and the origin of cosmic rays.

An observer at the Earth detects changes of primary and secondary cosmic radiations of many types. There are intensity variations of non-recurring and recurring types, variations extending from seconds to 11-year periods, and variations in amplitude from barely detectable cosmic-ray-"noise" fluctuations to the 11-year variations where more than one-half the cosmic-ray flux disappears and the spectrum changes drastically during the solar maximum, or where approximately one-third of the primary flux may disappear within a few hours as in the case of sharp decreases of cosmic-ray intensity. To emphasize the importance of the solar modulation process and its relation to questions of solar production of particles, and the connection of these phenomena to the interpretation of interplanetary fields and plasmas, we shall consider here only two kinds of variations as examples.

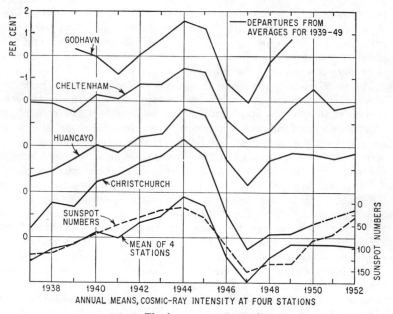

FIG. 2. The inverse correlation between ionization-chamber intensity and solar activity by Forbush.[1] More recent results show that the relativistic-energy portion of the primary spectrum changed by more than a factor 2 between solar minimum (1954) and solar maximum (1958) as indicated in Fig. 6.

2. PRIMARY-COSMIC-RAY SPECTRAL CHANGES WITH THE SOLAR ACTIVITY CYCLE

It was observed first by Forbush that there existed a 4 per cent variation in cosmic-ray intensity for each of two solar cycles and that there was an anticorrelation between solar activity and cosmic-ray intensity[1] (Fig. 2). We now know that the phenomenon is energy-dependent to the lowest energies and that the nucleonic component will display a change throughout the solar cycle of approximately five times the amplitude of the variation observed in the ion chambers.[6-9]

Spectral changes in the primary radiation which occur between solar maximum and solar minimum from 1948 to 1954 can be understood if the primary spectrum is represented by the function

$$j = \left(\frac{1}{pc/Ze}\right)^{-\gamma}$$

where Ze is the charge of the particle, and p is its momentum.   Then, for a primary spectrum where $\gamma = 2$ in 1948, the change in γ between 1948 and 1954 was $\nabla\gamma = +0.7$.   Between 1954 and 1958, γ changed from 2.7 back to 2 as shown in Fig. 3.[10]   The integrated flux from 1-Bv rigidity upward changed approximately 60 per cent between 1954 and 1958. High-altitude balloon flights demonstrate this convincingly.[9,11]   Figure 4 shows the integrated nucleonic-component intensity, 1954 to 1958.[9] The changes measured in the secondary nucleonic component deep in the atmosphere were > 20 per cent at sea level for this period of the integrated spectrum.   The changes occurred out to magnetic rigidities in excess of 50 Bv and in both the $A/Z = 1$ and $A/Z = 2$ classes of charged particles as shown in Fig. 5.[4]   A high degree of isotropy prevailed through-

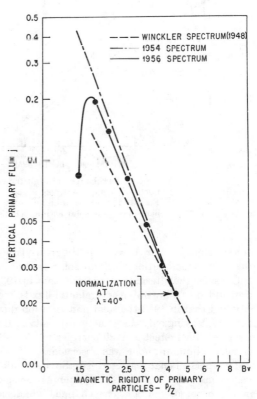

FIG. 3. The changes in the primary-cosmic-ray spectrum measured by Meyer and Simpson, 1948 to 1956,[10] arising from modulation of solar origin. See Fig. 6 for an over-all view of spectral changes. By 1958 the slope had changed to $\gamma \pm 2$.

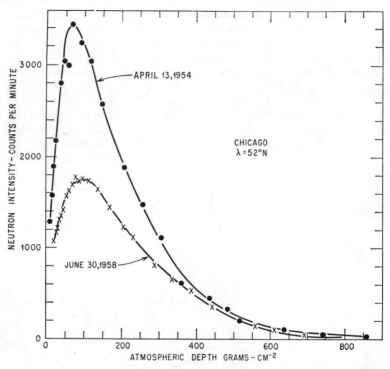

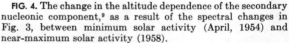

FIG. 4. The change in the altitude dependence of the secondary nucleonic component,[9] as a result of the spectral changes in Fig. 3, between minimum solar activity (April, 1954) and near-maximum solar activity (1958).

out the changes over the years in the relativistic-particle range, suggesting that it was modulation, and not solar production.

Consider the alternative, namely, that in 1954 there was solar production added to a low-intensity galactic flux to yield a high observed intensity and that in 1958 the solar contribution disappeared because of solar activity, leaving only the galactic intensity. If this were so, an outstanding directional effect at high energies would be observed during the year of solar minimum: none was observed.

The spectral changes described above are different from other intensity variations to be discussed later, such as the sharp decreases which occur in the order of hours. The changes which contribute to the over-all

11-year intensity variations occur irregularly in time but generally at times of greatest solar activity. It can be shown that the 11-year variation is not only the sum of a large number of short-term variations at the Earth. However, there is evidence that the short-term variations are related to the long-range behavior of the 11-year variations.

The above remarks have been directed to the relativistic particles in the spectrum, i.e., for example, down to proton energies $\sim$1 Bev. At lower energies there are even greater changes in spectrum throughout the solar cycles.

First, the so-called particle-energy cutoff, which had in early years been assumed to be invariant in time, was shown to change after the year 1948

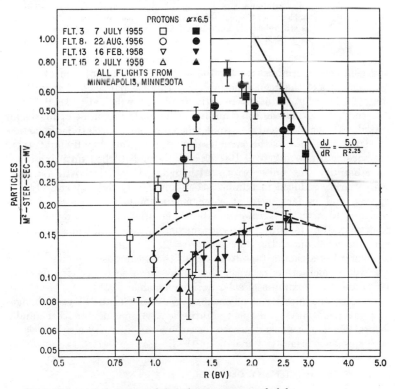

FIG. 5. The spectral changes of the primary-proton and alpha-particle components measured by McDonald.[4] Here the particle magnetic rigidity $R = pc/Ze$ in 10^9 volts,

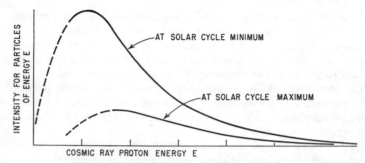

FIG. 6. The changes in the cosmic-radiation spectrum between solar minimum and solar maximum is not drawn to scale.   The behavior of the spectrum over the dashed portions of the curve is still relatively uncertain.   The range of energies shown here is 0–50 × 10⁹ ev.

and completely disappeared by 1954.[10,11]   This was not due to world-wide changes of the geomagnetic field.   In 1954 particles of energy less than 150 Mev for protons were arriving at high polar latitudes.[11]

Second, following the solar minimum in 1954, the onset of first solar activity at the Sun had a strong effect on the nonrelativistic-particle spectrum, with most of the particles disappearing very rapidly but leaving the spectrum above 2 to 3 Bev essentially undisturbed until increased solar activity was under way.   Although the nonrelativistic particles were sharply reduced in number, they apparently did not entirely disappear, and in fact even at solar maximum nonrelativistic particles continue to arrive.[12]   However, the differential spectrum developed a peak near 1 Bev for protons at solar maximum, this peak being associated with the spectrum at the time when $\gamma \approx 2$.

Figure 6 is a sketch (not to scale) of these composite changes in the spectrum which occur between the minimum of solar activity (such as 1954) and the maximum of solar activity (such as 1958).

We defer the question of physical interpretation of the 11-year changes of primary-cosmic-ray intensity until we also consider another fundamental effect: the sharp decreases of cosmic-ray intensity also associated with special solar-activity events on the Sun.

3. THE FORBUSH INTENSITY DECREASE

The ionization-chamber data analyzed by Forbush displayed sharp decreases of intensity, following by approximately 1 day certain large-scale solar flares.[1] The decreases were approximately 1 to 5 per cent in amplitude. A typical event is shown in Fig. 7 for a neutron intensity monitor of the nucleonic component. The overall effect is world-wide, with small variant features dependent upon local time. At first it was thought that an external ring current, generating a variable component in a geomagnetic field, was responsible for the observed changes at the surface of the Earth, but experiments have now shown that no axially symmetric ring current could account for these sharp decreases and that their origin must be more directly connected with modulation by solar activity.[3]

A unique feature of this effect is the decrease in the primary beam that may occur at rates up to 3 per cent or higher per hour and produce decreases of intensity integrated over the relativistic spectrum of more than 30 per cent. The recovery of the cosmic-ray intensity has a "half-life" of order 1 to 2 days, but on some occasions much longer. The spectral changes extend out beyond ≈ 50 By rigidity and are much less dependent upon particle rigidity than for the spectral changes in the 11-year intensity variation described above.[6-9] This has been shown in

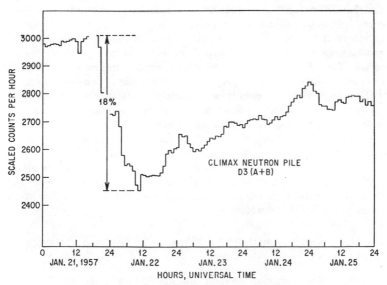

FIG. 7. A rapid decrease of secondary-nucleonic-component intensity arising from a change in primary-cosmic-ray intensity of more than 36 per cent in the interplanetary medium near the Earth. We call this a Forbush decrease.

several ways. For very large events, the energy dependence of the variation may be so small as to suggest that the predecrease spectrum is multiplied by an almost non-energy-dependent factor to yield the spectrum
at the time of decreased intensity. The energy dependence appears to
change throughout the developments of the solar cycle, but always it is
less than the 11-year cycle. A search for a large shift in the position of
the maximum in the differential spectrum (near the times of solar maximum) with the onset of a sharp decrease shows that shifts are negligible.
This is consistent with the modulation mechanism being nearly as effective at high as at low magnetic rigidities. (There exist, however, a few
events, such as the Feb. 11, 1958, event, which appear to be more energy-
dependent at low energies than the sharp Forbush decreases and are
treated as a separate group of events; they are not discussed here since
they show a shift of the differential spectrum maximum.*)

The high correlation with solar outbursts and the 24- to 40-hour transit
time before the effects are observed at the Earth suggest that the sharp
intensity decrease is a phenomenon characteristically related to the vicinity of the Earth or at least to a restricted volume around the Sun-Earth
line, rather than a heliocentric effect. Geomagnetic storms are loosely
correlated to these sharp decreases of intensity, and an extensive investigation is under way to understand the relationship of the origin of the
geomagnetic storm to these sharp decreases of cosmic-ray intensity and
to the Type III cosmic-noise-absorption events discussed in Chap. 13.
It is not always true, however, that geomagnetic storms are connected
with sharp decreases of cosmic-ray intensity. The mechanism producing
the changes of intensity acts upon both protons and alpha particles, and
hence probably upon the heavier nuclei also.

With these two types of intensity variations in mind, we direct our
attention to the question: What physical process underlies the modulation
mechanism or mechanisms? We do not here go into detail on all the
various hypotheses which are currently being considered, but only outline
the main features to illustrate the character of experiments being undertaken to resolve these problems.

4. MODELS AND EXPERIMENTS TO EXPLAIN THE SPECTRAL CHANGES OF SOLAR ORIGIN

In the above discussion we have considered two of the major spectral
changes that occur in the primary cosmic radiation. There are also

* J. A. Simpson, unpublished.

recurring 27-day variations of approximately 5 per cent amplitude at sea level, 24-hr variations that recur, and in addition the several irregular variations that are related to minor solar events. They are all important for a complete understanding of the phenomena taking place in space. However, the 11-year intensity variation accompanied by low-energy changes and the sharp Forbush decrease are so outstanding that they have priority in attempting a first-order explanation for solar modulation.

We first note that the Forbush decrease is a temporary depletion of particles from the average spectrum and that the 11-year-cycle intensity changes probably represent a depletion of particles at maximum solar activity, according to our previous discussion. Therefore we interpret the relativistic spectrum of the cosmic radiation (and possibly part or all of the nonrelativistic part of the spectrum) at solar minimum as representing the nonsolar spectrum of radiation as we would find it outside the solar system. At solar maximum, therefore, we observe the resultant spectrum of particles at the Earth as a consequence of the propagation through magnetic fields of solar origin and therefore as a solar modulation of the galactic beam.

If so, then what kinds of mechanisms could change temporarily the intensity and spectral distribution of particles from the Galaxy? This question has been under discussion for over a decade, and experiments have led successively to improved ideas. First guesses, invoking a moving ion beam carrying within it a "frozen-in" magnetic field as suggested by Alfvén and more recently advocated by Dorman,[13] to account for the small 24-hr variations, do not account for the large-scale effects discussed here. Following original ideas by Fermi[14] for the galactic acceleration of particles and magnetohydrodynamic concepts extending from ideas of Alfvén and others, Morrison[15] and Parker[16] during the past few years have proposed models based on the evidence derived from experiments on the magnetic-rigidity dependence of the modulation effects. Disordered magnetic fields carried into space by plasma may intervene between the radiation arriving from the far side of the solar system and the position of measurement at the Earth. The radiation arriving from the far side of irregular magnetic fields must diffuse through the advancing field region. (See Chap. 13 for a discussion of particle diffusion in magnetic fields.)

It can be shown that if an expanding region is initially free of cosmic radiation, the cosmic radiation will require time to diffuse through the magnetic-field region before the intensity inside the region will rise to the intensity outside the magnetic-field region. If the Earth is temporarily inside such a region, then there are times when the observed intensity may be expected to be less than the intensity outside the region of the surrounding magnetic fields. The magnitude of the depression and the magnetic-rigidity dependence of the variation determines the rms value of the magnetic-field region. This fact places severe conditions on such a model for the sharp Forbush decreases where $B_{rms} \geq 10^{-2}$ to 10^{-3} gauss. Parker has tried to place disordered fields around the Earth so that particles inside could be so rapidly removed by the solid Earth that the intensity inside would remain depressed when diffusion took place.[16] This model suffers from several difficulties, especially for the 11-year cycle. It is more attractive for the Forbush decrease since B_{rms} may be the order of 10^{-4} to 10^{-5} gauss and sufficient for even large effects, but even for this effect it requires a larger magnetic-rigidity dependence than is observed for the large, sharp decreases.

New experimental data on differences in the spectrum of the 11-year and the sharp Forbush decreases, along with information on the effect of these phenomena upon $A/Z = 2$ particles,[9] suggest a heliocentric origin for the modulation of 11-year changes. This evidence, along with the results from the flare of February, 1956, for the storage and escape of solar-flare particles, discussed in Chap. 13, begins to suggest the existence of a large-scale interplanetary magnetic field of roughly heliocentric origin and is consistent with radial fields inside the orbit of Earth.

For the sharp Forbush decreases, the remarkable insensitivity of the large events to particle magnetic rigidity suggests the existence of very intense magnetic-field regions. This evidence, along with the recent observations of the nonrelativistic solar protons connected with large solar flares, Type III cosmic-noise absorption, and sudden-commencement geomagnetic storms, has suggested revisions of the magnetic-field modulation for Forbush decreases, but we do not consider the theoretical models here.

Experimental evidence, in any case, shows that the sharp Forbush decrease is local to the extent that it is intimately related with the Sun-Earth system: a depression of intensity throughout the solar system does not occur. Over how large a volume is the total cosmic-ray intensity depressed for each event? This is under investigation, using space-probe experiments where particle detectors are placed at large distances from the Earth. A comparison with the intensity changes in neutron monitors at the Earth should be conclusive in setting lower limits for volumes of depressed intensity, and hence for limitations on the theory of the Forbush decrease.

Recently, direct experiments using the space vehicles Explorer VI and Pioneer V (which measured inward to the sun $\sim$0.1 A.U. from the

Earth) have been carried out. These experiments prove that (1) the rapid (Forbush) decrease of cosmic-ray intensity is *not* a geocentric phenomenon; (2) there is strong evidence for a bulk motion outward from the Sun of conducting plasma ejected in association with a solar flare which either carries magnetic fields within itself or manipulates an interplanetary magnetic field to remove convectively some galactic cosmic radiation from a limited volume of the inner solar system.[17,18]

These same experiments prove for the 11-year changes that (1) any solar mechanism changing the cosmic-ray intensity over 11 years is centered about the Sun; (2) the scale size for the volume in space, in which the cosmic-ray intensity is reduced in 1960, is greater than 1 A.U.; and (3) the *radial gradient* of cosmic-ray intensity near the orbit of Earth is so small as to suggest (since the difference in flux level between interstellar space and the inner solar system is greater than a factor 2) that modulation of galactic intensity in 1960 occurs at distances greater than the orbit of Earth.[19]

5. THE LOW-ENERGY PARTICLES—CONFINEMENT TO LINES OF FORCE IN INTERPLANETARY FIELDS

Since the relativistic particles undergo large-scale changes in spectral distribution and intensity due to interplanetary magnetic fields of solar origin, clearly the nonrelativistic, very low energy particles generated at the Sun must be strongly constrained to the motions of the existing magnetic lines of force. The recent evidence mentioned in Chap. 13, Sec. 4, on the solar production of nonrelativistic particles and the likely presence of a vast range and intensity distribution of very low energy particles from the Sun at all times not so far detected (as indicated by Fig. 1 of Chap. 11) suggests that they may be accessible to the Earth from time to time as the Earth moves in and out of such field regions connecting with the Sun and carrying these low-energy particles. At the orbit of the Earth, the motions and transport of these magnetic fields are determined by the prevailing interplanetary, tenuous plasma motions. Hence a search outside the geomagnetic field of the Earth as a function of time for the very low energy charged particles, their charge, and their energy distributions is important for understanding not only the modulation and production of more energetic particles by solar processes, but also the electromagnetic conditions of interplanetary space. For example, even in the energy range of <0.1 to 1 Bv rigidity, we now know of remarkably large changes in the particle spectrum, arising from modulation and production, i.e., the so-called change in the low-energy cutoff of the primary-cosmic-ray spectrum referred to earlier. How closely related are the changes in this low-energy maximum in the primary-particle distribution to the 11-year intensity variations observed throughout the relativistic range? To what extent do the changing electromagnetic conditions in the nearby planetary medium influence the population of trapped particle radiation in the geomagnetic field? The answers to questions of this kind will contribute to knowledge of the magnetic-field structure producing modulation of the low- and intermediate-energy particles.

The cosmic-ray neutron-intensity monitor and charged-particle detector networks have contributed to an understanding of the energy dependence of the primary relativistic particle; the high-altitude balloon measurements made at various geomagnetic latitudes have extended the energy range of these studies down to ~0.1-Bev energy; beyond this, however, as indicated by the blank area in Fig. 1 of Chap. 11, particle spectra at lower energies and plasma densities and flow directions must await detailed studies using detectors on satellites and space probes.

REFERENCES

1. S. E. Forbush: *J. Geophys. Research*, *59*, 525 (1954).
2. J. A. Simpson, W. H. Fonger, and S. B. Trieman: *Phys. Rev.*, *90*, 934 (1953).
3. J. A. Simpson: *Proc. Natl. Acad. Sci. U.S.*, *43*, 42 (1957).
4. F. G. McDonald: *Phys. Rev.*, *116*, 462 (1959).
5. P. Meyer: *Phys. Rev.*, *115*, 1734 (1959).
6. A. G. Fenton, K. B. Fenton, and D. C. Rose: *Can. J. Phys.*, *36*, 824 (1958).
7. J. A. Lockwood: *Phys. Rev.*, *112*, 1750 (1958).
8. K. G. McCracken: *Phys. Rev.*, *113*, 343 (1959).
9. K. B. Fenton, P. Meyer, and J. Simpson (to be published).
10. P. Meyer and J. A. Simpson: *Phys. Rev.*, *106*, 568 (1957).
11. H. V. Neher: *Phys. Rev.*, *107*, 588 (1957).
12. P. S. Freier, E. P. Ney, and P. H. Fowler: *Nature*, *181*, 1319 (1958); J. R. Winckler and L. Peterson: *Nature*, *181*, 1317 (1958).
13. L. I. Dorman: "Cosmic Ray Variations," State Publishing House for Theoretical Literature, Moscow, 1957 (translated: Technical Doc. Liaison Office, Wright-Patterson A.F.B.).
14. E. Fermi: *Phys. Rev.*, *81*, 683 (1951); *Progr. Theoret. Phys.*, *5*, 570 (1950).
15. P. Morrison: *Phys. Rev.*, *101*, 1397 (1956).
16. E. N. Parker: *Phys. Rev.*, *103*, 1518 (1956).
17. C. Y. Fan, P. Meyer, and J. A. Simpson: *Phys. Rev. Letters*, *4*, 543 (1960).
18. *Ibid.*, *5*, 269 (1960).
19. *Ibid.*, *5*, 272.

15

THE GEOMAGNETICALLY TRAPPED
CORPUSCULAR RADIATION

James A. Van Allen

1. INTRODUCTION

One of the most interesting geophysical discoveries of recent years was that made with the early U.S. IGY satellites Explorer I (Satellite 1958 Alpha) and Explorer III (Satellite 1958 Gamma). It was found[1,2] that an immense region around the Earth is occupied by a very high intensity of charged particles (protons and electrons), temporarily "trapped" in the geomagnetic field. Detailed study of this radiation has been a major endeavor of the past year and a half by a group at the State University of Iowa in the United States and by Soviet IGY workers. Important additional information at relatively low altitudes has been obtained by brief rocket flights by other workers. Although knowledge of the trapped radiation is still incomplete, very substantial progress has been made in observing and interpreting this new phenomenon.[3-13] The reader is referred to Refs. 3, 4, and 10 for the most complete accounts presently available in print.

Understanding of the dynamics of the trapping of charged particles in the geomagnetic field has also been considerably advanced by the Argus experiments of August-September, 1958. These experiments comprised the artificial injection of beta-decay electrons from the fission fragments of high-altitude detonations of small-yield atomic devices and the subsequent observation by Explorer IV (Satellite 1958 Epsilon), by sounding rockets, and by other techniques of the geophysical effects produced.[14]

Figure 1 gives an over-all view of the intensity structure of the two principal radiation zones (or belts) around the Earth as derived from our Geiger-tube observations[3,4] with Explorer IV and with Pioneer III. Generally confirmatory results have been obtained by the Soviets with radiation instrumentation on Sputnik III and Mechta.[9,10,13]　An immense amount of more detailed information at the lower altitudes is available

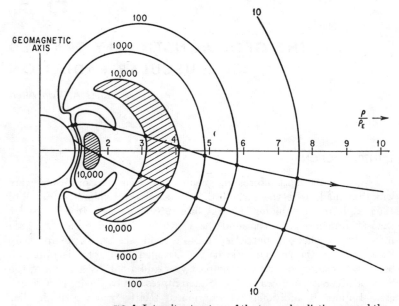

FIG. 1. Intensity structure of the trapped radiation around the Earth. The diagram is a geomagnetic meridian section of a three-dimensional figure of revolution around the geomagnetic axis. Contours of constant intensity are labeled with numbers 10, 100, 1000, and 10,000. These numbers are the true counting rates of an Anton type 302 Geiger tube carried by Explorer IV and Pioneer III. The linear scale of the diagram is relative to the radius of the Earth—6371 km. The outbound and inbound legs of the trajectory of Pioneer III are shown by the slanting, undulating lines. The intensity structure is, of course, a function of detector characteristics. See text.

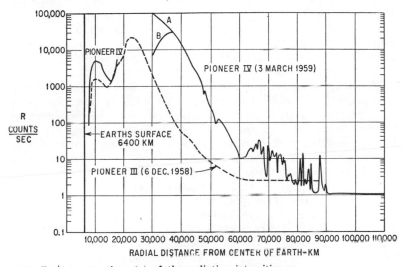

FIG. 2. A comparative plot of the radiation intensities as measured with nearly identical Anton 002 Geiger tubes in Pioneer III and Pioneer IV. The trajectories were not identical, the most important difference being that Pioneer IV cut through the inner zone several degrees closer to the equator, at a radial distance of about 10,000 km.

in the full gamut of Explorer IV observations with a variety of detectors.[3] These observations are still under intensive study.

The most recent data[15] from Pioneer IV on Mar. 3 to 6, 1959, again confirm the general structure of the region of trapped radiation but show a very great enhancement of intensity and a considerable extension of the outer zone—following the great M-region event on the Sun on Feb. 25, 1959 (Fig. 2). In addition, these data provide information on the absorptivity of the radiation in both inner and outer zones and give a new determination of the cosmic-ray intensity in interplanetary space.

2. NATURE OF THE TRAPPED RADIATION

On the basis of the extremely rapid increase of intensity with altitude above some 1000 km, it was immediately evident[1] that the newly discovered radiation must consist of charged particles constrained by the Earth's magnetic field since the additional atmospheric absorption between altitudes of, say, 1000 and 2000 km was several orders of magnitude less than the wall thickness of the detectors used in 1958 Alpha and

1958 Gamma.   There is now a wealth of evidence supporting this conclusion in full detail, and we regard it as established beyond all reasonable
doubt, that the observed radiation consists of charged particles trapped
in the Earth's magnetic field in the manner visualized by Poincaré, Stoermer, and Alfvén in classical theoretical studies.

The nature of the particles and their detailed energy spectra are much
more difficult to establish conclusively.   We originally reasoned as follows: On the grounds of their universality in nature it is reasonable to
suppose that electrons are present.   And among the many nuclear possibilities, protons are likely dominant because of the preponderance of
hydrogen as an atomic constituent of matter.   The simplest working
hypothesis, then, is that the trapped radiation consists of electrons and
protons.   If this be granted, then the problem becomes one of measuring
the absolute differential energy spectrum of each of the two components as
a function of position in space and direction and as a function of time.

It is immediately evident from the extensive Explorer IV observations[3]
that there is no simple, universal answer to the above problem.   The
intensity of the radiation *and* its composition are strong functions of
position in space, of direction, and of time.   A thoroughly satisfactory
study of the problem must await more elaborate experimental
observations.

Meanwhile, the presently available observations (obtained with relatively rudimentary equipment, by laboratory standards) have served to
provide a good reconnaissance of the nature of the trapped radiation.
Indeed, it is the writer's opinion that the present state of knowledge is
such that the full determination of the nature of the radiation, when
finally available, will be quite interesting and valuable but probably not
markedly different than that sketched below:

1. The observations with the diversity of detectors carried by Explorer
IV, Sputnik III, Pioneer IV, and Mechta demonstrate conclusively that
the nature of the radiation (i.e., its composition and the energy spectra
of its components) in the inner zone is quite different from that in the
outer zone—more different, that is, than the nature of the radiation in
different positions within either one of the two zones considered separately.

2. The integral range spectrum of the radiation in the inner zone falls
by about two orders of magnitude from 1 mg per cm^2 to about 140 mg
per cm^2, then trails out more gradually toward greater stopping powers.
Of the radiation which penetrates 140 mg per cm^2, a fraction of 1 per cent
also penetrates several grams per square centimeter.   On the basis of
crude range and specific ionization measurements in Explorer IV, the
latter, more penetrating component is tentatively identified as consisting

of protons having energies of the order of magnitude of 100 Mev. The less penetrating radiation has a low specific ionization, and hence quite likely consists of electrons having energies up to about 1 Mev and having a spectrum rising strongly (though not as rapidly as that of the auroral soft radiation) toward lower energies. Energy fluxes as high as 100 ergs per cm² sec steradian have been found beneath an absorber 1 mg per cm² in thickness at altitudes of 2000 km near the geomagnetic equator. As measured within a thin (0.92 g per cm²) CsI(T 1) crystal,[3] over 0.95 of the energy flux is in the less penetrating, electronic component.

3. The outer zone has a quite different nature. All evidence is consistent with an exclusive electron content, in so far as the characteristics of detectors used thus far permit observations (smallest value of absorber used: 1 mg per cm²). The energy spectrum apparently resembles that of the auroral soft radiation, rising sharply toward low energies from a practical upper limit of about 100 kev. The omnidirectional flux of electrons of energy greater than 20 kev is of the order of 10^{11} particles per cm² sec in the heart of the outer zone, on the basis of the simplest (though not conclusively the only possible) interpretation.[10,15]

4. The inner zone is relatively stable as a function of time during the period of available observations.

5. There are marked temporal fluctuations in the "slot" between the two zones and ones of very great magnitude in both intensity and spatial structure in the outer zone. These fluctuations are apparently associated with solar activity.[15]

6. Several recent rocket experiments into the lower fringe of the inner zone are of considerable interest.[16-18]

Holly and Johnson, using a simple magnetic spectrometer, find at 1000 km altitude over the central Atlantic Ocean that particles having a range greater than that of 160 kev electrons are predominantly electrons, with possibly 3 to 7 per cent protons being present. Of the electrons in the energy range 30 kev to 4 Mev, 99 per cent have energy less than 600 kev. Freden and White have flown a package of heavily shielded (6 g per cm²) photographic emulsion to a maximum altitude of 1230 km (also on the southeasterly missile range from Cape Canaveral, Florida). By a standard range-and-specific-ionization measuring technique, they find only protons under the specified absorber. The spectrum in the range of energy 75 to 700 Mev is well represented by $E^{-1.8}$. The results summarized in this paragraph are consistent with the earlier observations with Explorer IV and are considerably more decisive in respect to particle identification. Absolute values of intensity and the spatial dependence of intensity are best provided by Explorer IV data. As remarked earlier, the relative composition of the radiation is a function of position. For example, the radiation in the upper portion of the inner zone is considerably softer than that in the lower portion, and the radiation in the outer zone is almost completely absorbed by 4 g per cm^2 of lead.

3. ORIGIN OF THE TRAPPED RADIATION

In view of the extensive body of knowledge concerning "solar-terrestrial" relationships[19,20] and the earlier discovery of the auroral soft radiation,[21,22] we originally suggested[1] that the trapped corpuscular radiation consisted of ionized solar gas which had been injected into the geomagnetic field, with perhaps acceleration to the observed energies a local phenomenon in the geomagnetic field.

Subsequently, various workers have proposed that the trapped radiation may arise, at least in part, from other processes. Neher[23] suggested that a penetrating component may arise from the delayed radioactive decay of μ-mesons emerging from the Earth's atmosphere as part of the cosmic-ray "albedo." Christofilos,[24] Vernov,[9] Kellogg,[11] and Singer[7,8] have drawn attention to the neutron component of the cosmic-ray albedo as a possible source, and the last-named author has emphasized the potentiality of such neutrons of high energy for generating the penetrating component in the inner zone. These suggestions depend upon the ability of neutrons from cosmic-ray-induced nuclear disintegrations in the atmosphere to move outward through the geomagnetic field without deflection until they undergo radioactive decay. The decay products of a neutron (half-life at rest 11.7 min) are an electron, a proton, and a neutrino. The kinetic energy of the proton is comparable to that of its parent neutron, the electron has a well-known beta-decay spectrum (upper limit 782 kev for a neutron at rest), and the neutrino does not contribute to the observed geophysical phenomena.

The observed spectrum and composition of the radiation in the *inner zone* resemble those expected on the neutron-decay hypothesis of origin, the major component being electrons having an energy spectrum resembling that of neutron-decay electrons and the minor (but penetrating) component being protons of energy of the order of 100 Mev. (See Ref. 3 for further discussion.) Many quantitative considerations (source strength, trapped lifetimes, equilibrium spectra, etc.) remain to be examined before the neutron-decay origin of the inner zone can be regarded as established. Present knowledge favors it, though the source strength[25] of the mechanism may be inadequate; and it may be that the inner zone contains an important admixture of particles which have been "convected" inward from the outer zone.[26]

There is very little doubt that the great *outer zone* and the rich variety of associated geophysical effects (aurorae, airglow, atmospheric heating, geomagnetic storms, etc.) are directly attributable to solar gas, injected into (temporarily) trapped orbits in the geomagnetic field. The site and mechanism of the acceleration of the particles therein to the observed energies constitute major, unsettled problems. The two immediately evident possibilities are (1) acceleration within the Sun by betatron or other mechanisms and "piping" to the Earth's vicinity along extended magnetic lines of force, and (2) arrival in a cloud of solar gas as low-energy particles ($\sim 10^4$ ev), intrusion into the Earth's field, trapping, and subsequent acceleration by magnetohydrodynamic waves or by other processes in the local environment of the Earth. Radiation monitoring in interplanetary space for an extended period of time is the straightforward method for substantiating or eliminating possibility 1 and thereby making local acceleration either necessary or unnecessary. But of course the true situation may be a complex of possibilities 1 and 2.

4. TIME VARIATIONS

On Dec. 6 and 7, 1958 (Pioneer III) and on Jan. 2, 1959 (Mechta), the outer zone was apparently similar. But on Mar. 3, 1959 (Pioneer IV), the maximum intensity was much greater and the zone extended out some 15,000 km farther. This huge difference is the most prominent temporal fluctuation thus far observed. Indeed it provides the most striking evidence for the solar origin of, at least, the outer zone.

At the lower altitudes of the observations with Explorers I, III, and IV a wealth of observational material is available for study of temporal fluctuations. The inner zone is relatively stable, but intensities in the "slot" between the two zones and in the lower "horns" of the outer zone are subject to considerable fluctuations in a manner which tends to establish their connection with other geophysical phenomena.

5. GEOPHYSICAL ROLE OF THE TRAPPED RADIATION

The writer has suggested that the trapped radiation plays an essential role as an intermediate reservoir of charged particles between the Sun as a source and the Earth's atmosphere as a sink (aurorae, airglow, and atmospheric heating). In addition, the trapped radiation may be the seat of the electric current ("ring current") long supposed[19] to be responsible for the main phase of geomagnetic storms.

On the basis of energetic considerations, of the geometric form of the zones of trapped particles, of the estimated leakage rates, of the particle intensities, and of general considerations of plasma physics, these views appear plausible. But much more detailed observational and theoretical study will be required before each of the many phenomena can be conclusively examined.

6. SOME SAMPLE TENTATIVE INTENSITIES

In the *heart of the inner zone* at altitude about 3600 km on the geomagnetic equator:

1. Electrons of energy greater than 20 kev, maximum unidirectional intensity $\approx 2 \times 10^9$ per cm^2 sec steradian
2. Electrons of energy greater than 600 kev, maximum unidirectional intensity $\approx 1 \times 10^7$ per cm^2 sec steradian
3. Protons of energy greater than 40 Mev, omnidirectional intensity $\approx 2 \times 10^4$ per cm^2 sec

In the *heart of the outer zone* at altitude of about 16,000 km on the geomagnetic equator (on a day of high intensity):

1. Electrons of energy greater than 20 kev, omnidirectional intensity $\approx 1 \times 10^{11}$ per cm^2 sec
2. Electrons of energy greater than 200 kev, omnidirectional intensity is less than 1×10^8 per cm^2 sec
3. Protons of energy greater than 60 Mev, omnidirectional intensity is less than 10^2 per cm^2 sec
4. Protons of energy less than 30 Mev, no significant information

7. TRAPPED CORPUSCULAR RADIATION AROUND THE MOON AND AROUND OTHER PLANETS

The trapping of charged particles in the vicinity of astronomical bodies is doubtless a quite general astrophysical phenomenon. Indeed, it has already been proposed as a mechanism essential to the dynamics of the solar corona.[27] More immediate observational interest perhaps attaches to the possibility of trapped, corpuscular radiation around our Moon and around other planets (e.g., Mars and Venus).

The emergence of cosmic-ray-produced neutrons from the atmosphere or solid surface of astronomical bodies is probably a universal phenomenon (at least within our Galaxy).

Also, all the bodies of the solar system are subjected to the impact of plasma from the Sun with greater or lesser intensity in accordance with their distances from the Sun. Hence both of the (presumably most important) sources of trapped radiation are present throughout the solar system.

The principal parameters which enter into a general quantitative discussion of trapping are the magnetic moment of the body, the radius of the body, and the density and radial extent of its atmosphere.

The mechanism of trapping is now sufficiently well understood so that a reasonably confident assessment can be made for any known set of the above parameters. Generally speaking, the greater the magnetic moment and the less extended the atmosphere, the more favorable are the conditions for a high intensity of trapped radiation. There remains the obscurity of the mechanism for local acceleration of charged particles (if indeed such is necessary) which might be peculiarly favored around the Earth (though this seems unlikely).

Consideration of present knowledge makes it appear likely that the Moon is surrounded by little or no trapped radiation, in view of its probably small magnetic moment. The closest observations to the Moon (about 61,000 km) with Pioneer IV showed no discernible radiation belt, but because of the large miss distance, this result must be regarded as inconclusive.

Mars and Venus, for example, may well have substantial radiation belts.

The observational undertaking for settling these matters is one of the most enthralling of contemporary space science.*

* Note by author Oct. 19, 1960: The above account was prepared in June, 1959, and remains substantially correct. The reader is referred to the special comprehensive bibliography following the regular reference section at the end of the chapter for a more complete knowledge of pertinent work.

REFERENCES

1. J. A. Van Allen: Paper presented at joint meeting of National Academy of Sciences and American Physical Society on May 1, 1958.
2. J. A. Van Allen, G. H. Ludwig, E. C. Ray, and C. E. McIlwain: "Observation of High Intensity Radiation by Satellites 1958 Alpha and Gamma," *Jet Propulsion*, *28*, 588–592 (1958).
3. J. A. Van Allen, C. E. McIlwain, and G. H. Ludwig: "Radiation Observations with Satellite 1958 Epsilon," *J. Geophys. Research*, *64*, 271–286 (1959).
4. J. A. Van Allen and L. A. Frank: "Radiation around the Earth to a Radial Distance of 107,400 Kilometers," *Nature*, *183*, 430–434 (1950).
5. P. J. Coleman, Jr., C. P. Sonett, and A. Rosen: "Ionizing Radiation at Altitudes of 3500 to 36,000 Km.: Pioneer I," *Bull. Am. Phys. Soc.*, Ser. II, *4*, No. 4, 223 (1959).

6. A. Rosen, C. P. Sonett, and P. J. Coleman, Jr.: "Ionizing Radiation Detected by Pioneer II," *Bull. Am. Phys. Soc.*, Ser II, *4*, No. 4, 223 (1959).
7. S. F. Singer: "'Radiation Belt' and Trapped Cosmic Ray Albedo," *Phys. Rev. Letters*, *1*, 171–173 (1958)
8. S. F. Singer: "Trapped Albedo Theory of the Radiation Belt," *Phys. Rev. Letters*, *1*, 181–183 (1958).
9. S. N. Vernov: Special Lecture, Fifth General Assembly of C.S.A.G.I. in Moscow, July 30–Aug. 9, 1958.
10. S. N. Vernov, A. Y. Chudakov, P. V. Vakulov, and Y. I. Logachev: "Study of Terrestrial Corpuscular Radiation and Cosmic Rays during Flight of the Cosmic Rocket," *Doklady Akad. Nauk S.S.S.R.*, *125*, 304–307 (1959).
11. P. J. Kellogg: "Possible Explanation of the Radiation Observed by Van Allen at High Altitudes in Satellites," *Nuovo Cimento* (in publication).
12. T. Gold: "Origin of the Radiation near the Earth Discovered by Means of Satellites," *Nature*, *183*, 355–358 (1959).
13. S. N. Vernov, A. E. Chudakov, E. V. Gorchakov, J. L. Logachev, and P. V. Vakulov: "Study of the Cosmic-ray Soft Component by the 3rd Soviet Earth Satellite," *Planetary and Space Science*, *1*, 86–93 (1959).
14. "Symposium on Scientific Effects of Artificially Introduced Radiations at High Altitudes," *J. Geophys. Research*, *64*, 865 (1959) and in *Proc. Natl. Acad. Sci. U.S.*, *45*, 1141 (1959); also as separate reprint in *IGY Satellite Report Series No. 9* (1959):
    R. W. Porter: "Introduction"
    N. C. Christofilos: "The Argus Experiment"
    J. A. Van Allen, C. E. McIlwain, and G. H. Ludwig: "Satellite Observations of Radiation Artificially Injected into the Geomagnetic Field"
    L. Allen, Jr.: "Measurement of Trapped Electrons from a Nuclear Device by Sounding Rockets"
    J. A. Welch, Jr.: "Theory of Geomagnetically Trapped Electrons from an Artificial Source"
    P. Newman: "Optical, Electromagnetic, and Satellite Observations of High-altitude Nuclear Detonations—Part I"
    A. M. Peterson: "Optical, Electromagnetic, and Satellite Observations of High-altitude Nuclear Detonations—Part II"
15. J. A. Van Allen and L. A. Frank: "Radiation Measurements to 658,000 Kilometers with Pioneer IV," *Nature*, *184*, 219 (1959).
16. L. Allen, Jr., R. B. Walton, W. A. Whitaker, and J. A. Welch: "Angular Distribution of Van Allen Radiation with Respect to Geomagnetic Field" (private communication, May, 1959).
17. F. E. Holly and R. G. Johnson: "Composition of Radiation Trapped in the Geomagnetic Field at Altitudes up to 1000 Kilometers" (private communication, May, 1959).
18. S. C. Freden and R. S. White: "Protons in the Earth's Magnetic Field" (private communication, May, 1959).
19. S. Chapman and J. Bartels: "Geomagnetism," Vols. 1 and 2 (Oxford: Clarendon Press, 1940).
20. S. K. Mitra: "The Upper Atmosphere," The Asiatic Society Monograph Series, Vol. 5, 2d edition, Calcutta, 1952.
21. L. H. Meredith, M. B. Gottlieb, and J. A. Van Allen: "Direct Detection of Soft

Radiation above 50 Kilometers on the Auroral Zone," *Phys. Rev.*, *97*, 201–205 (1955).
22. J. A. Van Allen: "Direct Detection of Auroral Radiation with Rocket Equipment," *Proc. Natl. Acad. Sci. U.S.*, *43*, 57–92 (1957).
23. H. V. Neher: Private communication, April, 1958.
24. N. Christofilos: Private communication, April, 1958.
25. W. N. Hess: "Van Allen Belt Protons from Cosmic-ray Neutron Leakage," private communication, May, 1959.
26. T. Gold: "Energetic Particle Fluxes in the Solar System and Near the Earth," private communication, April, 1959.
27. P. J. Kellogg and E. P. Ney: "A New Theory of the Solar Corona," private communication, March, 1959.

A BIBLIOGRAPHY CONCERNING GEOMAGNETICALLY TRAPPED CORPUSCULAR RADIATION AND RELATED TOPICS, OCTOBER, 1960

J. A. VAN ALLEN

Akasofu, S. I.: "The Ring Current and the Outer Atmosphere," *J. Geophys. Research*, *65*, 535–543 (1960).
Alfvén, H.: "Cosmical Electrodynamics" (Oxford: Clarendon Press, 1950, 237 pp.).
——. "On the Electric Field Theory of Magnetic Storms and Aurorae," *Tellus*, *7*, 50–64 (1955).
——: "Momentum Spectrum of the Van Allen Radiation," *Phys. Rev. Letters*, *3*, 459–460 (1959).
Allen, L., Jr., J. L. Beavers, II, W. A. Whitaker, J. A. Welch, Jr., and R. B. Walton: "Project Jason Measurement of Trapped Electrons from a Nuclear Device by Sounding Rockets," *J. Geophys. Research*, *64*, 893–907 (1959)
Anderson, K. A.: "Ionizing Radiation Associated with Solar Radio Noise Storm," *Phys. Rev. Letters*, *1*, 335–337 (1958).
——: "Soft Radiation Events at High Altitude during the Magnetic Storm of August 29–30, 1957," *Phys. Rev.*, *111*, 1397–1405 (1958).
——: "Balloon Observations of X-rays in the Auroral Zone, I," *J. Geophys. Research*, *65*, 551–564 (1960).
—— and D. C. Enemark: "Observations of Auroral Zone X-rays and Solar Cosmic Rays," in H. Kallmann Bijl (ed.), "Space Research," pp. 702–714, Proceedings of the First International Space Science Symposium (North-Holland Publishing Co., Amsterdam, 1960, 1195 pp.).
Aono, Y., and K. Kawakami: "Cosmic Rays Observed by Satellite 1958 Alpha," *Report Ionosphere Research Japan*, *12*, 28–36 (1958).
Armstrong, A. H., F. B. Harrison, and L. Rosen: "Flux and Energy of Charged Particles at 300- and 600-mile Altitude," *Bulletin American Physical Society*, Ser. II, *4*, No. 6, 360 (1959).
Arnoldy, R., R. Hoffman, and J. R. Winckler: "Measurements of the Van Allen Radiation Belts during Geomagnetic Storms," in H. Kallmann Bijl (ed.), "Space Research," pp. 877–896, Proceedings of the First International Space Science Symposium (North-Holland Publishing Co., Amsterdam, 1960, 1195 pp.).

——, ——, and ——: "Observations of the Van Allen Radiation Regions during August and September 1959, Part 1," *J. Geophys. Research, 65*, 1361–1375 (1960).

——, ——, and ——: "Solar Cosmic Rays and Soft Radiation Observed at 5,000,000 Kilometers from Earth," *J. Geophys. Research, 65*, 3004–3007 (1960).

Askaryan, G.: "On the Nature of the External Radiation Belt of the Earth," in S. I. Syrovatsky (ed.), Proceedings of the Moscow Cosmic Ray Conference, Vol. III, pp. 81–82 (International Union of Pure and Applied Physics, Moscow, 1960).

Bartels, J.: "Geophysical Evidence Bearing on Orbital Variations of Satellites and on the Radiation Belts," in H. Kallmann Bijl (ed.), "Space Research," pp. 841–844, Proceedings of the First International Space Science Symposium (North-Holland Publishing Co., Amsterdam, 1960, 1195 pp.).

Basler, R. P., R. N. Dewitt, and G. C. Reid: "Radiation Information from $1958\delta_2$," *J. Geophys. Research, 65*, 1135–1138 (1960).

Beard, D. B.: "Interaction of the Solar Plasma with the Earth's Magnetic Field," *Phys. Rev. Letters, 5*, 89–91 (1960).

Bennett, W. H.: "Proposed Measurement of Solar Stream Protons," in J. A. Van Allen (ed.), "Scientific Uses of Earth Satellites," Chap. 22, pp. 194–197 (University of Michigan Press, 1956, 316 pp.).

——: "Solar Proton Stream Forms with a Laboratory Model," *Rev. Sci. Instr., 30*, 64–69 (1959).

Berkner, L. V., J. G. Reid, J. Hanessian, Jr., and L. Cormier (eds.): "Annals of the International Geophysical Year," Vol. VI, pts. I–V (Pergamon Press, London, 1958, 508 pp.). A general reference on matters of satellite technology.

Berthold, W. K., A. K. Harris, and H. J. Hope: "World-wide Effects of Hydromagnetic Waves due to Argus," *J. Geophys. Research, 65*, 2233–2239 (1960).

Blackwell, D. E., D. W. Dewhirst, E. P. Ney, and P. J. Kellogg: "Kellogg and Ney's Model of the Solar Corona," *Nature (London), 184*, 1120–1123 (1959).

Bless, R. C., C. W. Gartlein, D. S. Kimball, and G. Sprague: "Auroras, Magnetic Rays and Protons," *J. Geophys. Research, 64*, 949–953 (1959).

Block, L.: "Model Experiments on Aurorae and Magnetic Storms," *Tellus, 7*, 65–86 (1955).

Bobrov, M. S.: "A Study of Solar Corpuscular Streams Based on World-wide Disturbances Observed during the IGY," *Soviet Astronomy AJ, 3*, No. 6, 943–950 (May-June, 1960).

Chamberlain, J. W.: "Theories of the Aurora," in H. E. Landsberg and J. Van Mieghem (eds.), "Advances in Geophysics," Vol. 4, pp. 109–215 (Academic Press, Inc., 1958).

——, J. Kern, and E. H. Vestine: "Some Consequences of Local Acceleration of Auroral Primaries," *J. Geophys. Research, 65*, 2535–2537 (1960).

Chandrasekhar, S.: "Adiabatic Invariants in the Motions of Charged Particles," in R. K. M. Landshoff (ed.), "The Plasma in a Magnetic Field" (Stanford University Press, 1958, 130 pp.).

Chapman, S., and J. Bartels: "Geomagnetism," Vols. I and II (Oxford: Clarendon Press, 1940, 1049 pp.).

Charakhchian, A. N., V. F. Tulinov, and T. N. Charakhchian: "Cosmic Rays Emitted by the Sun," in H. Kallmann Bijl (ed.), "Space Research," pp. 649–661, Proceedings of the First International Space Science Symposium (North-Holland Publishing Co., Amsterdam, 1960, 1195 pp.).

Christofilos, N. C.: "The Argus Experiment," *J. Geophys. Research, 64*, 869–875 (1959).

Cole, K. D.: "Low Energy Corpuscular Radiation at High Latitudes," *Nature (London), 183*, 738 (1959).

Coleman, P. J., Jr., L. Davis, and C. P. Sonett: "Steady Component of the Interplanetary Magnetic Field: Pioneer V," *Phys. Rev. Letters, 5*, 43–46 (1960).

——, C. P. Sonett, and D. L. Judge: "Some Preliminary Results of the Pioneer V Magnetometer Experiment," *J. Geophys. Research, 65*, 1856–1857 (1960).

Crawford, J. A.: "Fermi Acceleration of Electrons in the Outer Van Allen Belt," *Phys. Rev. Letters, 3*, 316–318 (1959).

Cullington, A. L.: "A Man-made or Artificial Aurora," *Nature (London), 162*, 1365 (1958).

Davis, L. R., O. E. Berg, and L. H. Meredith: "Direct Measurement of Particle Fluxes in and near Auroras," in H. Kallmann Bijl (ed.), "Space Research," pp. 721–735, Proceedings of the First International Space Science Symposium (North-Holland Publishing Co., Amsterdam, 1960, 1195 pp.).

Dessler, A. J.: "Effect of Magnetic Anomaly on Particle Radiation Trapped in Geomagnetic Field," *J. Geophys. Research, 64*, 713–715 (1959).

—— and E. N. Parker: "Hydromagnetic Theory of Geomagnetic Storms," *J. Geophys. Research, 64*, 2239–2252 (1959).

—— and R. Karplus: "The Gap in the Electron Component of the Outer Zone of the Van Allen Radiation," *J. Geophys. Research, 65*, 2486 (1960). (Abstract.)

—— and ——: "Some Properties of the Van Allen Radiation," *Phys. Rev. Letters, 4*, 271–274 (1960).

—— and E. H. Vestine: "Maximum Total Energy of the Van Allen Radiation Belt," *J. Geophys. Research, 65*, 1069–1071 (1960).

Dolginov, S. S., E. G. Eroshenko, L. N. Zhugov, N. V. Pushkov, and L. O. Tyurmina: "Measuring the Magnetic Fields of the Earth and Moon by Means of Sputnik III and Space Rockets I and II," in H. Kallmann Bijl (ed.), "Space Research," pp. 863–868, Proceedings of the First International Space Science Symposium (North-Holland Publishing Co., Amsterdam, 1960, 1195 pp.).

—— and N. V. Pushkov: "Magnetic Field of the Outer Corpuscular Region," in S. I. Syrovatsky (ed.), Proceedings of the Moscow Cosmic Ray Conference, Vol. III, pp. 30–31 (International Union of Pure and Applied Physics, Moscow, 1960).

Dorman, L. I.: "On the Problem of the Nature of Soft Radiation in the Upper Atmosphere," in S. I. Syrovatsky (ed.), Proceedings of the Moscow Cosmic Ray Conference, Vol. III, pp. 74–80 (International Union of Pure and Applied Physics, Moscow, 1960).

Dyce, R. B., and M. P. Nakada: "On the Possibility of Detecting Synchrotron Radiations from Electrons in the Van Allen Belts," *J. Geophys. Research*, pp. 1163–1168 (1959).

Fan, C. Y., P. Meyer, and J. A. Simpson: "Preliminary Results from the Space Probe Pioneer V," *J. Geophys. Research, 65*, 1862–1863 (1960).

——, —— and ——: "Rapid Reduction of Cosmic-radiation Intensity Measured in Interplanetary Space," *Phys. Rev. Letters, 5*, 269–271 (1960).

——, —— and ——: "Experiments on the Eleven Year Changes of Cosmic Ray Intensity Using A Space Probe," *Phys. Rev. Letters, 5*, 272–274 (1960).

——, —— and ——: "Trapped and Cosmic Radiation Measurements from Explorer VI," in H. Kallmann Bijl (ed.), "Space Research," pp. 951–966, Proceedings of the First International Space Science Symposium (North-Holland Publishing Co., Amsterdam, 1960, 1195 pp.).

Field, G. B.: "The Source of Radiation from Jupiter at Decimeter Wavelengths," *J. Geophys. Research, 64,* 1169–1177 (1959).

——: "The Source of Radiation from Jupiter at Decimeter Wavelengths. 2. Cyclotron Radiation by Trapped Electrons," *J. Geophys. Research, 65,* 1661–1671 (1960).

Finch, H. F., and B. R. Leaton: "The Earth's Main Magnetic Field—Epoch 1955.0," *Monthly Notices of the Royal Astronomical Society* (Geophysical Supplements), 7, No. 6, 314–317 (November, 1957).

Fowler, P. H., and C. J. Waddington: "An Artificial Aurora," *Nature (London), 182,* 1728 (1958).

Francis, W. E., M. I. Green, and A. J. Dessler: "Hydromagnetic Propagation of Sudden Commencements of Magnetic Storms," *J. Geophys. Research, 64,* 1643–1645 (1959)..

Freden, S. C., and R. S. White: "Protons in the Earth's Magnetic Field," *Phys. Rev. Letters, 3,* 9–10, 145 (1959).

—— and ——: "Particle Fluxes in the Inner Radiation Belt," *J. Geophys. Research, 65,* 1377–1383 (1960).

Gall, R., and J. Lifshitz: "Temporary Capture of Cosmic Ray Particles and Their Contribution to the High Intensity Belts," in S. I. Syrovatsky (ed.), Proceedings of the Moscow Cosmic Ray Conference, Vol. III, pp. 64–73 (International Union of Pure and Applied Physics, Moscow, 1960).

Gibson, G., W. C. Jordan, and E. J. Lauer: "Containment of Positrons in a Mirror Machine," *Phys. Rev. Letters, 5,* 141–144 (1960).

Gold, T.: "Origin of the Radiation near the Earth Discovered by Means of Satellites," *Nature (London), 183,* 355–358 (1959).

——: "Motions in the Magnetosphere of the Earth," *J. Geophys. Research, 64,* 1219–1224 (1959).

——: "Plasma and Magnetic Fields in the Solar System," *J. Geophys. Research, 64,* 1665–1674 (1959).

Herz, A. J., K. W. Ogilvie, J. Olley, and R. B. White: "Radiation Observations with Satellite 1958δ_2 over Australia," in S. I. Syrovatsky (ed.), Proceedings of the Moscow Cosmic Ray Conference, Vol. III, pp. 32–40 (International Union of Pure and Applied Physics, Moscow, 1960).

Hess, W. N.: "Van Allen Belt Protons from Cosmic-ray Neutron Leakage," *Phys. Rev. Letters, 3,* 11–13, 145 (1959).

—— and A. J. Starnes: "Measurement of the Neutron Flux in Space," *Phys. Rev. Letters, 5,* 48–50 (1960).

Hirtzler, J. H., and J. Hirshman: "Measurements of the Geomagnetic Field Near Capetown," *J. Geophys. Research, 65,* 3016–3018 (1960).

Holly, F. E., and R. G. Johnson: "Measurement of Radiation in the Lower Van Allen Belt," *J. Geophys. Research, 65,* 771–772 (1960).

Hultqvist, B.: "Auroral Isochasms," *Nature (London), 183,* 1478–1479 (1959).

Inove, Y.: "Physical Properties in the Outer Van Allen Belt and Their Relations to the Phenomena in the Exosphere," in H. Kallmann Bijl (ed.), "Space Research," pp. 828–840, Proceedings of the First International Space Science Symposium (North-Holland Publishing Co., Amsterdam, 1960, 1195 pp.).

Jastrow, R.: "Density and Temperature of the Upper Atmosphere," *Astronautics*, July, 1959, pp. 24–25, 108.

———: "Geophysical Effects of the Trapped Particle Layer," in H. Kallmann Bijl (ed.), "Space Research," pp. 1009–1018, Proceedings of the First International Space Science Symposium (North-Holland Publishing Co., Amsterdam, 1960, 1195 pp.).

——— and G. J. F. MacDonald: "Highlights of the Planetary Sciences Program," *Trans. Am. Geophys. Union, 41,* 430–434 (1960).

Josias, C.: "Pioneer's Radiation-detection Instrument," *Astronautics*, July, 1959, pp. 32–33, 114–115.

Kasper, J. E.: "The Earth's Simple Shadow Effect on Cosmic Radiation," *Nuovo Cimento*, Ser. X, Suppl. Vol. 11, No. 1, pp. 1–26 (1959).

———: "Geomagnetic Effects on Cosmic Radiation for Observation Points above the Earth," *J. Geophys. Research, 65,* 39–53 (1960).

Kellogg, P. J.: "Possible Explanation of the Radiation Observed by Van Allen at High Altitudes in Satellites," *Nuovo Cimento*, Ser. X, *11,* 48–66 (1959).

———: "Electrons of the Van Allen Radiation," *J. Geophys. Research, 65,* 2705–2713 (1960)

——— and E. P. Ney: "A New Theory of the Solar Corona," *Nature (London), 183,* 1297–1301 (1959).

———, ———, and J. R. Winckler: "Geophysical Effects Associated with High altitude Explosions," *Nature (London), 183,* 358–361 (1959).

Korff, S. A., and R. C. Haymes: "Radiation Observed at Balloon Levels with Cosmic-ray Counters during an Auroral Display," *J. Geophys. Research, 65,* 2504 (1960). (Abstract.)

Krassovsky, V. I.: "Energy Sources of the Upper Atmosphere," *Planetary and Space Science, 1,* 14–19 (1959).

———: "Results of Scientific Investigations Made by Soviet Sputniks and Cosmic Rockets," *Astronautica Acta, 6,* 32–47 (1960).

———, I. S. Shklovsky, G. I. Galperin, and E. M. Svetlitsky: "On Fast Corpuscles of the Upper Atmosphere," in S. I. Syrovatsky (ed.), Proceedings of the Moscow Cosmic Ray Conference, Vol. III, pp. 59–63 (International Union of Pure and Applied Physics, Moscow, 1960).

Kurnosova, L. V., V. I. Logachev, L. A. Razorenov, and M. I. Fradkin: "Cosmic Ray Investigation by the Second Cosmic Rocket Landed on the Moon," in H. Kallmann Bijl (ed.), "Space Research," pp. 852–862, Proceedings of the First International Space Science Symposium (North-Holland Publishing Co., Amsterdam, 1960, 1195 pp.).

Lawrie, J. A., V. B. Gerard, and P. J. Gill: "Magnetic Effects Resulting from Two High-altitude Nuclear Explosions," *Nature (London), 184,* B.A. 34, 51, 52 (1959).

Leipunskii, O. I.: "Possibility of a Magnetic Effect of High-altitude Explosions of Atom Bombs," *Zh. Eksper. Teor. Fiz., 83,* 302–304 (1960).

Ludwig, G. H.: "Cosmic Ray Instrumentation in the First U.S. Earth Satellite," *Rev. Sci. Instr., 30,* 223–229 (1959).

——— and W. A. Whelpley: "Corpuscular Radiation Experiment of Satellite 1959 Iota (Explorer VII)," *J. Geophys. Research, 65,* 1119–1124 (1960).

Maeda, H.: "Geomagnetic Disturbances due to Nuclear Explosion," *Jour. Geophys. Research, 64,* 863–864 (1959).

Malville, J. M.: "Artificial Auroras Resulting from 1958 Johnston Island Nuclear Explosions," *J. Geophys. Research, 64*, 2267–2270 (1959).

———: "The Effect of the Initial Phase of a Magnetic Storm upon the Outer Van Allen Belt," *J. Geophys. Research, 65*, 3008–3010 (1960).

Mason, R. G., and M. J. Vitousek: "Some Geomagnetic Phenomena Associated With Nuclear Explosions," *Nature (London), 184*, B.A. 52–54 (1959).

Matsushita, S.: "On Artificial Geomagnetic and Ionospheric Storms Associated with High-altitude Detonations," *J. Geophys. Research, 64*, 1149–1161 (1959).

McIlwain, C. E.: "Scintillation Counters in Rockets and Satellites," *I.R.E. Transactions in Nuclear Science*, NS, *7*, No. 2–3, 159–164 (June–September, 1960).

———: "Direct Measurement of Particles Producing Visible Aurorae," *J. Geophys. Research, 65*, 2727–2747 (1960).

———: "Direct Measurement of Protons and Electrons in Visible Aurorae," in H. Kallmann Bijl (ed.), "Space Research," pp. 715–720, Proceedings of the First International Space Science Symposium (North-Holland Publishing Co., Amsterdam, 1960, 1195 pp.).

——— and P. Rothwell: "Satellite Observations of Time Variations of Charged Particle Intensities at High Latitudes," *Bulletin of the American Physical Society*, Ser. II, *4*, No. 4, 238 (1959). (Abstract.)

——— and ———: "Spatial Dependence of the Intensity of Charged Particles Trapped in the Earth's Field between 50°N and 50°S Geographic Latitude, and 300- to 2000-km. Altitude," *J. Geophys. Research, 65*, 2508–2509 (1960). (Abstract.)

McNish, A. G.: "Geomagnetic Effects of High-altitude Nuclear Explosions," *J. Geophys. Research, 64*, 2253–2265 (1959).

Meredith, L. H., M. B. Gottlieb, and J. A. Van Allen: "Direct Detection of Soft Radiation above 50 Kilometers in the Auroral Zone," *Phys. Rev., 97*, 201–205 (1955).

Miyazaki, Y., and H. Takeuchi: "Altitude Dependence and Time Variation of the Radiation Intensity Observed by U.S. Satellite 1958α," *Report of Ionosphere Research in Japan, 12*, No. 4, 448–458 (1958).

——— and ———: "Altitude Dependence and Time Variation of the Radiation Intensity Observed by U.S. Satellite 1958α," in S. I. Syrovatsky (ed.), Proceedings of the Moscow Cosmic Ray Conference, Vol. III, pp. 41–45 (International Union of Pure and Applied Physics, Moscow, 1960).

——— and ———: "Radiation Measurements from Satellite 1958 Epsilon," in H. Kallmann Bijl (ed.), "Space Research," pp. 869–876, Proceedings of the First International Space Science Symposium (North-Holland Publishing Co., Amsterdam, 1960, 1195 pp.).

Montalbetti, R., and A. V. Jones: "H$_\alpha$ Emissions during Aurorae over West-Central Canada," *J. Atmos. Terrest. Phys., 11*, 43–50 (1957).

Newman, P.: "Optical, Electromagnetic, and Satellite Observations of High-altitude Nuclear Detonations, Part I," *J. Geophys. Research, 64*, 923–932, 2036 (1959).

Northrop, T. G., and E. Teller: "Stability of the Adiabatic Motion of Charged Particles in the Earth's Field," *Phys. Rev., 117*, 215–225 (1960).

Obayashi, T.: "The Acceleration of Particles in the Outer Atmosphere," *J. Geomagn. Geoelect., 10*, 151–152 (1959).

———: "Physical State of Outer Atmosphere and the Origin of Radiation Belts," in H. Kallmann Bijl (ed.), "Space Research," pp. 821–827, Proceedings of the

First International Space Science Symposium (North-Holland Publishing Co., Amsterdam, 1960, 1195 pp.).

——— and Y. Hakura: "Enhanced Ionization in the Polar Ionosphere and Solar Corpuscular Radiation," in H. Kallmann Bijl (ed.), "Space Research," pp. 665–694, Proceedings of the First International Space Science Symposium (North-Holland Publishing Co., Amsterdam, 1960, 1195 pp.).

O'Brien, B. J., J. A. Van Allen, F. E. Roach, and C. W. Gartlein: "Correlation of an Auroral Arc and a Subvisible Monochromatic 6300Å Arc with Outer-zone Radiation on November 28, 1959," *J. Geophys. Research, 65,* 2759–2766 (1960).

———, and G. H. Ludwig: "Development of Multiple Radiation Zones on October 18, 1959," *J. Geophys. Research, 65,* 2695–2699 (1960).

Omholt, A.: "Studies on the Excitation of Aurora Borealis, I. The Hydrogen Lines," *Geofys. Publ., 20,* No. 11, 40 pp. (1959).

Papazian, H. A.: "The Colors of Jupiter," *Publ. Astron. Soc. Pacific, 71,* 237–239 (1959).

Parker, E. N.: "The Gross Dynamics of a Hydromagnetic Gas Cloud," *Astrophysical Journal* (Supplement), *3,* 51–76 (1957).

———: "Interaction of the Solar Wind with the Geomagnetic Field," *Physics of Fluids, 1,* 171–187 (1958).

———. "Extension of the Solar Corona into Interplanetary Space," *J. Geophys. Research, 64,* 1675–1681 (1959).

Peterson, A. M.: "Optical, Electromagnetic, and Satellite Observations of High-altitude Nuclear Detonations, Part II," *J. Geophys. Research, 64,* 933–938 (1959).

Piddington, J. H.: "Geomagnetic Storm Theory," *J. Geophys. Research, 65,* 93–106 (1960).

Pikel'ner, S. B.: "The Origin of the Outer Radiation Band of the Earth," *Soviet Astronomy AJ, 3,* No. 6, 1043–1044 (May-June 1960).

Porter, R. W.: "Introductory Remarks: Symposium on Scientific Effects of Artificially Introduced Radiations at High Altitudes," *J. Geophys. Research, 64,* 865–867 (1959).

Radhakrishnan, V., and J. A. Roberts: "Polarization and Angular Extent of the 960 Mc/sec Radiation from Jupiter," *Phys. Rev. Letters, 4,* 493–494 (1960).

Ray, E. C.: "On the Theory of Protons Trapped in the Earth's Magnetic Field," *J. Geophys. Research, 65,* 1125–1134 (1960).

Rees, M. H., and G. C. Reid: "The Aurora, the Radiation Belt and the Solar Wind: A Unifying Hypothesis," *Nature (London), 184,* 539–540 (1959).

Richter, H. L., Jr., W. Pilkington, J. P. Eyrand, W. S. Shipley, and L. W. Randolph: "Instrumenting the Explorer I Satellite," *Electronics, 32,* No. 6, 39–43 (1959).

Rosen, A., P. J. Coleman, Jr., and C. P. Sonett: "Ionizing Radiation Detected by Pioneer II," *Planetary and Space Science, 1,* 343–346 (1959).

———, T. A. Farley, and C. P. Sonett: "Soft Radiation Measurements on Explorer VI Earth Satellite," in H. Kallmann Bijl (ed.), "Space Research," pp. 938–950, Proceedings of the First International Space Science Symposium (North-Holland Publishing Co., Amsterdam, 1960, 1195 pp.).

———, C. P. Sonett, P. J. Coleman, Jr., and C. E. McIlwain: "Ionizing Radiation at Altitudes of 3,500 to 36,000 Kilometers, Pioneer I," *J. Geophys. Research, 64,* 709–712 (1959).

Rosenbluth, M. N., and C. L. Longmire: "Stability of Plasmas Confined by Magnetic Fields," *Annals of Physics, 1,* 120–140 (1957).

Rossi, B.: "Scientific Results of Experiments in Space," *Trans. Am. Geophys. Union*, *41*, 410–434 (1960).

Rothwell, P.: "Magnetic Cut-off Rigidities of Charged Particles in the Earth's Field at Times of Magnetic Storms," *J. Geophys. Research, 64*,.2026–2028 (1959).

—— and C. E. McIlwain: "Satellite Observations of Solar Cosmic Rays," *Nature* (*London*), *184*, 138–140 (1959).

—— and ——: "Magnetic Storms and the Van Allen Radiation Belts: Observations from Satellite 1958 Epsilon (Explorer IV)," in H. Kallmann Bijl (ed.), "Space Research," pp. 897–909, Proceedings of the First International Space Science Symposium (North-Holland Publishing Co., Amsterdam, 1960, 1195 pp.).

—— and ——: "Magnetic Storms and the Van Allen Radiation Belts: Observations with Satellite 1958ε (Explorer IV)," *J. Geophys. Research, 65*, 799–806 (1960).

—— and ——: "Satellite Observations of Solar Cosmic Rays," in S. I. Syrovatsky (ed.), Proceedings of the Moscow Cosmic Ray Conference, Vol. III, pp. 14–18 (International Union of Pure and Applied Physics, Moscow, 1960).

Schwartz, M.: "Penumbra and Simple Shadow Cone of Cosmic Radiation," *Nuovo Cimento*, Ser. X, Suppl. Vol. 9, No. I, 27–59 (1959).

Singer, S. F.: "A New Model of Magnetic Storms and Aurorae," *Trans. Am. Geophys. Union, 38*, 175–190 (1957).

——: "'Radiation Belt' and Trapped Cosmic Ray Albedo," *Phys. Rev. Letters, 1*, 171–173 (1958).

——: "Trapped Albedo Theory of the Radiation Belt," *Phys. Rev. Letters, 1*, 181–183 (1958).

——: "Cause of the Minimum in the Earth's Radiation Belt," *Phys. Rev. Letters, 3*, 188–190 (1959).

——: "Properties of the Upper Atmosphere and Their Relation to the Radiation Belts of the Earth," *Planetary and Space Science, 2*, 165–173, 263 (1960).

——: "The Nature and Origin of the Earth's Radiation Belts: Their Relation to Upper Atmosphere Densities and Their Geophysical Effects," in S. I. Syrovatsky (ed.), Proceedings of the Moscow Cosmic Ray Conference, Vol. III, pp. 50–58 (International Union of Pure and Applied Physics, Moscow, 1960).

——: "On the Nature and Origin of the Earth's Radiation Belts," in H. Kallmann Bijl (ed.), "Space Research," pp. 797–820, Proceedings of the First International Space Science Symposium (North-Holland Publishing Co., Amsterdam, 1960, 1195 pp.).

——: "Latitude and Altitude Distribution of Geomagnetically Trapped Protons," *Phys. Rev. Letters, 5*, 300–303 (1960).

Snyder, C. W.: "The Upper Boundary of the Van Allen Radiation Belts," *Nature* (*London*), *184*, 439–440 (1959).

Sonett, C. P.: "Coupling of the Solar Wind and the Exosphere," *Phys. Rev. Letters, 5*, 46–48 (1960).

——: "Experimental Physics Using Space Vehicles," in F. I. Ordway III (ed.), "Advances in Space Science," Vol. 2, pp. 1–115 (Academic Press, 1960).

——, E. J. Smith, D. L. Judge, and P. J. Coleman, Jr.: "Current Systems in the Vestigial Geomagnetic Field: Explorer VI," *Phys. Rev. Letters, 4*, 161–163 (1960).

——, ——, and A. R. Sims: "Surveys of the Distant Geomagnetic Field: Pioneer I and Explorer VI," in H. Kallmann Bijl (ed.), "Space Research," pp. 921–937, Proceedings of the First International Space Science Symposium (North-Holland Publishing Co., Amsterdam, 1960, 1195 pp.).

————, D. L. Judge, A. R. Sims, and J. M. Kelso: "A Radial Rocket Survey of the Distant Geomagnetic Field," *J. Geophys. Research*, *65*, 55–68 (1960).

Spitzer, L., Jr.: "Physics of Fully Ionized Gases" (Interscience Publishers, Inc., 1956, 105 pp.).

Steiger, W. R., and S. Matsushita: "Photographs of the High-altitude Nuclear Explosion 'Teak'," *J. Geophys. Research*, *65*, 545–550 (1960).

Stoermer, C.: "The Polar Aurora" (Oxford: Clarendon Press, 1955, 403 pp. and 213 figs.).

Stuart, G. W.: "Satellite Measured Radiation," *Phys. Rev. Letters*, *2*, 417–418 (1959).

Treiman, S. B.: "The Cosmic-ray Albedo," *Phys. Rev.*, *91*, 957–959 (1953).

Van Allen, J. A.: "Study of the Arrival of Auroral Radiations," in J. A. Van Allen (ed.), "Scientific Uses of Earth Satellites," Chap. 21, pp. 188–193 (University of Michigan Press, Ann Arbor, Mich., 1956, 316 pp.).

————: "Direct Detection of Auroral Radiation with Rocket Equipment," *Proc. (U.S.) Nat. Acad. Sciences*, *43*, 57–92, 1957.

————: "Radiation Belts around the Earth," *Scientific American*, *200*, No. 3, 39–47 (March, 1959).

————: "The Geomagnetically-trapped Corpuscular Radiation," *J. Geophys. Research*, *64*, 1683–1689 (1959).

————: "The Geomagnetically Trapped Corpuscular Radiation," in S. I. Syrovatsky (ed.), Proceedings of the Moscow Cosmic Ray Conference, Vol. III, pp. 7–13 (International Union of Pure and Applied Physics, Moscow, 1960).

————: "Radiation Belts of the Earth," U.S. National Report 1957–1960, Twelfth General Assembly, International Union of Geodesy and Geophysics, Helsinki, Finland, July 25–August 6, 1960, pp. 246–248 (A.G.U./NAS-NRC), 1960.

————: "Origin and Nature of the Geomagnetically-trapped Radiation," in H. Kallmann Bijl (ed.), "Space Research," pp. 749–750, Proceedings of the First International Space Science Symposium (North-Holland Publishing Co., Amsterdam, 1960, 1195 pp.).

———— and L. A. Frank: "Radiation around the Earth to a Radial Distance of 107,400 Kilometers," *Nature (London)*, *183*, 430–434 (1959).

———— and ————: "Radiation Measurements to 658,300 Km. with Pioneer IV," *Nature (London)*, *184*, 219–224 (1959).

———— and W. C. Lin: "Outer Radiation Belt and Solar Proton Observations with Explorer VII during March–April 1960," *J. Geophys. Research*, *65*, 2998–3003 (1960).

————, G. H. Ludwig, E. C. Ray, and C. E. McIlwain: "Observation of High Intensity Radiation by Satellites 1958 Alpha and Gamma," *Jet Propulsion*, *28*, 588–592 (1958).

————, C. E. McIlwain, and G. H. Ludwig: "Radiation Observations with Satellite 1958 Epsilon," *J. Geophys. Research*, *64*, 271–286 (1959).

————, ————, and ————: "Satellite Observations of Electrons Artificially Injected into the Geomagnetic Field," *J. Geophys. Research*, *64*, 877–891 (1959).

Vernov, S. N., and A. E. Chudakov: "Terrestrial Corpuscular Radiation and Cosmic Rays," in H. Kallmann Bijl (ed.), "Space Research," pp. 751–796, Proceedings of the First International Space Science Symposium (North-Holland Publishing Co., Amsterdam, 1960, 1195 pp.).

———— and ————: "Investigation of Radiation in Outer Space," in S. I. Syrovatsky (ed.), Proceedings of the Moscow Cosmic Ray Conference, Vol. III, pp. 19–29 (International Union of Pure and Applied Physics, Moscow, 1960).

————, ————, E. V. Gorchakov, J. L. Logachev, and P. V. Vakulov: "Study of the Cosmic-ray Soft Component by the 3rd Soviet Earth Satellite," *Planetary and Space Science, 1*, 86–93 (1959).

————, ————, A. I. Lebedinsky, and I. P. Ivanenko: "Composition of the Earth's Corpuscular Radiation and Possible Mechanisms of Its Origination," in S. I. Syrovatsky (ed.), Proceedings of the Moscow Cosmic Ray Conference, Vol. III, pp. 46–49 (International Union of Pure and Applied Physics, Moscow, 1960).

————, ————, P. V. Vakulov, and Y. I. Logachev: "Study of Terrestrial Corpuscular Radiation and Cosmic Rays by the Flight of a Cosmic Rocket," *Doklady Akademii Nauk SSSR, 125*, 304–307 (1959).

————, ————, ————, and ————: "Mechta Radiation Data," *Astronautics,* July, 1959, pp. 23, 86–88.

————, ————, ————, ————, and A. G. Nikolaev: "Radiation Measurements during the Flight of the Second Cosmic Rocket," *Dokl. Akad. Nauk. SSSR, 130*, 517–520 (1960).

————, ————, ————, and ————: "Radiation Measurements during the Flight of the Second Soviet Space Rocket," in H. Kallmann Bijl (ed.), "Space Research," pp. 845–851, Proceedings of the First International Space Science Symposium (North-Holland Publishing Co., Amsterdam, 1960, 1195 pp.).

————, N. L. Grigorov, Y. I. Logachev, and A. Y. Chudakov. "Artificial Satellite Measurements of Cosmic Radiation," *Doklady Akademii Nauk SSSR, 120*, 1231–1233 (1958).

————, Y. I. Logachev, A. Y. Chudakov, and Y. G. Shafer: "Research on Variations of Cosmic Radiation," in L. V. Berkner, J. G. Reid, J. Hanessian, Jr., and L. Cormier (eds.), Annals of the International Geophysical Year, Vol. VI, "Manual of Rockets and Satellites," pp. 263–275 (Pergamon Press, London, 1958). [*Uspekhi Fizicheskikh Nauk, Akademia Nauk Soiuza S.S.R., 63*, 149–162 (1957).]

Vestine, E. H.: "Note on Conjugate Points of Geomagnetic Field Lines for Some Selected Auroral and Whistler Stations of the I.G.Y.," *J. Geophys. Research, 64*, 1411–1414 (1959).

————: "Polar Auroral, Geomagnetic, and Ionospheric Disturbances," *J. Geophys. Research, 65*, 360–362 (1960).

————, L. Laporte, I. Lange, C. Cooper, and W. C. Hendrix: "Description of the Earth's Main Magnetic Field and Its Secular Change, 1905–1945," Carnegie Institution of Washington, Publication 578, Washington, D.C., 1947, 532 pp.

———— and W. L. Sibley: "Remarks on Auroral Isochasms," *J. Geophys. Research, 64*, 1338–1339 (1959).

———— and ————: "The Geomagnetic Field in Space, Ring Currents, and Auroral Isochasms," *J. Geophys. Research, 65*, 1967–1979 (1960).

Walt, M., L. F. Chase, Jr., J. B. Cladis, W. L. Imhof, and D. J. Knecht: "Energy Spectra and Altitude Dependence of Electrons Trapped in the Earth's Magnetic Field," in H. Kallmann Bijl (ed.), "Space Research," pp. 910–920, Proceedings of the First International Space Science Symposium (North-Holland Publishing Co., Amsterdam, 1960, 1195 pp.).

Warwick, J. W., and R. H. Lee: "Observations of the Spectrum of Jupiter's Decametric Radio Emission, January and February 1960," *J. Geophys. Research, 65*, 2531 (1960). (Abstract.)

Welch, J. A., Jr., and W. A. Whitaker: "Theory of Geomagnetically Trapped Electrons from an Artificial Source," *J. Geophys. Research*, *64*, 909–922 (1959).

Wentworth, R. C., W. M. MacDonald, and S. F. Singer: "Lifetimes of Trapped Radiation Belt Particles Determined by Coulomb Scattering," *The Physics of Fluids*, *2*, 499–509 (1959).

Winckler, J. R.: "Balloon Study of High-altitude Radiations during the International Geophysical Year," *J. Geophys. Research*, *65*, 1331–1359 (1960).

——— and L. Peterson: "Large Auroral Effect on Cosmic-ray Detectors Observed at 8 g/cm² Atmospheric Depth," *Phys. Rev.*, *108*, 903–904 (1957).

———, ———, R. Arnoldy, and R. Hoffman: "X-rays from Visible Aurorae at Minneapolis," *Phys. Rev.*, *110*, 1221–1231 (1958).

Yagoda, Herman: "Star Production by Trapped Protons in the Inner Radiation Belt," *Phys. Rev. Letters*, *5*, 17–18 (1960).

Yoshida, S., G. H. Ludwig, and J. A. Van Allen: "Distribution of Trapped Radiation in the Geomagnetic Field," *J. Geophys. Research*, *65*, 807–813 (1960).

16 ≡

ON PARTICLES AND FIELDS PERTINENT
TO AURORAL THEORY

Joseph W. Chamberlain

For over fifty years scientists have felt fairly certain that the aurora is produced by the bombardment on the Earth's upper atmosphere of high-speed particles, ejected from the Sun during periods of solar activity. But the precise manner in which these particles escape from the Sun, travel the intervening 93 million miles from the Sun to the Earth, eventually interact with the Earth's magnetic field, and finally make their way into the Earth's atmosphere to produce the aurora have all been subjects steeped in mystery. A variety of theories for these processes have been proposed, but none has been especially satisfactory.

Our inability to fully understand the aurora is not so surprising when one recalls that all our information about the streams of particles from the Sun has been indirect. We observe activity on the Sun, and a day or so later we have an aurora on the Earth, accompanied by substantial changes in the Earth's magnetism—a so-called "geomagnetic storm." In addition, the spectrum of auroral light shows that protons (hydrogen nuclei) are striking the atmosphere with speeds of several thousand kilometers per second during an aurora, forming impressive evidence that the aurora is indeed due to hydrogen gas ejected from the Sun.

297

Nevertheless, our knowledge of the behavior of the particles in space has remained obscure, and only the possibility of their direct detection, by satellites and space probes, offers real hope of understanding the auroral phenomenon.

In this section I wish to sketch the information that has so far entered into the construction of auroral theories and to indicate the principal problems that still remain and the manner in which space experiments may be expected to solve them.

1. STREAMS OF SOLAR GAS

At the core of an auroral theory lies a hypothesis on the manner in which a solar disturbance is propagated. Usually the hypothesis has involved clouds or streams of plasma or ionized gas. Several attempts have been made[1-4] to detect calcium atoms in such streams spectroscopically through abnormal absorptions shortward of the solar H and K spectral lines prior to magnetic storms, but the results have been mostly negative.

The angular diameter of geoactive streams is often thought to be several degrees[5] as deduced from (1) the duration for strong magnetic storms of a few days at most, (2) the tendency for active solar regions to have their maximum geomagnetic influence near central-meridian passage, (3) the yearly variation, interpreted as due to the ejection of particles from regions on the Sun that are localized near the sunspot belts,[6] and (4) the 11-year cycle, with an observed lag in the geoactive maximum behind the sunspot maximum attributed to the higher solar latitude of sunspots early in the sunspot cycle.

That corpuscular emission from the Sun is more widespread and frequent than had been inferred from geophysical observations is indicated by the acceleration of comet tails away from the Sun. Formerly attributed to radiation pressure, these accelerations now appear to involve particle collisions. Biermann[7-10] has developed this hypothesis and concludes that densities of the order of 100 particles per cm^3 and stream velocities of the order of 500 to 1500 km per sec are present at all times near the Earth, with a flux increased over 100 times during magnetic storms. This proposal for such a strong "solar wind," as Parker[11,11a] calls it, offers difficulties in accounting for neutral hydrogen in the solar system and is not substantiated by observations of continuous outward motions in the corona. Thus the reality of a steady solar wind is still uncertain. Some theoretical work on the solar corona and interplanetary gas suggests no more than a "solar breeze."[12,13]

Solar-particle streams appear to originate in the active regions around sunspots and may consequently carry magnetic fields.[14] Mustel[15] estimates that fields as high as 10^{-2} gauss might be transported to the Earth in this fashion, "frozen" to the gas. Such fields would contribute to the large accelerations of ions in comet tails, reducing the momentum otherwise required for solar streams; would have a profound bearing on the interaction of the streams with the Earth; and may account for time variations in cosmic rays, such as the Forbush decrease.

A considerable number of models for solar streams have been proposed.[16] Here we must confine the discussion to a brief resumé of the principal works. All these models have attempted to elucidate the interaction between charged particles and the terrestrial magnetic field. The theories differ according to the assumptions made regarding the relative speeds of protons and electrons, the importance of a particle's electric and magnetic forces on its neighbors in the stream, and the influence of solar or interplanetary magnetic fields.

Störmer's[17-19] theory of single particles in a dipole field is the prototype for stream models in which the motions of charged particles of one sign are predominant. A precursor to Störmer's work was the theory for a particle in the field of a monopole developed by his teacher, Poincaré.[20] The stimulus was the experimental work of Birkeland,[21] who fired particles at a magnetized sphere (terrella). A modification of the Störmer theory was proposed by Bennett and Hulburt[22,23] and Bennett,[24,25] and it is also suitably illustrated by a modified terrella experiment designed by Bennett.[26,27]

A stream composed of equal numbers of positive ions and electrons, all moving with essentially the same velocity, was first proposed by Lindemann (Lord Cherwell)[28] and subsequently developed by Chapman and Ferraro[29-31] and Ferraro.[32] It was assumed that interplanetary space had little or no effect on the stream, which carried no magnetic field of its own. Extensions have been proposed by Martyn,[33] Landseer-Jones,[34] and Warwick,[35] regarding the interaction of such a stream with the terrestrial field to produce aurora.

Streams moving through an external field in interplanetary space or carrying a magnetic field frozen to the cloud have been considered by Alfvén,[36-40] Aström,[41] Landseer-Jones,[42] Piddington,[43] and Gold.[44,45] Again, appropriate terrella experiments have been designed in support of some of this work.[46-48]

2. THE PRINCIPAL PROBLEMS REGARDING THE ORIGIN OF AURORA

One of the most significant advances in our understanding of auroral particles the past few years is the realization that at least some of the particles have speeds much faster than the 1000 km per sec implied by delay times of geophysical events following solar events and that there is a wide energy or velocity spread among auroral particles. These conclusions are based on the profiles of hydrogen lines in auroral spectra,[49] the brightness distribution with height in aurorae,[49] balloon measurements of X rays from incident electrons,[50-56] and rocket and satellite data on the particles themselves.[57,58]

The fundamental question to auroral theory today is whether auroral particles spend an appreciable amount of time in the Van Allen belt. That is to say, do auroral particles impinge on the atmosphere directly from interplanetary space, or do they enter the atmosphere by way of the Van Allen regions, wherein their energies may be altered and their geographic distribution regulated? One means of resolving this problem is to compare the energies of the particles in the solar stream far out in space with the energies of particles in the trapped-radiation belt and with the energies of particles striking the atmosphere and producing the aurora.

The spectrum of auroral energies might conceivably be explained in two quite different ways. On the one hand, the auroral particles may be accelerated locally[49] (i.e., within the terrestrial magnetic field). On the other hand, the energy spectrum may be produced by acceleration at the Sun. In the latter case particles of all energies (in the low-energy, auroral region) must be held together, presumably by a magnetic field. When the magnetized cloud or stream material merges with the terrestrial field, the particles might then flow directly into the polar atmosphere, producing the aurora.

With the first picture (local acceleration), the existence of trapped particles would be an essential feature of the production of aurorae. With the second picture, the outer Van Allen belt would be only a secondary effect of the general auroral process, the trapped particles representing the residue of particles that were unable to penetrate into the atmosphere. These leftover particles would then constitute the trapped-radiation belt, replenishing it from time to time.

A combination of these two pictures may also eventually emerge, with local acceleration of electrons, say, being important, the proton energy spectrum being modified near the Earth in a relatively less important manner. In that event, a solar or interplanetary magnetic field may be of paramount importance in holding the protons together in spite of their large energy dispersion, but local acceleration would be responsible for producing the electron energy spectrum. A pertinent experiment to be conducted well outside the Earth's field, around the time of a strong aurora, would measure the number of protons and electrons with different velocities and moving in different directions (since a magnetic field in space would superimpose a spiraling motion on the velocity away from the Sun).

A final auroral theory must explain such items of the auroral morphology as the appearance of aurorae predominantly on the night side of the Earth (and even with a maximum probability of appearance near the midnight meridian of the Earth), the fine structure in an auroral display, and motions of the auroral patterns as seen visually and detected by radar reflections. These problems are evidently all related to the areas on the Earth where auroral particles precipitate and to the trajectories of the auroral particles in space.

If the aurora arises from particles bombarding the atmosphere directly from the solar corpuscular stream, then the geographic location of the aurora, its structure, and its motions must be related to the manner in which the auroral particles are bent around the Earth and precipitated directly into the atmosphere. Until the discovery of the Van Allen belts this type of theory was generally favored, but no detailed theory ever offered a satisfactory explanation for these phenomena. Störmer's theory of particle trajectories attempted to cope with these matters, but his explanation is now known to be inadequate, dealing as it did with particles of a single energy and not allowing for the wide energy spread now known to characterize the auroral particles.

With the viewpoint that the aurora arises from the Van Allen belt, the geographic location, the structure, and the motions become problems of ascertaining why and where particles are dumped out of the belt. Theoretical discussions of these problems are still so speculative as to leave unexplained these major features of aurorae.   Direct measurement of the particles in the radiation belt at the times and above the places where aurorae are produced are expected to elucidate the problem and give sufficient clues to the actual mechanisms at work so that a phenomenological theory of the aurora may soon be constructed.

Detection of aurorae on other planets also becomes a possibility with space probes and will be of interest for several reasons. First, the emitted auroral light may show the presence of such constituents in the planetary atmosphere as nitrogen, which cannot be detected in the spectrum of reflected sunlight, as can carbon dioxide, for example. Second, the presence of an auroral zone would be an indicator of a planetary magnetic field and perhaps of low-energy trapped particles around the planet. Finally, when the strength of the magnetic field becomes measured by other means and the planet's Van Allen belt is explored directly, we shall have an entire new set of data, very likely on a completely different scale from the terrestrial phenomena, with which to test hypotheses for auroral mechanisms.

The matters discussed in this section are treated in more detail elsewhere.[59]

REFERENCES

1. R. S. Richardson: "Results of an Investigation to Detect an Inter-solar Cloud of Charged Particles during Magnetic Storms," *Transact. Amer. Geophys. Un.*, *25*, 558–560 (1944).
2. H. A. Brück and F. Rutllant: "Some Observations of the H and K Lines in the Solar Spectrum during a Magnetic Storm," *Monthly Not. Roy. Ast. Soc.*, *106*, 130–134 (1946).
3. M. F. Smyth: "Photoelectric Investigations of Solar Corpuscular Radiation, I," *Monthly Not. Roy. Ast. Soc.*, *114*, 137–153 (1954).
4. M. F. Smyth: "Photoelectric Investigations of Solar Corpuscular Radiation, II," *Monthly Not. Roy. Ast. Soc.*, *114*, 503–513 (1954).
5. M. N. Gnevyshev and A. I. Ol: "The Solid Angle of the Sun's Corpuscular Streams" (translated title), *Ast. Zhur.*, *22*, 151–157 (1945).
6. A. L. Cortie: "Sunspots and Terrestrial Magnetic Phenomena, 1898–1911: The Cause of the Annual Variation in Magnetic Disturbances," *Monthly Not. Roy. Ast. Soc.*, *73*, 52–60, 136 (1912).
7. L. Biermann: "Kometenschweife und Solare Korpuskularstrahlung," *Z. Astrophys.*, *29*, 274–286 (1951).
8. L. Biermann: "Über den Schweif des Kometen Halley im Jahre 1910," *Z. Naturforsch.*, *7a*, 127–136 (1952).
9. L. Biermann: "Physical Processes in Comet Tails and Their Relation to Solar Activity," *Mém. Soc. Roy. Sci. Liège*, Ser. 4, *13*, 291–302 (1953).
10. L. Biermann: "Solar Corpuscular Radiation and the Interplanetary Gas," *Observatory*, *77*, 109–110 (1957).
11. E. N. Parker: "Dynamics of the Interplanetary Gas and Magnetic Fields," *Astrophys. J.*, *128*, 664–676 (1958).
11a. E. N. Parker: "The Hydrodynamic Treatment of the Expanding Solar Corona," *Astrophys. J.*, *132*, 175–183 (1960).
12. J. W. Chamberlain: "Interplanetary Gas. II. Expansion of a Model Solar Corona," *Astrophys. J.*, *131*, 47–56 (1960).
13. J. W. Chamberlain: "Interplanetary Gas. III. A Hydrodynamic Model of the Corona," *Astrophys. J.*, *133* (1961, in press).
14. F. Hoyle: "Some Recent Researches in Solar Physics" (University Press, Cambridge, England, 1949).
15. E. R. Mustel: "Corpuscular Streams during the Years of Minimum Activity and Their Properties" (translated title), *Ast. Zhur.*, *35*, 351–365 (1958).

16. J. W. Chamberlain: "Theories of the Aurora," in H. E. Landsberg and J. Van Mieghem (eds.), "Advances in Geophysics," pp. 109–215 (Academic Press, 1958).

17. C. Störmer: "Sur les trajectories des corpuscles électrisés dans l'espace sous l'action du magnétisme terrestre avec application aux Aurores Boréales," Arch. Sci. Phys. et Nat. (Genève), [4], 24, 5–18, 113–158, 221–247, 317–354 (1907).

18. C. Störmer: "Sur les trajectories des corpuscles électrisés dans l'espace sous l'action du magnétisme terrestre avec application aux Aurores Boréales," Arch. Sci. Phys. et Nat. (Genève), [4], 32, 117–123, 190–219, 277–314, 415–436, 501–509 (1911); 33, 51–69, 113–150 (1912).

19. C. Störmer: "The Polar Aurora" (Clarendon Press, Oxford, 1955).

20. H. Poincaré: "Remarques sur une expérience de M. Birkeland," Compt. rend., 123, 530–533 (1896).

21. K. Birkeland: "Sur les rayons cathodiques: sous l'action de forces magnétiques intenses," Arch. Sci. Phys. et Nat. (Genève), 1, 497–512 (1896).

22. W. H. Bennett and E. O. Hulburt: "Magnetic Self-focused Solar Ion Streams as the Cause of Aurorae," J. Atm. Terr. Phys., 5, 211–218 (1954).

23. W. H. Bennett and E. O. Hulburt: "Theory of Aurora Based on Magnetic Self-focusing of Solar Ion Streams," Phys. Rev., 95, 315–319 (1954).

24. W. H. Bennett: "Self-focusing Streams," Phys. Rev., 98, 1584–1593 (1955).

25. W. H. Bennett: "Auroral and Magnetic-storm Theory," Astrophys. J., 127, 731–742 (1958).

26. W. H. Bennett: "The Störmertron," Ann. Géophys., 14, 206–207 (1958).

27. W. H. Bennett: "Solar Proton Stream Forms with a Laboratory Model," Rev. Sci. Instrum., 30, 63–69 (1959).

28. F. A. Lindemann: "Note on the Theory of Magnetic Storms," Phil. Mag. [6], 38, 669–694 (1919).

29. S. Chapman and V. C. A. Ferraro: "A New Theory of Magnetic Storms," Terr. Magn., 36, 77–97, 171–186 (1931); 37, 147–156, 421–429 (1932); 38, 79–96 (1933).

30. S. Chapman and V. C. A. Ferraro: "The Theory of the First Phase of a Geomagnetic Storm," Terr. Magn., 45, 245–268 (1940).

31. S. Chapman and V. C. A. Ferraro: "The Geomagnetic Ring Current. I. Its Radial Stability," Terr. Magn., 46, 1–6 (1941).

32. V. C. A. Ferraro: "Theory of the First Phase of a Magnetic Storm," J. Geophys. Research, 57, 15–49 (1952).

33. D. F. Martyn: "The Theory of Magnetic Storms and Auroras," Nature, 167, 92–94 (1951).

34. B. C. Landseer-Jones: "The Streaming of Charged Particles through a Magnetic Field as a Theory of the Aurora," J. Atm. Terr. Phys., 3, 41–57 (1952).

35. C. Warwick: "Green Coronal Line Intensity and Geomagnetism," J. Geophys. Research, 64, 527–531 (1959).

36. H. Alfvén: "A Theory of Magnetic Storms and Aurorae I," Kungl. Sv. Vetenskapsakad. Handl., 18, No. 3, 1–39 (1939).

37. H. Alfvén: "A Theory of Magnetic Storms and Aurorae II and III," Kungl. Sv. Vetenskapsakad Handl., 18, No. 9, 1–39 (1940).

38. H. Alfvén: "Cosmical Electrodynamics" (Clarendon Press, Oxford, 1950).

39. H. Alfvén: "On the Electric Field Theory of Magnetic Storms and Aurora," *Tellus, 7,* 50–64 (1955).
40. H. Alfvén: "On the Theory of Magnetic Storms and Aurorae," *Tellus, 10,* 104–116 (1958).
41. E. Aström: "On the Theory of Magnetic Storms and Aurorae," *Tellus, 8,* 239–240 (1956).
42. B. C. Landseer-Jones: "The Significance of a Nonterrestrial Magnetic Field in Neutral Stream Theories of the Aurora," *J. Atm. Terr. Phys., 6,* 215–226 (1955).
43. J. H. Piddington: "Interplanetary Magnetic Field and Its Control of Cosmic-ray Variations," *Phys. Rev., 112,* 589–596 (1958).
44. T. Gold: "Plasma and Magnetic Fields in the Solar System," *J. Geophys. Research, 64,* 1665–1674 (1959).
45. T. Gold: "Origin of the Radiation near the Earth Discovered by Means of Satellites," *Nature, 183,* 355–358 (1959).
46. K. G. Malmfors: "Experiments on the Aurorae," *Ark. Mat. Astr. Fysik, 34B,* No. 1, 1–8 (1946).
47. L. Block: "Model Experiments on Aurorae and Magnetic Storms," *Tellus, 7,* 65–86 (1955).
48. L. Block: "On the Scale of Auroral Model Experiments," *Tellus, 8,* 234–238 (1956).
49. J. W. Chamberlain: "On a Possible Velocity Dispersion of Auroral Protons," *Astrophys. J., 126,* 245–252 (1957).
50. L. H. Meredith, M. B. Gottlieb, and J. A. Van Allen: "Direct Detection of Soft Radiation above 50 Kilometers in the Auroral Zone," *Phys. Rev., 97,* 201–205 (1955).
51. J. A. Van Allen: "Direct Detection of Auroral Radiation with Rocket Equipment," *Proc. Natl. Acad. Sci., 43,* 57–62 (1957).
52. K. A. Anderson: "Soft Radiation Events at High Altitude during the Magnetic Storm of August 29–30, 1957," *Phys. Rev., 111,* 1397–1405 (1958).
53. K. A. Anderson: "Balloon Observations of X-rays in the Auroral Zone I," *J. Geophys. Research, 65,* 551–564 (1960).
54. J. R. Winckler and L. Peterson: "Large Auroral Effect on Cosmic-ray Detectors Observed at 8 g/cm² Atmospheric Depth," *Phys. Rev., 108,* 903–904 (1957).
55. J. R. Winckler, L. Peterson, R. Arnoldy, and R. Hoffman: "X-rays from Visible Aurorae at Minneapolis," *Phys. Rev., 110,* 1221–1231 (1958).
56. J. R. Winckler, L. Peterson, R. Hoffman, and R. Arnoldy: "Auroral X-rays, Cosmic Rays, and Related Phenomena during the Storm of February 10–11, 1958," *J. Geophys. Research, 64,* 597–610 (1959).
57. L. H. Meredith, L. R. Davis, J. P. Heppner, and O. E. Berg: "Rocket Auroral Investigations," in J. Hanessian, Jr. and I. Guttmacher (eds.), "Experimental Results of the U.S. Rocket Program for the IGY to 1 July 1958," pp. 169–178 (National Academy of Sciences, IGY Rocket Report Series No. 1, 1958).
58 C. E. McIlwain: "Direct Measurement of Protons and Electrons in Visible Aurorae," *State University of Iowa, Dept. Physics-Astronomy, Report* 59-29, pp. 1–8, 1959.
59. J. W. Chamberlain, "Physics of the Aurora and Airglow" (Academic Press, 1960).

PART **6** $\equiv$

THE STARS

THE SUN

Leo Goldberg and Edward R. Dyer, Jr.

1. BACKGROUND

1.1 Introduction

The Sun is a typical member of the family of stars in which energy production takes place in the core, but in which the conversion of hydrogen into helium has not progressed far enough to introduce profound changes in the structure. This family appears on the Hertzsprung-Russell diagram (plot of luminosity versus spectral type or surface temperature, Fig. 2 of Chap. 18) as the main sequence. Luckily for stellar astrophysics, the Sun is an average sort of star, occupying a central position in the distribution of main-sequence stars according to luminosity and surface temperature, radius, mass, and perhaps even relative age. This fact gives the astrophysicist a good deal of confidence in extending theories derived from solar studies toward the two extremes of bigger, brighter stars and smaller, fainter ones.

Furthermore, the Sun is tremendously important from the standpoint of astrophysics because it is the only star that can be examined in considerable detail from a relatively close distance. Other stars are so remote (the nearest is 300,000 times as far as the Sun) that they appear as optical point sources, and only the integrated starlight from their disks is received on the Earth. In the case of the Sun, however, it is possible by existing techniques to resolve details smaller than 1 second of arc, or about one-thousandth the Sun's radius. Much smaller details are easily observable from above our lower atmosphere: this point will be discussed later.

Naturally the scrutiny, analysis, and correlation of the detailed features of the visible surface of the Sun and its extended outer atmosphere yield vastly more data than does integrated light for the formulation of theories about energy production, transfer, and conversion and for the formulation of models for the interior and atmosphere. Despite the Sun's proximity, however, the amounts and types of data that have been secured till now with earth-bound instruments are inadequate for the solution of most of the basic solar problems. Extension of the range of observation to cover the entire electromagnetic spectrum and the elimination of bad seeing caused by the Earth's atmosphere are likely to fill the most important gaps in our knowledge.

Before discussing the specific applications of satellite techniques to solar physics, we shall summarize briefly the present state of knowledge in the field.*

Radiation from the Sun as a whole is only very slightly variable. But the radiation from localized regions or in restricted frequency ranges is extremely variable, and this variability is associated with activity in the solar atmosphere in the form of sunspots and sunspot groups, prominences, flares, etc. In astrophysical studies of the Sun it is useful to make a distinction between those that refer to the "quiet" and the "active" Sun. The terms "quiet" and "active" were originally introduced by radio astronomers to contrast the radio behavior of the Sun during periods of solar activity with that in the absence of activity, but they now also serve more generally to distinguish the normal Sun from its disturbed regions.

1.2 Quiet Sun

In discussing solar physics, it is convenient to divide the Sun into four concentric regions with more or less well defined properties:

1. *The interior* is the region from which no radiant energy escapes directly; i.e., it has been intercepted at least once. The interior may be subdivided further into (a) a core, a region in which the radiant energy is produced by thermonuclear reactions, predominantly near the center,

---

* More detailed and technical accounts will be found in *Handbook of the Solar System*, Vol. I,[1] in *Handbuch der Physik*, Vol. 52,[2] and in other references listed in the bibliography at the end of this chapter.

and through which it seeps by radiative transfer along the temperature gradient toward the outside, and (*b*) a convective envelope, whose depth is uncertain, but which is at most 140,000 km thick (one-fifth the radius). It extends up to a layer just below the visible exterior. and contains no more than one two-hundredth of the total mass.

The Sun and cooler, less massive stars are believed to run on the proton-proton cycle, whose temperature dependence is about T^4. Hotter, more massive stars operate on the carbon cycle with energy-production rate proportional to T^{16} to T^{19} or so. This extreme temperature dependence creates such a steep gradient that convection is promoted in the inner cores of the larger stars; in stars as small as the Sun one does not expect such a convective inner core.[3]

The convective instability in the envelope just beneath the visible surface is due partly to the recombination of ions, especially the very abundant He^{++}, He^+, and H^+, which releases radiant energy into the surroundings, and partly to the proximity of this region to the outer low-temperature boundary. The magnitude of these effects on the extent of the convective region is not precisely known[4]

The temperature, pressure, and density decline through the interior from extremely high values at the center to relatively low values at the visible surface.

2. *The photosphere* is the apparent surface, actually a relatively thin layer from which practically all optical radiation comes. In a region several hundred kilometers in thickness, the optical depth τ for visible radiation increases inward from zero to a large value. Hence the emergent radiation contains contributions from many different layers, but its intensity is approximately equal to that radiated by the gas at an optical depth of unity. (Unit optical depth or thickness corresponds to the distance in which the traversing radiation is attenuated by the factor $1/e$.) At the distance of the Earth from the Sun, a layer of unit optical depth seen edge on subtends less than 1 second and therefore appears sharp. The continuous spectrum of this radiation is a mean of near black-body radiation whose temperature ranges from perhaps 4500 to 7500°K, weighted according to the contribution of each shell to the emergent radiation. At the center of the disk the resulting blended spectrum resembles that of a black body near 6000°K. Near the limb, along oblique lines of sight where the contribution of the deeper, hotter layers is proportionately less, the continuous spectrum corresponds to a lower temperature. This is the physical explanation of limb darkening and limb reddening. The temperature of a black body that most nearly matches the continuous spectrum of sunlight integrated over the whole

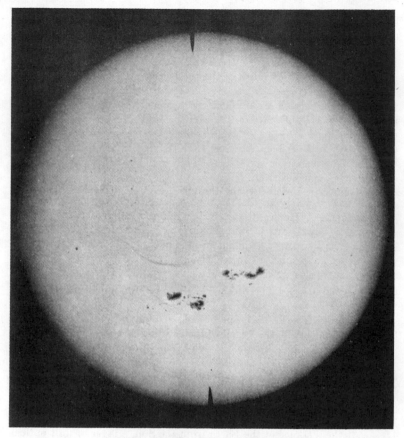

FIG. 1. The Sun in integrated white light. (*a*) Two exceptionally large sunspot groups and some smaller spots; (*b*) limb darkening or dimming of solar radiation coming from near the apparent edge; and (*c*) faculae, the regions slightly hotter than their surroundings that are most easily visible near the limb. (*Courtesy of Mt. Wilson and Palomar Observatories.*)

visible disk is thus somewhat lower (about 5750°K), and this "effective temperature" is the one which most logically fits into the effective temperature scale for stars, from which with very few exceptions only the integrated radiation can be observed. (See Fig. 1 for a photograph of the Sun in white light.)

Under high resolution, the photosphere is seen to be mottled with granules (Fig. 2), small areas of the order of 1 or 2 seconds of arc (about 1000 km) in diameter, slightly hotter and brighter than their surroundings and having a mean lifetime of several minutes. These appear to be regions where currents emerge with upward velocities of the order of 1 km per sec, and the surrounding darker interstices are the regions of subsidence. The detailed nature of the granules and of the mechanism underlying them have eluded understanding, chiefly because the turbu-

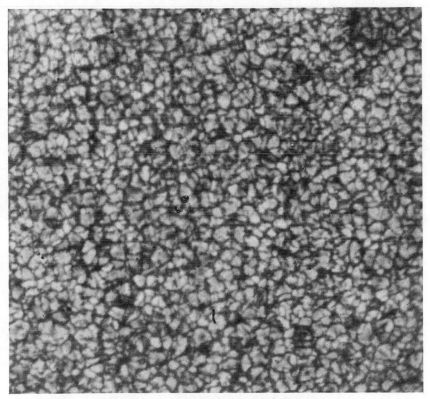

FIG. 2. Solar granules taken on Aug. 17, 1959, with a balloon-borne telescope (scale: 1 cm on print = 4600 km on Sun). (*Courtesy of Project Stratoscope of Princeton University, sponsored by the Office of Naval Research and the National Science Foundation.*)

lence of the Earth's atmosphere has prevented precise measurements of the distribution of granular sizes, velocities, and temperatures.

Within the past two or three years, the turbulence of the Earth's atmosphere has been eliminated as an obstacle to the achievement of high-definition direct photographs of the Sun as a result of the observations by Schwarzschild from high-altitude balloons.[5] Whereas earlier ground-based observations were frequently controversial, because of their marginal character, the balloon results seem to establish conclusively that (a) the solar granules appear to have a great range of apparent diameters, extending from about 300 km or less to about 1800 km; (b) the granules are strikingly irregular in shape, many of them simulating irregular polygons; (c) there is a striking topological asymmetry between the brighter-than-average and darker-than-average areas; (d) the root-mean-square temperature fluctuation is probably not larger than $\pm 100°$.

The energy that drives the convective currents is undoubtedly derived from the region of convective instability just below the photosphere. Until recently it was impossible to decide conclusively whether the cells are of the stationary Bénard type or whether there is present the whole spectrum of nonstationary turbulence, right down to the microturbulence thought to be responsible for the more-than-thermal Doppler broadening of the Fraunhofer lines.   The new observations by Schwarzschild seem to leave little doubt, however, that the real situation is intermediate between these two extremes and that the character of the solar granulation is most closely represented by nonstationary convection.   Unfortunately, all the observational data required for full theoretical understanding are not yet available.   In particular, the mean upward velocity of the granules and the spectrum of velocities as a function of size are both uncertain.

The photosphere is also the seat of such solar activity as sunspots and faculae (see Fig. 1) and of associated local variable magnetic fields (described below under the heading Active Sun and Active Regions).

3. *The chromosphere* is a dynamic transition region about 10,000 to 15,000 km thick, lying between the relatively cool outer layers of the photosphere (about 4500°K) and the million-degree corona. It is extremely inhomogeneous, and small volumes are far from being in a steady state.   The light of the chromosphere, when viewed against the background of space (as during an eclipse or through a coronagraph), has an emission-line spectrum that corresponds more or less to the absorption-line spectrum of the photosphere.   In the extreme lower chromosphere the line intensities of the metals indicate for the most part a temperature not much different from the upper photosphere, namely, of the order of 4000 to 5000°K.   The intensity of the Balmer continuum and of the

Balmer "jump" also points in this direction. On the other hand, certain high-excitation lines (He I $\approx$ 20 ev, He II $\approx$ 40 ev, etc.) are already strongly enhanced only a few hundred kilometers above the photosphere. The width of the H and He lines also can be interpreted as resulting from higher temperatures. The intensity of the highest-frequency radio radiation ($\lambda \lesssim 1$ cm), which originates in the low chromosphere, indicates an electron-kinetic temperature of about 8000°K, but the intensity of slightly lower frequency radiation, coming from regions just a little higher, points to much higher temperatures.

The normal structure of the chromosphere consists of fairly closely packed spicules—small jetlike prominences with lifetimes of the order of

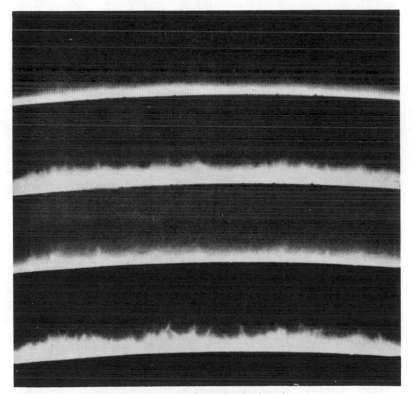

FIG. 3. Enlarged view of the chromosphere, showing its spicular structure. (*Courtesy of the Sacramento Peak Observatory, Geophysics Research Directorate, AFCRC.*)

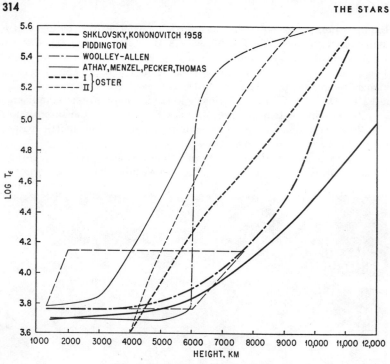

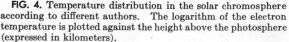

FIG. 4. Temperature distribution in the solar chromosphere according to different authors. The logarithm of the electron temperature is plotted against the height above the photosphere (expressed in kilometers).

several minutes and upward velocities of the order of 20 km per sec—whose tops reach a height of roughly 10,000 km (see Fig. 3). The appearance of the chromosphere in the light of Hα that arises from this structure has been compared to a prairie fire.

Theoretical astrophysicists have been attempting to construct a coherent model of the chromosphere which explains both the low- and high-temperature phenomena, both the optical and radio results. There is little uniformity of opinion except perhaps on the following: the chromosphere, especially in the region below 6000 km, is a complex inhomogeneous region probably comprising cells of high and low temperature, perhaps as different as 30,000 and 4000°; in the upper chromosphere (above 6000 km) the temperature rises steadily and rapidly to several hundred thousand degrees at the base of the corona. There is no sharp

division between the top of the chromosphere and the base of the corona
since the tops of spicules sometimes project into the corona.

Figures 4 and 5 show the run of temperature and electron density with
height according to several recent models of the chromosphere.[6] Some
of these are based on optical data alone, others on radio data; still others
represent an attempt to reconcile the two. Present theoretical disagreements about the structure of the chromosphere (which apply equally to
the corona, discussed in the next section) arise only partly from the
difficulty of securing data of high resolution, as in the case of the photosphere. In addition to this grave difficulty, there have been two other

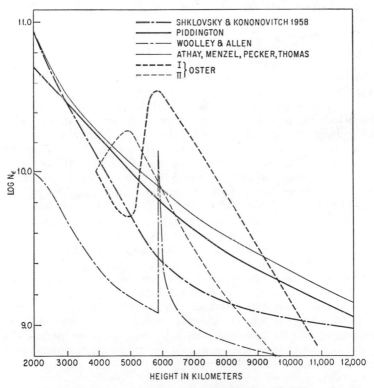

FIG. 5. The electron density in the chromosphere. The logarithm of the electron density expressed in particles per cubic
centimeter is plotted against the height in kilometers. (*From
University of Michigan Research Institute Report, Nov.* 1958.)

stumbling blocks.   It is intrinsically harder to construct a model for the very complex and dynamic outer envelopes than for the relatively simpler photosphere.   Furthermore, most of the radiation from the photosphere is in the visible region of the spectrum and has thus been under detailed investigation for some time.   By contrast, the most distinctive and, relative to the photosphere, strongest radiations that emanate from the outer envelope are in the extreme short-wave (ultraviolet and X-ray) and long-wave (radio-frequency) regions of the spectrum.   On this account it is only very recently that we have begun to accumulate data through the new techniques of radio astronomy and rocketry.

Types of activity associated most closely with the chromosphere (aside from the spicules which may be regarded as a feature of the "quiet" chromosphere) are plages, flares, and prominences.   These phenomena are discussed below.   It might be noted in passing that the association of these active regions with the chromosphere is based in part upon their spectral characteristics rather than on their location, since most prominences actually project into the corona whereas flares may occur in the upper photosphere as well as in the chromosphere.

4. *The corona* (see Fig. 6) is the very tenuous outer atmosphere of the Sun, which can be traced out into space for a distance of several solar radii.   In it the electron density is believed to fall from about 10^9 per cubic centimeter at the base to interplanetary values (up to 10^2 per cubic centimeter) at the outside.   The intensity of coronal light is approximately 10^{-6} of the total sunlight, and most of this is continuous radiation from the photosphere scattered by electrons, as shown by its color and radial polarization.   Most of the Sun's X radiation originates in the corona and in certain active regions of the chromosphere.   A number of phenomena concur in indicating that the kinetic temperature of the corona is of the order of $10^{6°}$K.   Among these phenomena are (*a*) the appearance of the forbidden emission lines of multiply ionized Fe, Ni, and Ca, requiring several hundred electron volts for their excitation; (*b*) the complete washing out of the Fraunhofer lines in the scattered photospheric spectrum by the high thermal velocities of the scattering electrons; (*c*) the temperature deduced from radio-frequency radiation in this region; (*d*) the low-density gradient or large scale height of the corona, if it is assumed to be in approximate hydrostatic equilibrium with the Sun's gravitational field.

The corona is only very approximately spherically symmetrical. Actually, it exhibits a considerable amount of both regular and irregular structure.   The regular structure goes through a cycle in phase with the 11-year activity cycle: at sunspot minimum the corona shows broad

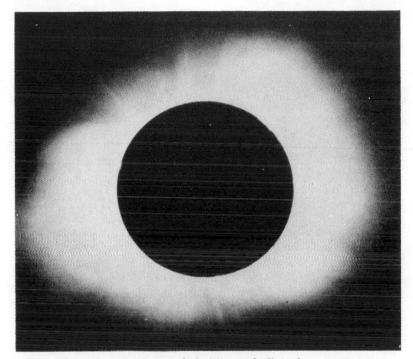

FIG. 6. The solar corona photographed at the total eclipse of June 8, 1918. The streamers at the North and South Poles strongly suggest the presence of a general magnetic field. (*Courtesy of Mt. Wilson and Palomar Observatories.*)

extensions above the equatorial region and fine striated streamers fanning out from each pole, while at sunspot maximum the structure is more nearly the same over equator and pole, with the polar streamers much less pronounced.   The corona also shows localized inhomogeneities, e.g., regions of greater radio opacity when occulting radio stars, "hot spots" over regions of obvious activity in the chromosphere, etc.   Some of these features are more properly associated with the active Sun.   The two sorts of active regions, as indicated by strong line emission and strong radio noise, respectively, are by no means identical.   There is some evidence, chiefly from radio observations, that the outer corona is a relatively loose collection of clouds of highly ionized gas.

1.3   Magnetic Fields in the Quiet Sun

There remains the general question of the Sun's magnetic field, which is not definitely associated with any particular one of the four separate concentric regions discussed above.   The polar streamers in the solar corona seem to require the presence of a permanent general dipole field, although its strength need be only a small fraction of a gauss.   Hale's[7] early attempts to measure the Sun's magnetic field, using the Zeeman effect in the Fraunhofer lines, led to conflicting results, which have only been resolved in the last few years.   All the more recent investigations, especially those of the Babcocks,[8] with their much more sensitive photo-electric scanning equipment, have agreed in showing that the general field is of the order of 1 gauss (see also Thiessen,[9] Kiepenheuer,[10] and von Klüber[11]).   The Babcocks show that the general dipole magnetic field merges at medium heliographic latitudes into a toroidal field whose pattern is masked, especially during active phases, by the much stronger local temporary fields which are possibly derived from the toroidal field. The Babcocks have shown the existence of localized bipolar and unipolar fields of several gauss lasting from days to months, the strongest of which are associated with faculae (see below).   Their earlier technique, though sensitive to 0.2 gauss, integrated the line-of-sight component of the field over the slit, which corresponds to a strip of the Sun's surface about 50,000 km long, so that the values represented the average of considerably stronger fields of even finer structure.   This structure was later revealed when the technique was further refined to a resolving power of 5 seconds.[12] As is well known, the field in a large sunspot may reach a value higher than 3000 gauss.

Although these strong local fields apparently do not persist to high latitudes, and thus do not interfere there with the detection of a general dipole field, the observational difficulties become worse near the poles because the line-of-sight component of the field approximately normal to the surface approaches zero.

In a recent paper, H. D. Babcock[13] reports that the dipole field has reversed polarity since 1956, which indicates that the Sun is magnetically less rigid than some theories have indicated.

Looking ahead a moment, we know enough about the behavior of solar activity to say positively that any theory which claims to explain such things as coronal and chromospheric heating, the support of prominences, the generation of flares, the production of sunspots, together with the cyclical nature of solar activity, must take account of the presence of magnetic fields.   The liberation of energy by a flare provides a good example of the crucial role played by magnetic fields in the origin of solar phenomena. The energy liberated per unit volume during a typical flare is frequently greater by more than a factor of 10 than the combined thermal and turbulent energy of the gas, which is no more than 10 ergs per cm^3. On the other hand, the magnetic energy associated with a field of only 50 gauss is 100 ergs per cm^3.

1.4 Active Sun and Active Regions

Although sunspots and the 11-year sunspot cycle are familiar phenomena, they are only one manifestation of disturbance on the photosphere of the Sun. Furthermore, disturbances are not limited to the photosphere but occur in the whole visible part of the Sun, and certainly in parts of the interior as well (see Figs. 1 and 7). The principal types of disturbance may be listed as follows.

1. *Sunspots and Sunspot Groups.* These regions, some 1000 or 1500° cooler than the surrounding photosphere, range in size from intergranular dark spots to areas nearly 100,000 km in diameter. The mean lifetime is correlated with size, and is of the order of several months for the largest spot groups. They have strong magnetic fields, mostly perpendicular to the surface, with intensities up to several thousand gauss for the largest spots. They very frequently occur in pairs of opposite magnetic polarity but, even when single, are normally associated with bipolar fields, as described by the Babcocks. The fields develop slightly before the visible spot and persist much longer, after the spot itself has decayed. The circulation of material in the neighborhood of a spot is inward toward the center in the higher layers (chromosphere) and outward in the lower layers (photosphere), with almost no suggestion of rotation around the spot.

Spots and spot groups hardly ever occur at heliographic latitudes higher than 35 to 40°—near this limit at the beginning of an 11-year cycle (as marked by a minimum of activity) but near the solar equator toward the end. Individual spots and groups tend to drift relative to their surroundings during the course of their lifetimes, mainly in longitude. Spots in the two hemispheres tend to have opposite magnetic polarity, and the polarity reverses in alternate 11-year cycles.

2. *Faculae or Plages.* These are areas somewhat brighter than their surroundings, much larger than granules, frequently visible in continuous radiation, but more conspicuous and showing a more detailed pattern in monochromatic light. They occur up to much higher latitudes than spots and cover about 10 per cent of the Sun's disk (time average). All spots and spot groups are surrounded by plages, which as a rule survive

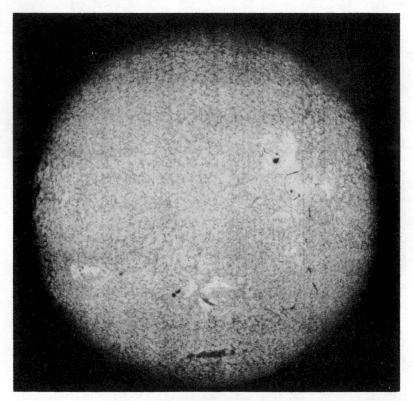

FIG. 7. A spectroheliogram taken in the light of Hα (hydrogen). It shows sunspots, plages (regions brighter than their surroundings in monochromatic light found frequently near spots), filaments (narrow dark structures, which are prominences seen in silhouette), and flocculi (wormy fine structure). (*Courtesy of Mt. Wilson and Palomar Observatories.*)

much longer than the spot. Plages, always associated with magnetic fields, may be expected to occur if the average value of the field over an extended area is more than 2 gauss or locally more than about 20 gauss.[14,15]

3. *Prominences.* These look roughly like projections of the chromosphere into the corona. They take many forms and follow many patterns of development.

Many prominences are associated with the disturbed areas around sunspots. Those in middle to high heliographic latitudes are not so associated, but they nevertheless behave as if governed by local magnetic fields and follow an 11-year cycle of activity.

The typical large prominence (if any may be called typical) is a region of the order of 10^5 km in its longest dimension—an appreciable fraction of the solar radius and somewhat cooler, denser, and more opaque than the surrounding coronal material in which it is embedded. The typical large prominence has a lifetime of the order of several weeks; during this interval it may disappear suddenly and apparently catastrophically; it may then sometimes reappear in practically the same place with the same form. This may happen several times.

The prominences seem to be shaped by the magnetic lines of force in rather localized and moderately persistent fields; the photographs with the best resolution show a fibrous or webby fine structure. The stable filamentary prominences appear to be supported in "hammocks" of magnetic lines (see paragraph 4 below).[15] The velocity of the material in an active prominence is frequently of the order of hundreds of kilometers per second, and in about 50 per cent of the cases the motion is along paths that resemble lines of force. Ordinary prominences are smaller and shorter-lived or take other less active forms.

4. *Filaments and Flocculi*. Thin or blade-shaped prominences, when they appear dark against the solar disk in monochromatic photographs (spectroheliograms), are sometimes called "filaments." This separate designation survives from the day when it was not realized that filaments and prominences are simply two aspects of the same phenomenon. In particular, filaments are the projection, as viewed from above, of quite stable prominences lying across the lines of force at the top of an arch connecting two magnetic regions of opposite polarity. Flocculi, small wormy-looking details that show up bright or dark in spectro-heliograms, may perhaps be regarded as small short filaments, i.e., projections of small prominencelike structures. Some astronomers have tentatively identified them as spicules seen in projection. Without necessarily being identical with the spicules, flocculi are possibly the monochromatic indication of the presence of the hypothetical small hot and cool regions that seem required to explain the chromospheric structure. It seems more likely, however, that the very finest structure in spectroheliograms—finer than flocculi—correspond to the spicules and that these mottlings are the objects to be identified with either the hot or cool regions.

5. *Flares*. These are catastrophic disturbances whose sudden onset and more gradual decay usually takes less than an hour (see Fig. 8). The spectrum of a flare in the visible region consists chiefly of strong

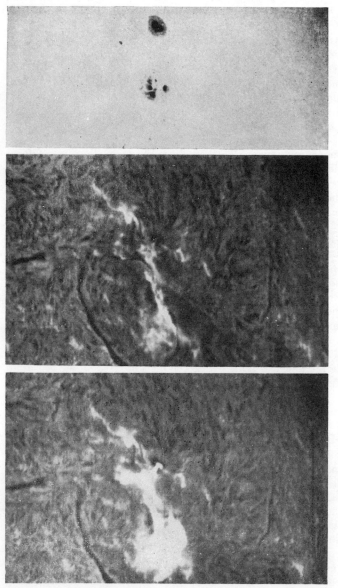

FIG. 8. From left to right, the development of a solar flare. The first picture is a direct white-light photograph of a sunspot group; the mottling of the apparent surface is due to granules. The next two pictures were taken in the monochromatic light of Hα, 11 and 22 min later, respectively. Besides the conspicuously bright flare, they show filaments (the conspicuous dark strips) and flocculi (very small wormy-looking details). (*Courtesy of Mt. Wilson and Palomar Observatories.*)

emission lines with occasionally a weak continuum. Rocket observations of the whole Sun during flares have shown greatly enhanced X radiation, which presumably originates in the flare.

The latest series of measurements by Chubb, Friedman, and Kreplin[16] were carried out from July 14 to Sept. 1, 1959, and yielded highly spectacular results. In the early phases of large flares, X rays with energies as high as 70 kev were detected, and in each of three large flares the emission persisted for the full 6 min that the rockets remained above the height of 45 km to which the hardest X rays penetrated. From the spectral distribution of the X-ray flux, a collection of thermal sources is inferred which would require local temperatures of the order of 100 million degrees Kelvin in the solar atmosphere.

It is to be expected that ultraviolet emission lines (e.g., Lyman-α) will also be strongly enhanced in a flare. However, rocket observations of Lyman-α radiation from the entire Sun are not conclusive; this follows from the fact that the area of a large flare is only 10^{-4} times that of the Sun, so that enhancement in the flare by a factor of 10^3 would result in only a 10 per cent increase in the integrated intensity. Under these circumstances it is remarkable that the total X-ray flux during a Class 2+ flare was roughly twice the quiet Sun value.

Strong flares are nearly always accompanied by a strong increase in radio noise. Another characteristic of the flare is its correlation with sudden ionospheric disturbances (SIDs), a consequence of the great increase of ionization in the D layer (50 to 100 km up) instantly upon the arrival of the enormously enhanced X radiation. These events are frequently followed within 15 to 50 hr by streams of charged particles, probably chiefly protons and electrons. According to the recent work of Van Allen (see Chap. 15), the solar stream perturbs the Earth's magnetic field and allows the particles trapped in the outer belt to stream down toward the ground at geomagnetic latitudes $\pm70°$, thus causing the aurorae. The solar stream simultaneously replenishes the outer belt. The accompanying disturbance to communications of the currents induced by the geomagnetic storms has pushed efforts to predict the magnitude and nature of these storms from the size and position of flares, but with only moderate success. The enhanced radio noise is undoubtedly connected with the passage of the charged particle stream through the ionized outer envelope of the Sun.

Flares occur only in active regions occupied by plages, usually near sunspots. They frequently break out near the boundary between two strong, opposing spot-connected fields where the local field intensity is close to zero. The detailed mechanism is not clear, although the abrupt-

ness of their onset has suggested that they are sudden electric discharges. Various theories have been advanced, based on a variety of
ideas such as the local building up of charge density, magnetic pinch
effects, local changes in conductivity, the rate of change of the magnetic
flux, etc.

6. "*Hot Spots.*" These are regions in the corona from which the
emission lines of multiply ionized iron, etc., are particularly strong. They
are transitory and seem to be closely correlated in position with obviously
disturbed regions in the photosphere.

7. *Variable Radio-frequency Radiation.* Radio-frequency radiation
from the Sun is characterized by its great diversity in frequency and time.
The following is a description of these events by Wild.[17]

The Sun is the only individual star yet detected at radio wavelengths. The
observed emission originates entirely in the ionized solar atmosphere where the
concentration of free electrons is sufficient to reflect and absorb radio waves.
At any one frequency the radiation that escapes from the Sun originates outside
the critical surface at which the electron density reduces the refractive index
to zero. At short (centimeter and decimeter) wavelengths, radiation can
escape from the innermost shell of the atmosphere—the solar chromosphere;
at long (meter) wavelengths the region of origin is restricted to the more
tenuous solar corona.

The intensity of the solar radio emission varies with time. The minimum
level of intensity is due to thermal radiation. The spectrum and disk distribution of the thermal emission gives data on the temperature and electron-density
distribution of the solar atmosphere. The radio observations have confirmed
that the coronal temperature is about $10^{6\circ}$K and provide one of the best known
methods of studying chromospheric temperatures ($\sim 10^{4\circ}$K) and densities.
At centimeter wavelengths the radiation originates mainly in the chromosphere.

The variable components of the radiation are associated with sunspots and
other solar activity. Their characteristics are complex and depend on the
wavelength.

At meter wavelengths, enhancements may exceed the thermal level by a
factor of 10^4 or more. In this range three components have been recognized by
their temporal and spectral characteristics:

(i) Radio "noise storms," of unknown origin, lasting for hours or days, during
which the level shows a series of bursts of seconds' duration superimposed on a
more slowly varying background. The bursts ("type I") are of narrow bandwidth (~ 5 Mc/sec), and the background is a broader continuum. The storms
originate in localized regions above large sunspots, but occur only during
restricted periods in the lifetime of a spot. The onset of a storm frequently
occurs up to half an hour after a solar eruption for which the principal optical
manifestation is a solar flare. The radiation is strongly circularly polarized,

indicating that the magnetic fields of sunspots influence its generation or propagation.

(ii) Intense "outbursts" of radio emission, lasting for some minutes and fluctuating violently. These correlate closely with flares. Their radio spectrum ("type II") shows narrow peaks which gradually drift in frequency toward the lower frequencies. They originate from localized regions, initially approximately above the optical flare; if the active region is displaced from the center of the disk, the source is observed to move gradually toward and even beyond the limb. The spectral and directional drifts both indicate a source which travels outward through the solar atmosphere at velocities of the order of 1000 km/sec. On the basis of this velocity the sources have been tentatively identified with the corpuscular streams that geophysicists have postulated to account for the onset of aurorae and terrestrial magnetic storms about one day after the flares. The mechanism of radio-energy production is not understood. A clue is given, however, by the spectrum which sometimes shows intense narrow peaks which are duplicated at second-harmonic frequencies. This and other evidence point to a mechanism involving gross oscillations of charge at the natural ("plasma") frequency of the emitting region.

(iii) Intense short-lived bursts, lasting a few seconds, whose frequency of maximum intensity drifts rapidly from high to low frequencies. Groups of them occur near the start of some solar flares and spasmodically at other times of solar activity. Their rapid frequency-drift indicates a source traveling outward with velocities up to 10^5 km/sec ($c/3$). It has been suggested that corpuscular streams of this velocity could be the causal link between solar flares and the increases in cosmic-ray intensity which occasionally follow the flares after a delay of about one hour. There is evidence that the fast (type III) streams and slow (type II) streams are ejected simultaneously, at the start of a flare, from a common source low in the solar atmosphere.

At centimeter and decimeter wavelengths, the enhancements are much smaller and smoother, rarely exceeding the thermal level by a factor of more than two. Two components have been recognized:

(i) The "slowly varying component," believed to originate in thermal radiation from localized regions of abnormally high density and temperature ($\approx 10^7 °K$) above active centers. The radio emission occurs throughout, and often beyond, the life of the visible spot, and the component shows a high statistical correlation with sunspot area.

(ii) Disturbances (the high-frequency component of "outbursts") which start at the beginning of solar flares and last for some minutes. Two phenomena may be present: a sudden burstlike feature near the start of the flare, superposed on a more gradual rise and fall. Some, at least, are localized within the active regions. Their mechanism is unknown.

At millimeter wavelengths, the character of the emissions resembles more closely the character of the optical radiation. The intensity corresponds to a stable source of temperature about $10^4 °K$ with occasional slight increases at the time of large flares.

After the above was written, two new types of radio emission were identified and labeled types IV and V. These occur shortly after type II and type III burst events, respectively. The type IV event endures for one-half to several hours, the type V for only seconds or a few minutes. Both are broad-band, steady continuum radiation and devoid of type I bursts. It is believed that type IV and V radiation is generated by electrons at relativistic energies, accelerated in solar magnetic fields (synchrotron radiation). There is evidence that many of the bursts at centimeter wavelengths are types IV and V.

8. *Variable Magnetic Fields.* Magnetic fields have been discussed in connection with the general field of the Sun, sunspots, faculae, prominences, and flares. Weak, local, irregular magnetic fields are apparently always present on the face of the Sun. Those considerably stronger fields that are found in association with active phenomena (flares, spots, etc.) differ from the weakest fields only in degree. Furthermore, we can safely say that whenever there is an active phenomenon, it will be accompanied by a strong field, and whenever there is a strong field (of possibly a particular shape) there will be other manifestations of activity. Since the fields develop before and persist after the active phenomena, it seems certain that the fields are the controlling factor, and it is here that we must look for the specific underlying mechanisms of solar activity.

1.5 Review of Unsolved Problems and Broad Lines of Attack

Before proceeding to list some of the chief unsolved problems of solar astrophysics, we shall first review the ways in which space experiments can serve to advance their solution. The use of artificial satellites and probes confers advantages that can be classified as follows:

a. Observation and interpretation of the full electromagnetic spectrum of radiation received from extraterrestrial sources. Outside the Earth's atmosphere the cutoff on the low-frequency side would be determined by the density of the electrons in the interplanetary medium; this cutoff is expected to be in the neighborhood of 100 kc. There are also good reasons to expect that gamma rays with energies up to 200 to 300 Mev will be received. The total spectral range from 100 kc to 300 Mev (frequency $\sim 10^{23}$ cps) thus consists of about 18 decades in frequency, as compared with the 5 decades or so we now receive through the two windows in our otherwise opaque atmosphere.

Observations taking advantage of this expanded range are in effect extensions of classical techniques, and we shall be concerned almost exclusively with this category for the advancement of solar physics.

The next two categories are new departures made uniquely possible by the satellite or probe.

b. Investigation of physical conditions in accessible regions by direct exploration with space probes carrying thermometers, particle counters, radiation detectors, analyzers, sample collectors, etc.

c. Controlled experiments in celestial mechanics. (The principal applications of this type of experiment are in the fields of relativity, gravity, and geodesy; see Chaps. 3 and 5.)

For completeness, one may add two more advantages closely related to but distinct from category *a* above: elimination of the bright background of radiation scattered (sunlight, etc.) or emitted by our own atmosphere (airglow), which, in the case of the Sun, masks the corona; elimination of the scintillation and image distortion (poor seeing) caused by the optical inhomogeneity of our atmosphere, which obliterates fine detail.

Some of the obstacles to observation originate chiefly in the lower atmosphere and can be largely overcome at balloon altitudes (poor seeing, scattered light, some infrared absorption). Thus experiments that depend exclusively on an improvement in the resolution of details need not absolutely be conducted from satellites, unless it is also desirable to take advantage of the superior theoretical resolving power of ultraviolet radiation.

These matters are discussed somewhat more fully in Chap. 18.

In the following summary, the listing of outstanding problems goes more or less from the inside out (photosphere chromosphere-corona) but without any serious attempt to assign a definite location, for most of the phenomena are interconnected and transcend the somewhat arbitrary boundaries of the regions. Experiments of categories *a* and *b* will suggest themselves automatically to the reader.

1. *Granules.* The granules are certainly the tops of convective cells emerging through the photosphere from the convectively unstable layer immediately below. It was pointed out earlier that the recent balloon observations of Schwarzschild[5] show that the true character of the solar granulation strikingly resembles the pattern associated with nonstationary convection. However, if one calculates the Rayleigh number appropriate to the bottom of the solar photosphere, one finds that it exceeds the critical value by five powers of ten and therefore the solar granulation should on this basis be an entirely random phenomenon. The fact that the observed granules have a pronounced cellular structure and a bright-dark asymmetry has not yet been explained by theory. Much additional information remains to be secured before the problem of the granulation

will be completely solved, especially information on the distribution of the granules with respect to velocities and magnetic fields. It is probable that this information is more likely to be forthcoming in the near future from balloons than from satellites. Such investigations will obviously require a high degree of stability in directional control of the equipment.

2. *Flares.* The mechanism of their sudden onset and development and the acceleration of the high-velocity particle streams require explanation. Various theoretically possible interactions between the fairly strong local magnetic fields and the matter in which they are embedded have been suggested. What is needed is a detailed time sequence of the magnetic fields—their strength, polarity, direction, and rate of change with time— in the regions of near-zero longitudinal field intensity where flares have a tendency to break out. It is possible that measures with sufficient detail can be secured from the ground or balloon telescopes. But a parallel time sequence of ultraviolet and X-ray spectra and of detailed spectroheliograms necessary to supply data on excitation temperatures and electron density can be secured only from satellites.

3. *Sunspots.* Since many of the aspects of the sunspot phenomenon can be and have been studied in visible radiation, the difficulty here, more than in other cases, is one of theoretical interpretation: How is the sunspot cooled? Is the gas pressure reduced because part of the load has been taken over by the magnetic pressure? Or is the cooling due to a forced expansion of a rising gas column whose ionized elements spread out when following the diverging lines of force? On the other hand, there is no clear-cut evidence that the gas column is really rising. This last is not a theoretical but an observational difficulty, which might be resolved by data of higher resolution or deduced from radiation from a greater variety of optical depths, either of which would indicate the mode of vertical circulation inside a spot.

4. *Chromospheric Structure.* What is the structure of the chromosphere? In particular, what is the explanation for the simultaneous appearance of spectral features indicating temperatures ranging from about 4500° to 30,000°K? Can we verify the suggestion that it is a highly inhomogeneous mixture of cells of hot and cool gases?

What is the nature of the spicules? Are they either the hot or the cool elements in the suggested chromospheric structure? How are they related to the other features, like granules and flocculi? High-resolution spectra and spectroheliograms in the extreme ultraviolet and the millimeter-wave radio regions would help to decipher these questions, from which one might evolve a comprehensive and coherent theory of magnetohydrodynamic turbulence applicable to these phenomena. This type of investigation would require a high degree of stability and control of the satellite vehicle.

5. *Temperature Gradient.* What is the nature of the sharp rise in kinetic temperature from about 4500°K in the upper photosphere to about 1,000,000°K in the quiet corona? Here we might look at three of the competing mechanisms without considering their present apparent merits or their relative contribution: (a) The turbulent energy of granules, spicules, etc., in the photosphere and lower chromosphere is dissipated by acoustic waves into thermal energy in the upper chromosphere through shock-wave heating. (b) As strong magnetic fields decay, their energy is devoted to the acceleration of charged particles in great quantities; this kinetic energy is in turn dissipated into heat. (c) The kinetic energy of interstellar matter falling into the Sun is dissipated by collisions into heat. Probably the first two of these processes, and possibly the third, are all going on with various degrees of effectiveness.

It is difficult to decide the relative merits of these theories or the relative importance of the contribution of each mechanism on the basis of heating effects alone. On the other hand, certain attendant phenomena other than heating would be different. For example, theory a calls for a spectrum of turbulent velocities which would vary with height in a regular way; theory b requires certain patterns of fluctuating electromagnetic fields; theory c demands a fairly dense cloud of infalling particles around or near the Sun. These effects should all be observable in the foreseeable future with space techniques.

6. *Coronal Structure.* In view of the observed clumpiness in the corona, what is its detailed fine structure (electron density, magnetic fields, temperature, particle streams, etc.)? To what extent is this fine structure related to phenomena in the chromosphere or to possible or hypothetical events on the outside (e.g., particle infall)?

In regard to radio observation of the corona, the chief advantage of space experiments will lie in the ability to reach spectral regions below 20 Mc or so, now cut off by our ionosphere. This region of very low frequency is of particular interest, in that radiation here corresponds to plasma oscillations originating in clouds of very low electron density.

Finally, the mapping of "hot spots," which seem to exist even in the quiet corona, by extreme ultraviolet and X-ray spectroscopy, and the detailed study of the emission lines and continua of the highly ionized atoms in these localized regions would go a long way toward producing a satisfactory model of the corona. Furthermore, with the help of an occulting disk, it might be possible to secure by time-lapse photography a movie of the mass motions in the outer corona in the light of one of the strong resonance emission lines, similar to what has been done at Sacramento Peak for the inner corona with the visible forbidden line (Fe XIV) λ5303. A coronagraph would be useful down to about 1800 Å, but for shorter wavelengths the Sun's continuum is too weak to be troublesome.

7. *Magnetic Fields.* The evidence that local magnetic fields, sometimes of considerable strength, play a part in various phenomena has already been noted, e.g., in the generation of sunspots, plages, and flares, in prominence support, coronal structure, etc. It is no exaggeration to say that the relation of these local fields to the phenomena, on the one hand, and to the weaker general magnetic field of the Sun, on the other, together constitute the central problem.

The clarification of the relation of the fields to the phenomena really requires detailed measures of field strength in the specific features, e.g., in the specific flare or coronal streamer. These measurements are perhaps no more easily performed with the help of a satellite than by more conventional methods, except in so far as it is possible to isolate some particular short-wavelength radiation coming only from a given source. The relation of the local fields to the general field, however, and origin of the general field itself are largely theoretical problems, although one may still hope that the detailed treatment of interactions between fields and phenomena will provide fresh insights leading to a more satisfactory and comprehensive magnetohydrodynamic theory of solar activity.

2. OUTLINE OF INVESTIGATIONS

Although many references to specific instrumentation are made in the rest of this chapter, several lines of instrumental development which need considerable attention are noted at this point: (1) new types of detectors in the extreme ultraviolet and X-ray regions; (2) new types of detectors in the infrared and millimeter-wave regions; (3) a search for new materials with high reflectivity in the far ultraviolet and X-ray regions, for use in optical systems working in this area; (4) stabilization and control of an orbiting platform, to achieve the pointing accuracy necessary to realize the optical resolution of images theoretically attainable outside the Earth's atmosphere; (5) coding and transmission of large quantities of information (e.g., the amount in one detailed spectroheliogram).

2.1 The Solar Spectrum

1. *Ultraviolet Emission Spectra.* The ultraviolet emission spectrum has been photographed from rockets. Rense[18] has succeeded in reaching a short-wavelength limit of 84 Å, with a grazing-incidence spectrograph,

and Tousey et al.[19] have secured many excellent normal-incidence spectra reaching below 600 Å. Hinteregger's[20] technique has been to scan the ultraviolet spectrum to about 200 Å with a tungsten-cathode photomultiplier and to telemeter back the information (see Chap. 18). This technique is a promising one for satellites if the wear problems associated with mechanical motion for prolonged periods in vacuum can be solved.

X radiation has been observed in the wavelength range of about 10 to 50 Å. The spectral region intermediate between X rays and ultraviolet is still unknown, although progress in closing this gap has been encouraging. Further reconnaissance of this region of the spectrum by photography from rockets is urgently needed in order to plan sensibly for satellite experiments, from which the most significant results will be derived. The development of an X-ray telescope or other imaging device is also of vital importance.

Rocket photographs have shown that the continuous spectrum radiated by the solar photosphere diminishes very rapidly in intensity with decreasing ultraviolet wavelength, as would be expected from a black body with a temperature of about 5000°, and that below λ1700 the spectrum consists almost entirely of emission lines radiated by the solar chromosphere.

The ultraviolet spectrum on the longward side of 1000 Å contains the resonance lines of many elements, most of which are known or believed to occur in the Sun, but whose abundances are not well determined because the existing data are based on weak absorption lines representing transitions between two states of moderately high excitation, or because lines are entirely absent in the visible spectrum. Examples are C, N, O; the inert gases Ne, A, Kr, Xe, Rn; the halogens; As, Se, Tl, etc.

Since the temperature of the solar chromosphere increases with height from 5000° to about 1 million degrees and since, on the average, lines of high ionization occur at shorter wavelengths than do those of low ionization, the emission lines at short wavelengths will tend to originate higher in the atmosphere than those of longer wavelengths. In addition to the resonance emission lines of hydrogen, helium, and other abundant elements in various stages of ionization, the spectral region 100 to 1000 Å contains the bound-free continua associated with neutral hydrogen and with neutral and ionized helium. The relative intensities of these lines and continua should make possible a critical evaluation of the physical conditions in the chromosphere. For an unambiguous determination of the temperature gradient, the spectrum should be observed at various points along a solar radius, and this requires very high precision in pointing, which can probably only be achieved with a stabilized platform.

The intensities in the ultraviolet-emission spectrum will undoubtedly be highly sensitive to local physical conditions in the solar atmosphere. Hence such a program should include the recording of the spectra of solar flares and of other local disturbances in the solar atmosphere.

One of the most important experiments in the ultraviolet is one designed to measure and record the peak intensity of the solar Lyman-α line during each revolution of a satellite and also to measure the detailed variations in the intensity when the satellite is within range of a telemetry station. Early versions of this experiment have already been carried out by H. Friedman and his colleagues. The first flight, aboard Explorer VII, achieved only marginal success because of interference from the corpuscu-/ lar radiation in the Van Allen belts. In a later version, piggy-backed with the Transit satellite, this interference has been eliminated by magnetic shielding which deflects all electrons up to several Mev. Results from the first few months of observation show that Lyman-α is remarkably stable during disturbances such as solar flares. By contrast, solar X-ray emission, which is also being measured, is extremely sensitive to solar activity.

With the rapid increase in weight and telemetry capabilities, a second-generation Lyman-α experiment should be possible in the near future. For this, and for possibly other frequencies, it would be desirable to monitor the intensity of the radiation continuously and in detail. Lyman-α observations during the "flash" phase of a major flare are especially important.

2. *X Rays.* We have seen that the temperature of the solar corona is of the order of a million degrees. From the observation of forbidden lines in the visible region of the spectrum, it is known that metallic atoms such as iron, calcium, and nickel are very highly ionized (Fe X–XV, Ni XII–XVI, Ca XII–XV, etc.). The resonance lines of these ions occur chiefly in the spectral region below 50 Å. Efforts are being made to develop spectroscopic instrumentation with sufficient power to resolve these individual lines, for example, by grazing-incidence techniques. Friedman and his co-workers are working on a system using a proportional counter and pulse analyzer to resolve the X-ray region below 10 Å. It is hoped that the resolution will be sufficient to separate the groupings of emission lines, particularly in solar flares. Otherwise, the X-ray flux within wavelength bands a few angstroms wide should be monitored concurrently with ultraviolet observations.

Low-resolution broad-band synoptic surveys in the X-ray and ultraviolet regions, employing a technique developed also by the Friedman group, are an almost immediate possibility. This technique consists of combining a given gas in a detector with a thin-film window of a given metal; a suitable combination of gas and metal provides passbands of different locations and widths. Friedman is currently extending developments of this kind of detector to "free-flow" ionization chambers, (i.e., gas not contained in a tube) through which various gases with various ionization limits can be flowed to control the long-wavelength threshold of the passband.

Continuous monitoring of Lyman-α has already been mentioned. Monitoring of certain other frequencies is equally important to provide a mass of time-based data for investigating Sun-Earth relationships. Friedman has already gathered evidence that a high correlation exists between the X radiation emitted from solar flares and sudden D-layer ionization. Similarly, it is possible that there is a connection between the variable solar emission in the frequency range of the ozone bands and the marked temperature excursions in the ozone region of the Earth's atmosphere. This upset of the energy balance probably has in turn a second-generation effect on winds and weather. Obviously, continuous monitoring over a period of something like a year in these two wavelength regions will be extremely valuable in unraveling the suspected Sun-Earth correlations.

The monitoring of solar corpuscular radiation is treated in Chapter 13.

3. *Line Profiles.* Purcell and Tousey[21] achieved a very important advance during 1959 in the successful photography of the profile of Lyman-α with a resolving power of about 0.05 Å. The profile revealed a deep, narrow core of absorption which is believed to be produced by neutral hydrogen in the outer fringes of the Earth's atmosphere, the so-called geocorona. The experiment was carried out with a spectrograph having a resolving power of 40,000. Friedman hopes to obtain even higher resolving power (0.02 Å) by photographing the thirteenth-order image of Lyman-α formed by a concave grating, a procedure which has already been tested in the laboratory. A satellite version of the Lyman-α-profile experiment is being planned by Rense, who plans to use an echelle grating for this purpose. The variations in the intensity and shape of the solar Lyman-α profile as well as the temporal changes that may occur in the central absorption core lend very great importance to this experiment. Profile measurements from satellites are probably also immediately practicable for other strong lines and for weak lines of the very light elements, whose Doppler widths are relatively large.

4. *The Solar-energy Curve.* Observations from the ground of the solar-energy curve and of the monochromatic limb darkening have provided the observational basis for present knowledge of the structure of the

solar photosphere, including temperature and pressure gradients and the continuous opacity. Extension of such observations both to ultraviolet and infrared wavelengths would lead to improvement of existing solar photospheric models, especially in the higher layers where knowledge is incomplete, and would also result in precise determination of the solar constant.

Continuous monitoring of the total solar output to detect short-term changes in the solar constant, if any, would be of obvious value.

2.2 Ultraviolet and X-ray Spectroheliograms

Spectroheliograms, or monochromatic photographs of the Sun, made from the surface of the Earth in the line radiations of ionized calcium (H and K lines) and of hydrogen (Hα) have revealed a great variety of transient disturbances in the solar atmosphere. The most spectacular of these disturbances is the solar flare. The physical nature of a solar flare can best be studied through its spectrum, but the circumstances of its origin and development in relation to other kinds of activity can best be investigated from spectroheliograms. The most significant ultraviolet lines for this purpose would be Lyman-α of neutral hydrogen at λ1216, λ584 of He I, and λ304 of He II. If possible, solar images in these three lines should be recorded simultaneously. For studies of the development of solar activity, an initial angular resolution of about 1 minute of arc would be sufficient.

Tousey's group[22] has recently flown a rocket camera which secured some Lyman-α spectroheliograms with a resolution of 1 minute or better in 0.02 sec exposure. Because of the Van Allen radiation, it will probably not be feasible to use the photographic technique unless the altitude can be kept quite low.

It is more likely that scanning techniques, with their currently lower resolving power, but with the advantage of supplying data in easily codable and transmittable form, will continue to hold the field. Here it is possible to secure resolution of perhaps 1 minute of arc, either by bundles of tubular collimators or, in those cases where mirror material is sufficiently reflective in the wavelength region of interest, by wobbling a concave mirror with a photodetector at the focus.

If the angular resolution could be reduced to a few seconds of arc, the ultraviolet spectroheliograms would greatly advance knowledge of the structure of the chromosphere, particularly as regards its non-homogeneity. If, as the evidence suggests, there are large temperature fluctuations in the chromosphere, the spectroheliograms made in different lines should exhibit great differences in their intensity patterns, especially when spectroheliograms are made simultaneously (from the ground) in low-excitation lines.

The spectrum of the solar corona at wavelengths shorter than λ3000 is expected to contain a number of forbidden lines of highly ionized atoms strong enough to be observed with a satellite-borne coronagraph and spectrograph. The relative weakness of photospheric radiation in the ultraviolet would suppress the intensity of the coronal continuum as compared with the visible, and of course scattered skylight would also not be a factor. This experiment should probably first be flown in a rocket.

2.3 Dynamic Spectra of Solar Radio Bursts

Dynamic radio spectra of solar bursts were first obtained by Wild and his colleagues.[17] They are now observing over the frequency range of 25 to 240 Mc. Over part of this frequency band they measure the size, position, and polarization of the source of the bursts. More recently Warwick et al.[23] have obtained dynamic spectra over the band of 33 to 15 Mc which have revealed phenomena of great complexity and interest. The so-called type II and type III bursts, which begin at high frequencies and occur progressively later at the lower frequencies, have been interpreted by Wild as resulting from corpuscular streams propagated outward through the solar atmosphere at speeds varying from a few hundred kilometers per second to a few tens of thousands of kilometers per sec. It is suspected that some of the corpuscular streams have sufficient kinetic energy to escape from the solar atmosphere and to reach the Earth, while others of lower energy are turned back or stopped. To establish whether the radio bursts are caused by the same corpuscular streams which are also responsible for geomagnetic storms or for the very soft component of solar cosmic rays, Haddock[6] has proposed that the low-frequency end of the solar burst spectra be observed from a satellite. As a by-product of this experiment, it may be possible to determine the decrease of electron density with distance from the Sun and perhaps the acceleration or deceleration of the corpuscular stream in the initial phase of its flight from the Sun to the Earth.

2.4 Gamma Rays

The subject of gamma rays is taken up more fully elsewhere (cf. Chap. 18). In connection with the Sun and solar-terrestrial relationships, it should be mentioned that the experiments with gamma-ray detectors flown either in rockets or satellites can easily be arranged in such a way as to separate the following components: cosmic primaries, solar primaries, and various sorts of secondaries including bremsstrahlung from the Van Allen radiation belt. In a rocket, a certain amount of separation according to altitude and direction is possible; at high satellite altitudes the directional separation becomes important; and finally the solar component should disappear in the Earth's shadow.

In view of Winckler and Peterson's observation[24] of a flash of 0.5-Mev gamma rays $\frac{1}{2}$ min before a flare, continuous monitoring of solar gamma rays is most important.

2.5 Close-in Solar Probes

In the more distant future, it may become possible to build a probe rugged enough to function at the high radiant temperatures in the neighborhood of the Sun. (For example, at 4 solar radii from the Sun the radiant temperature is about 3000°K, roughly the melting point of the most refractory substances known. The present working limit is somewhere in the neighborhood of 700°K.) It may then become possible to carry on closer-in experiments of the same general type as those already discussed. More important, however, would be the possibility of magnetometer measurements of the general solar magnetic field, sampling the streams of particles emerging from the Sun to study their composition, velocity, distribution, and similar questions. We are obviously still some distance from accomplishing experiments of this sort very close to the Sun.

2.6 Current Developments: Satellite-borne Solar Experiments

Some of the experiments outlined above are already becoming an actuality. The flying of solar Lyman-α and X-ray detectors designed and built by the Naval Research Laboratory in Explorer VII and the Transit companion have already been mentioned. Figure 9 shows an artist's drawing of the National Aeronautics and Space Administration's S-16 satellite, which is the first of two simple "orbiting solar observatories" and which provides a versatile frame on which to mount experiments requiring only a modest degree of stabilization and accuracy in pointing.[25]

The largest part of this satellite is a wheel made up of nine triangular sectors; from this wheel project three booms tipped with spherical gas tanks. The tanks contain compressed nitrogen gas which is allowed to escape in a controlled manner through tangentially aimed reaction jets, thus providing the torque necessary to spin the wheel in its own plane up to 30 rpm and to keep it there, with occasional extra squirts, for a period of about 6 months. The booms, beside serving as radio antennas,

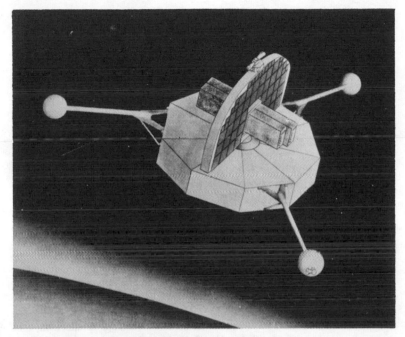

FIG. 9. Artist's drawing of the NASA S-16 satellite, an early version of the orbiting solar observatory. (*Courtesy of NASA.*)

thus increase the moment arm for the torque. In the satellite's finally stabilized orientation, the direction toward the Sun is in the plane of the wheel, within $\pm 5°$.

The fan-shaped frame projecting from the hub of the wheel rotates on an axle in the opposite direction from the wheel so that when the satellite is properly oriented it can present one flat face of the frame to the Sun. The bank of solar batteries on that face is designed to produce 25 watts of power, about half of which are for control, data recording and telemetry, etc., and the other half for experiments. The two long boxes represent sensors or telescopes; these are aimed in the same direction as the normal to the fan-shaped frame, that is, toward the Sun. In order to accomplish this, the axis of rotation of the wheel must be pointing perpendicular to the direction of the Sun. It is brought to this position by precessing the spin axis by means of thrust applied at the tip of the spin axis. Two tangential nozzles for this purpose can be seen in the drawing, at the near end of the spin axis where it projects through the edge of the fan-shaped frame. The instrumentation is carried in six of the nine wedge-shaped compartments that form the sectors of the main wheel, the other three being reserved for controls, data storage, telemetry, etc. The turning of the wheel brings each of the compartments into line with the Sun twice a minute. The long narrow boxes also contain instrumentation. As mentioned above, they are kept pointed at the Sun with an accuracy of $\pm 5°$ in the plane perpendicular to the plane of the wheel by the precession jets; this error is further reduced to 1 to 3 minutes by a servo motor which elevates and depresses the long axis of the boxes in relation to the plane of the wheel. The angle in the plane of the wheel is also maintained with this accuracy by means of a servo. It is expected that later models will do even better.

The following experiments have been proposed for the first two launchings of this model. For the stabilized section (long narrow boxes in Fig. 9) (1) apparatus to record continuously with high resolving power the profile of Lyman-α, (2) a device to observe the spectrum of soft X rays, (3) scanning spectrometers of moderate resolving power to cover the spectral region from $\lambda 75$ to $\lambda 1500$, and (4) a solar X-ray telescope for active regions on the solar disk and in the corona above it. The wedge-shaped compartments in the wheel would be suitable to carry equipment that does not require continuous pointing at the Sun. In the first vehicle these will be (1) devices to monitor the soft X-ray emission from the Sun, (2) detectors for 100-Mev solar gamma rays, (3) detectors for 0.1 to 1 Mev gamma rays to measure their intensity and distribution over the sky, and (4) equipment for auxiliary measurements of solar X rays in the spectral region 1 to 60 Å.

Acknowledgments at the end of Chapter 18 apply to this chapter as well. We are especially indebted to Drs. Walter Orr Roberts and Grant Athay for reviewing an earlier version of this chapter.

REFERENCES

1. G. P. Kuiper (ed.): *The Sun*, Vol. 1 of *The Solar System* (Chicago Press, 1953). A collection of detailed monographs:
   L. Goldberg: "Introduction"
   B. Strömgren: "The Sun as a Star"
   M. Minnaert: "The Photosphere"
   Charlotte E. Moore: "The Identification of Solar Lines"
   H. C. van de Hulst: "The Chromosphere and Corona"
   K. O. Kiepenheuer: "Solar Activity"

J. L. Pawsey and S. F. Smerd: "Solar Radio Emission"
T. G. Cowling: "Solar Electrodynamics"
C. W. Allen, P. C. Keenan, G. van Biesbroeck, R. R. McMath, J. W. Evans,
W. O. Roberts, R. Tousey, J. P. Wild, Helen W. Dodson, H. W. and H. D.
Babcock, A. Ehmert, and J. A. Simpson: "Empirical Problems and
Equipment"

2. Articles by L. Goldberg and A. K. Pierce and C. de Jager in *Handbuch der Physik*,
   52, rev. ed. (Berlin: Springer Verlag, 1959).

3. M. Schwarzschild: *The Structure and Evolution of the Stars*, Sections 15–16 and 23
   (Princeton University Press, 1958).

4. M. Schwarzschild: See Ref. 3, Section 11.

5. M. Schwarzschild: *Astrophys. J.*, *130*, 345 (1959).

6. Reprinted from *Final Report—Astronomical Experiments Proposed for Earth
   Satellites*, University of Michigan Research Inst., November, 1958.

7. G. E. Hale: *Astrophys. J.*, *38*, 27 (1913).

8. For example, H. D. Babcock: *Publ. Astr. Soc. Pacific*, *60*, 244 (1948); H. W. and
   H. D. Babcock: *Astrophys. J.*, *121*, 349 (1955). See also Refs. 14 and 15.

9. G. Thiessen: *Ann. d'Astrophys.*, *9*, 101 (1946); *Zeitschr. f. Astrophysik*, *26*, 16
   (1949); *ibid.*, *30*, 8 (1951); *Observatory*, *69*, 228 (1949) and *70*, 234 (1950);
   Nature, *169*, 147 (1952); *Naturwissensch.*, *40*, 218 (1953).

10. K. O. Kiepenheuer: *Proc. 9th Volta Meeting* (Rome: The National Academy).

11. H. von Kluber: *Observatory*, *71*, 9 (1951).

12. R. Howard: *Astrophys. J.*, *130*, 193 (1959). Recent results with Babcock-type
    magnetograph with resolution of 10″ × 10″. Plages coincide closely with
    10-gauss contours.

13. Harold D. Babcock: *Astrophys. J.*, *130*, 364 (1959).

14. H. W. and H. D. Babcock: "Photospheric Magnetic Fields," paper 26 in *Elec-
    tromagnetic Phenomena in Cosmical Physics*, I.A.U. Symposium No. 6, Stock-
    holm, August 1956 (London: Cambridge University Press, 1958).

15. H. W. Babcock, "The Magnetism of the Sun," *Scientific American*, *202*, 52 (1960).

16. T. A. Chubb, H. Friedman, and R. W. Kreplin: "X-ray Emission Accompanying
    Solar Flares," paper at the First International Space Science Symposium, Nice,
    January, 1960 (Amsterdam: North-Holland Publ. Co.).

17. J. P. Wild: "Observational Radio Astronomy," in L. Martin (ed.), *Advances in
    Electronics and Electron Physics*, *7*, 5 (Academic Press, 1955).

18. W. A. Rense: "Solar Ultraviolet Spectroscopy and Applications to Problems of
    the Upper Atmosphere and the Solar Corona," paper at the First International
    Space Science Symposium, Nice, January, 1960 (Amsterdam: North-Holland
    Publ. Co.).

19. J. D. Purcell, D. M. Packer, and R. Tousey: "The Ultraviolet Spectrum of the
    Sun," paper at the First International Space Science Symposium, Nice, January,
    1960 (Amsterdam: North-Holland Publ. Co.).

20. H. E. Hinteregger, K. R. Damon, L. Heroux, and L. A. Hall: "Telemetering
    Monochromator Measurements of Solar 304Å-Radiation and Its Attenuation
    in the Upper Atmosphere," paper at the First International Space Science
    Symposium, Nice, January, 1960 (Amsterdam: North-Holland Publ. Co.).

21. J. D. Purcell and R. Tousey: "The Profile of Solar Lyman Alpha," paper at the
    First International Space Science Symposium, Nice, January, 1960 (Amster-
    dam: North-Holland Publ. Co.).

22. J. D. Purcell, D. M. Packer, and R. Tousey: "Photographing the Sun in Lyman Alpha," paper at the First International Space Science Symposium, Nice, January, 1960 (Amsterdam: North-Holland Publ. Co.).
23. A. Boischot, R. H. Lee, and J. W. Warwick: *Astrophys. J.*, *131*, 61 (1960).
24. L. E. Peterson and J. R. Winckler: "Gamma-ray Bursts from a Solar Flare," *J. Geophys. Research*, *64*, 697 (1959).
25. The device is being designed and constructed for the NASA by the Ball Brothers Research Corporation of Boulder, Colorado, under the supervision of Dr. R. C. Mercure, to whom we are indebted for descriptive material used in the following paragraphs of the text.

SUPPLEMENTARY READING

General

G. Abetti: *The Sun*, transl. by J. B. Sidgwick (Macmillan, 1957).

W. H. McCrea: *Physics of the Sun and Stars* (London: Hutchinson House, 1950).

D. H. Menzel: *Our Sun* (Harvard Books on Astronomy), 2d ed. (Harvard University Press, 1959).

Radio Astronomy of the Sun

R. Hanbury Brown and A. C. B. Lovell: *The Exploration of Space by Radio*, Chap. 7 (London: Chipman and Hall, Ltd., 1957).

J. L. Pawsey and R. N. Bracewell: *Radio Astronomy* (London: Oxford University Press, 1955).

Solar Ultraviolet and X-ray Studies

Annals of the IGY, *12* (London: Pergamon Press, in press, 1959). Contains results reported at the 5th Meeting of CSAGI, Moscow, August, 1958. Section 8, "Solar Electromagnetic Radiation." Contributions by:

H. Friedman, T. A. Chubb, J. E. Kupperian, Jr., and J. C. Lindsay: "X-ray and Ultraviolet Emission of Solar Flares"

E. T. Byram, T. A. Chubb, H. Friedman, and J. E. Kupperian, Jr.: "Intensity of Solar Lyman-alpha and Adjacent Ultraviolet Emission Lines"

H. Friedman, T. A. Chubb, J. E. Kupperian, Jr., and J. C. Lindsay: "X-ray Emission of Solar Flares"

J. E. Kupperian, Jr., E. T. Byram, T. A. Chubb, and H. Friedman: "Far Ultraviolet Radiation in the Night Sky"

J. E. Kupperian, Jr., A. Boggess III, J. E. Milligan, and H. Friedman: "Rocket Astronomy in the Far Ultraviolet"

J. E. Kupperian, Jr., and H. Friedman: "Gamma Ray Intensities at High Altitudes"

J. D. Purcell, A. Boggess, and R. Tousey: "A High Resolution UV Spectrogram of the Sun"

H. Friedman: *Proceedings of the I.R.E.*, *47*, 272 (February, 1959, issue devoted to IGY). Reviews results to date on intensity and distribution of short-wave solar radiation and solar-terrestrial relationships.

18 ≡

GALACTIC AND EXTRAGALACTIC ASTRONOMY

Leo Goldberg and Edward R. Dyer, Jr.

1. INTRODUCTION

The introductory part of Chap. 17 on the Sun suggests that there are three distinct ways in which satellite investigations will advance the cause of astronomy: (1) the new capability of observing practically the entire spectrum of electromagnetic and particle radiation, without interference by the terrestrial atmosphere; (2) the ability to sample directly a physical environment with measuring devices; and (3) the control of the initial conditions of an orbit, in order to investigate certain effects in mechanics or basic physics (relativity, etc.).

The first of these categories, with which we are chiefly concerned in this chapter, is essentially an extension of time-honored classical methods of investigation. The other two are examples of entirely new departures that are made uniquely possible by the artificial satellite and probe. It is obvious that in the area of investigation of this chapter, namely, space beyond the confines of the solar system, it will be some time before methods of the second type (probes, etc.) will have developed to an operational state. Investigations of the third type, which have been called "experimental celestial mechanics," are discussed in Chap. 3 (The Nature of Gravitation) and in Chap. 5 (Geodesy).

The Earth's atmosphere hinders astronomical observation in three principal ways:

First, it is opaque to radiation, except through the "visual window" (about 0.3 to 1μ) and the "radio window" (about 3 mm to 15 m) (see Fig. 1). The visual window is cut off on the short-wave side at about 0.3μ by the ultraviolet absorption of ozone. Between the visual window and the radio window there is a region of infrared molecular band absorption (water vapor, carbon dioxide, oxygen, etc.) which is partially transparent in a few wavelength bands from 1 to 24μ, but is almost completely opaque from 24μ to the millimeter-wave region where the radio window begins. The radio window is limited on the long-wave side at about 15 m (20 Mc) by the critical frequency for reflection by the electron clouds of our ionosphere. Since the electron density and therefore the limiting frequency are variable, it is often possible to observe at frequencies below this limit, especially through "holes" in the ionosphere. Reber and

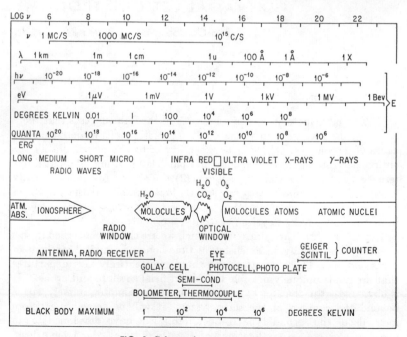

FIG. 1. Schematic representation of the transparency of the terrestrial atmosphere as a function of wavelength. (*Courtesy of A. D. Code*[15] *and the Editors of The Astronomical Journal.*)

Ellis,[1] working in Tasmania, have made observations at frequencies below 9 Mc and occasionally as low as 1 Mc.

Thus the radiation from the two extreme ends of the spectrum, both very important for astrophysical studies, is blocked off. The gap in the middle (the infrared-microwave region) is perhaps not quite so serious because to some extent one can interpolate into this region from both sides, but also because some of this radiation is absorbed chiefly in our lower atmosphere, and the region of greatest opacity can be surmounted at balloon altitudes.

Second, the upper-atmospheric airglow and scattering of sunlight and starlight in our lower atmosphere interfere with observations of extended cosmic sources: the solar corona, zodiacal light, faint emission or reflection nebulosities, integrated unresolved starlight in the Galaxy or in remote extragalactic nebulae, etc. The skylight in effect sets a lower limit to the surface brightness of any other source that can be detected against its background (more accurately its foreground). The scattered component diminishes quite rapidly with altitude, but the airglow originates in the very high atmosphere.

Third, the differential refractive and dispersive effects of small inhomogeneous cells in the lower atmosphere on rays passing through them, and their variation with time, impair and at times destroy the definition of optical images. On this account the theoretical resolving power of optical equipment is in fact never realized for apertures greater than about 12 in. Scintillation and "poor seeing" effectively prevent the resolution of details like solar granules, surface features of a planet, close double stars, closely packed star fields in distant clusters, and galaxies.

Since poor seeing originates in the lower atmosphere (below about 50,000 ft), it is completely surmounted at balloon altitudes and considerable improvement is achieved even on high mountaintops. The other obstacles—airglow, and molecular or ionospheric absorption—persist to extreme altitudes and cannot be overcome from balloons. In extreme-high-altitude observations, rockets are useful for reconnaissance, but satellites are essential whenever the collection of data requires more than a few minutes.

The accessibility to observation of the entire electromagnetic spectrum would tremendously broaden the observational basis for theories about the structure and physical state of individual objects (stars, nebulae, etc.), the structure of systems like our Galaxy and other galaxies, and their distribution in space. As an example, one of the most important questions that can now be treated is that of the detailed abundances of certain abundant light elements and their isotopes in the stars, the nebulae, and the interstellar medium. These data are of the utmost importance because of their close relationship to the cycles of thermonuclear energy generation in stellar interiors and to the subsequent history of the by-products.

For a spectral line to appear in the visible or near-visible spectrum, say, between 0.3 and 1.2μ, it must of course correspond to a transition between two energy states 1 to 4 ev apart. For the lighter, more abundant elements and their ions, the only transitions in this energy range are relatively weak ones between two excited states. Now the strength of a spectral line is a function of the number of atoms in the initial state of the transition, and the transition probability. The number in the excited state relative to the total number for the given element can be accurately calculated only if the temperature is known and thermodynamic equilibrium prevails. Under many conditions of observational interest neither of these conditions is met, so that assumptions of varying degrees of plausibility must be made. The astronomer is deeply interested in elements such as H, He, C, N, O, the halogens, the inert gases other than He, and other light elements. All of them are abundant in the Universe, but their leading lines fall in the ultraviolet and some of them do not have even one detectable line in the visible regions of stellar or nebular spectra.

Many other examples of new opportunities for research will be given below, but we can also count on many surprises. One has only to turn to the brief history of radio astronomy to find examples: the discrete sources of radio noise in space, the distribution of radio-noise sources in the Sun's corona, and the phenomenon of bursts, the localized sources on Jupiter, etc.

The rest of this chapter is divided into the following two divisions: Section 2, A Review, which consists of selected topics from astronomy and astrophysics treated in sufficient detail so that the nonspecialist will grasp the objectives of the research programs, and Section 3, Research Problems, which considers some specific problems that seem susceptible of solution with space techniques.

2. A REVIEW

This section is concerned with problems of current interest in astronomy and astrophysics, with special emphasis on such topics as stellar populations and evolution, the abundances of the elements, stellar radiation, discrete-emission-line gaseous nebulae, the interstellar medium, galaxies, and sources of radio-frequency radiation.

2.1 Stellar Populations and Evolution

The phrase "stellar population" denotes a collection of stars having either certain common properties (physical, chemical) or collectively conforming to some fairly well defined distribution (positions or velocities).

1. *Population Criteria.* Baade originated the notion of two stellar populations, which he labeled I and II: I is what you find in the arm of a spiral galaxy (like the solar neighborhood in the Milky Way), and II is what you find in a globular cluster. This basic idea is enlarged on in paragraphs *a* and *b* below. Today we use four observational criteria to classify stars or sets of stars into populations: (1) location or distribution on the Hertzsprung-Russell diagram, (2) membership, location, and spatial distribution in larger star systems, (3) velocity or velocity distribution, (4) chemical composition. All but the last are really statistical criteria, in that they deal with overlapping distributions and can be applied with certainty to individual bodies only in exceptional cases.

a. Differences in distribution on the Hertzsprung-Russell (H-R) diagram, in which the luminosity of an object is plotted against its spectral type or surface temperature (see Fig. 2). It will be noted that the upper part of the diagram is very different for the two populations. Population I is characterized by the very hot luminous stars of Types O-B-A at the upper end of the main sequence and by red giants of Types G-K-M of the order of 30 to 300 times as bright visually as the Sun and separated from the main sequence by the "Hertzsprung gap." In Population II there are no main sequence stars of Types O-B-A; its most luminous stars are red giants. These are somewhat brighter than those in Population I, and their distribution on the H-R diagram is connected with the main sequence somewhere around Type F. It has, in addition, a horizontal branch of stars about 100 times as bright as the Sun running through the Hertzsprung gap from the red giants across the main sequence, and this branch contains the cluster-type variables that are typical of Population II. Baade was the first to note that the brightest stars of the two populations that could be resolved in the arms and in the center of extragalactic nebulae (notably in M31) were, respectively, blue and red in color. It should be noted that not much can be said as yet about population differences on the H-R diagram in the distribution of faint stars. In globular clusters they are hard to resolve, and in the general population around the Sun they are hard to identify.

b. Differences in spatial distribution, or in their association with other matter. For example, Baade's Population I is confined to the arms of spiral galaxies and to irregular galaxies and is found in close association

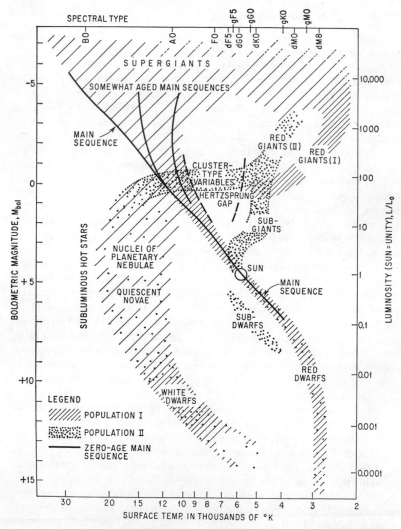

FIG. 2. Hertzsprung-Russell, or temperature-luminosity, diagram, showing the regions occupied by stars of various kinds or populations.

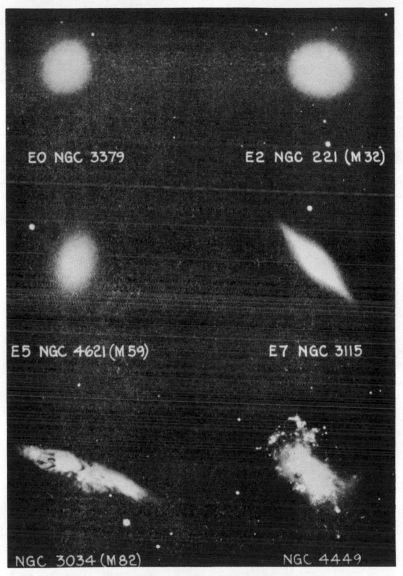

FIG. 3. Elliptical galaxies of Types E0 to E7 (top four), which are composed of Population II, and Irregular galaxies (bottom two), which are predominantly Population I. This figure and the next show the morphological types into which galaxies are classified. (*Courtesy of Mount Wilson and Palomar Observatories.*)

with discrete clouds of interstellar matter—gas and small solid grains, frequently referred to as dust. Baade's Population II (characteristic of a globular cluster by Baade's original definition) is also found in a pure state in elliptical galaxies, which are very like huge globular clusters; it is also found in a perhaps less pure state in the central region of spiral galaxies and in a large spheroidal distribution around the center (the galactic "halo"). See Figs. 3, 4, and 5.

c. *Differences in velocity distribution,* which are in fact very closely connected with and responsible for the spatial distributions mentioned in paragraph b. The spheroidal distribution typical of Population II results from elongated orbits of high eccentricity and nearly random inclinations to the plane of rotation of the galactic system. The stars in the spiral arms and the associated interstellar clouds have more nearly circular orbits, nearly in the plane of general rotation of the whole system. In any fairly small region where both populations are present, the local velocity distribution will differ and the members of one population will in general be moving rapidly with respect to members of the other population. These differences were first pointed out by Oort and his associates at Leiden.

d. *Differences in chemical composition.* Analysis of the absorption-line spectra of stellar atmospheres by the curve-of-growth technique has indicated that the stars of Population I have, in general, a higher ratio of heavy elements to hydrogen. There is a strong presumption that this difference reflects a difference in composition of the original nebular matter from which the star populations were formed, because according to currently accepted models of stellar interiors, it is only in exceptional cases that matter from the core, which has undergone transmutation by thermonuclear reactions, can reach the surface by convection or diffusion.

In conclusion, two matters should be noted: First, Populations I and II, in their purest form, appear to be the extreme ends of a continuous spectrum of populations, with characteristics intermediate between those described. Second, the four criteria are in general agreement in their assignment of stars to a place in this scale. Thus a fairly coherent picture of stellar evolution is just now emerging that accounts, at least in broad outline, for the observational facts so far as they are now known.

2. *Evolutionary Stages.* This theory of stellar evolution calls for a sequence of stages that follow each other in succession. How long each one lasts depends on such factors as the mass.

a. Protostars—fairly compact globules of interstellar matter—condense out of the clouds by self-gravity, possibly helped by the inward radiation pressure from other stars. Objects answering this description are relatively numerous in the Milky Way.

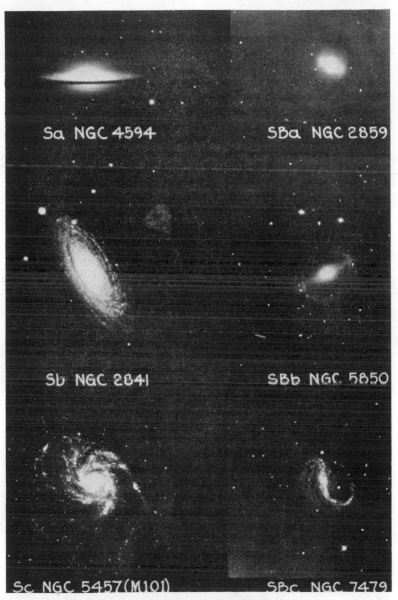

Sa NGC 4594   SBa NGC 2859

Sb NGC 2841   SBb NGC 5850

Sc NGC 5457 (M101)   SBc NGC 7479

FIG. 4. Spiral galaxies (Sa to Sc, left) and barred spirals (SBa to SBc, right). The central region, which becomes less prominent through the sequence, is Population II, like the Ellipticals, and the arms are predominantly Population I, like the Irregulars. (*Courtesy of Mount Wilson and Palomar Observatories.*)

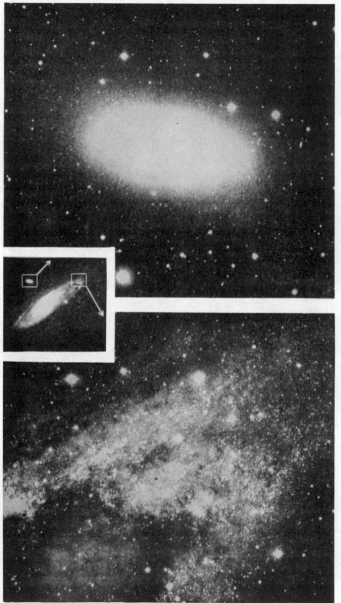

FIG. 5. Populations I and II contrasted. On the left: an outer arm of M31 (Type Sb), taken in blue light to bring out the hot giants and supergiants and associated nebulosity, typical of Population I. On the right, NGC 205 (Type E5), taken in yellow light to bring out the yellow giants typical of Population II. (*Courtesy of Mount Wilson and Palomar Observatories.*)

b. The protostars contract until they reach a spherical configuration where hydrostatic equilibrium prevails between self-gravity and the internal gas pressure plus the radiation pressure: they become stars. The range in mass appears to be limited at the lower end at something like 10^{-2} solar mass. Smaller objects do not develop high enough central pressures, densities, and temperatures to support thermonuclear processes. Similarly, the upper end of the range is limited at something like 10^2 solar masses by the instability resulting from too great a rate of energy production. These young stars, composed largely of hydrogen, form the "zero-age" main sequence on the H-R diagram (see Fig. 2).

During the contraction stage the effective surface temperature of a protostar will rise from a few degrees absolute to its equilibrium main-sequence value (see following paragraphs *c* and *d*). The time scale for the contraction phase required by theory is of the order of one-hundredth to one-thousandth of the time spent on the main sequence; during this stage the luminosity is believed to be only slightly less than the equilibrium main-sequence value, for the larger surface area nearly compensates for the lower temperature. Protostars in the contraction phase might therefore be detected with improved devices of sufficient sensitivity in the infrared.

c. In the cores of the stars, where the temperature is some millions or tens of millions of degrees and the density is of the order of 10^2 g per cm³, hydrogen is converted to helium and radiant energy, the latter working its way to the surface by radiative transfer. The internal balance is such that the luminosity L of a main-sequence star is proportional to a power of its mass M^n, where n is approximately 3 or 4. The Sun, with $L = 4 \times 10^{33}$ ergs per sec and $M = 2 \times 10^{33}$ g, is radiating away $L/M = 2$ ergs per sec per g of matter. From this figure an estimate of the Sun's maximum life expectancy τ can be made, under the assumptions that it began life as pure hydrogen, that the hydrogen is all accessible to thermonuclear processes in the core, that its luminosity remains unchanged, and that it exchanges only a negligible quantity of matter with its environment in comparison with its own mass. Remembering that less than 1 per cent of the mass of each proton is released as radiant energy, one obtains $\tau \cong 10^{11}$ years. A massive star of spectral type B, with $M \cong 10 M_{sun}$ and $L \cong 10^4 L_{sun}$, generates radiant energy at the rate $L/M \cong 10^3$ times that of the Sun, and thus has a maximum life expectancy only one-thousandth as long, or $\sim 10^8$ years.

d. Main-sequence stars brighter and more massive than the Sun, with higher central temperatures and densities, are believed to operate on the carbon cycle, which has a temperature dependence of T^{16} or higher. The

Sun and less massive stars operate on the proton-proton cycle, with a much less sensitive temperature dependence of about T^4. The extreme sensitivity of the carbon cycle to temperature makes for a convective core in the more massive stars, which entails a model somewhat different from the less massive stars. What happens as a star converts its hydrogen into helium, i.e., how it ages, depends on the model. Since both models have a deep nonconvective layer between the core and the outer shell, little internal mixing outside the core can take place. Such a star expands with hydrogen depletion, although the expansion probably does not become noticeable until a fairly large portion of the hydrogen in the core is consumed. For the most massive bright stars at the top of the main sequence, this expansion is accompanied by a cooling of the surface in such a way that the luminosity remains approximately constant. The stars become red giants and move more or less directly to the right on the H-R diagram. For smaller stars, the surface temperature remains more nearly constant or even increases at first, so that the motion on the H-R diagram is first upward, then up to the right. The aging process of becoming red giants proceeds much more rapidly in the most massive stars because of their large L/M.

   e. The red giants represent the stage in which a large dense core of more or less inactive helium is surrounded by a shell in which the thermonuclear cycles involving hydrogen are still taking place. The outer envelope is an overblown, turbulently convective region. Toward the end of this stage, when densities and pressures have built up sufficiently in the center, other cycles become successively possible, involving the conversion of helium to carbon, carbon to heavier elements, etc., leading finally to iron.[2-4] Instabilities may set in that account for the variable stars in this part of the H-R diagram.

   f. We skip now to the stage of the white dwarfs, globes of degenerate matter with masses of the order of the Sun's mass but with diameters of planetary dimensions. Their high density and low gravitational potential are so extreme that the injection of a tremendous amount of energy from the outside would be required to inflate them back to normal stars. Thus they must be the end-product of stellar evolution and are doomed inevitably to cool off by radiating away the store of thermal energy, thus to become "black dwarfs." The cooling-off process has a time constant of the order of 10^9 years.[5]

Neither the route from the red-giant and variable-star region of the H-R diagram to the white-dwarf sink, nor the processes involved, are clear. The model of a completely degenerate white dwarf which takes into account relativistic effects forbids a mass greater than approximately 1.4 solar masses. Thus it appears that a more massive star must somehow shed its excess matter—perhaps violently, perhaps in a steadier and smoother fashion. One current theory suggests that supernovae (which flare up to luminosities $\sim 10^8$ as bright as the Sun) exemplify the violent shedding of excess matter; another theory suggests that at sufficiently high densities ($\gtrsim 10^6$ g per cm^3) and temperatures (several billion degrees) the heavy-metal core suffers a collapse, with catastrophic results. Ordinary novae, repeating novae, planetary nebulae, and Wolf-Rayet stars have all been suggested as alternative, less active mechanisms for shedding excess mass and perhaps should not be excluded. In any case it is significant that all these objects lie in an ill-defined band on the H-R diagram stretching from the variable stars, leftward and downward to the white dwarfs.

g. The ejected matter, having been through various transmutations in the interior of the star, enriches the interstellar medium with a fraction of heavier elements. Stars formed later out of this material will thus start out with an enhanced ratio of heavy elements to hydrogen.

3. *Effects of Evolution on Stellar Populations.* Several other hypotheses will indicate how the theory of evolution rather neatly explains stellar populations in terms of age:

Stars continue to be formed as long as there is interstellar matter of the proper density distribution. This hypothesis has been strengthened by the discovery in recent years of stellar associations (groups of stars too loosely organized to be called a cluster, whose individual motions indicate a common origin in a region of dense nebulosity only a few million years ago [see Figs. 6 and 7]) and of T Tauri stars (stars embedded in nebulosity that have apparently just come into being). Such processes occur today only in Population I regions, where there is nebular matter. Regions occupied by a pure Population II—globular clusters and elliptical galaxies—have long since been swept clean of their interstellar matter, presumably by passages through other star systems, so that no stars have formed in them for some time. They may thus be regarded as an aged and sterile population.

The motion of a star in its galaxy is determined once and for all by the motion of the cloud from which it was formed. The collision cross section of the gravitational sphere of action around a star, in which appreciable deflection of a passing star can be brought about, is so small compared with the separations of the stars, that the relaxation time of stellar motions in the Sun's neighborhood is of the order of 10^{14} years. It would of course be shorter in more densely populated regions, but still long compared with 10^9 to 10^{10} years, the hypothetical age of the Galaxy.

FIG. 6. The Sc-type spiral M33. In the outer Population I arms and along their very faint extensions, the most conspicuous objects are asssociations of young hot stars embedded in nebulosity. (*Official U.S. Navy Photograph.*)

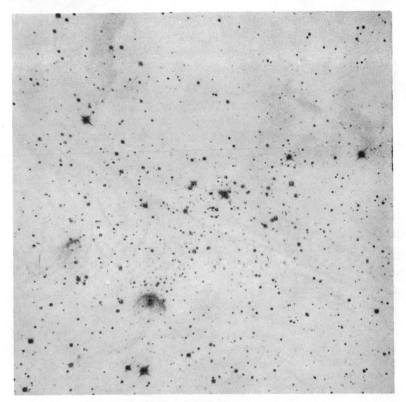

FIG. 7. A stellar association, in nebula IC 410, of newly formed stars in our own galaxy. (*Courtesy of Stewart Sharpless, U.S. Naval Observatory.*)

Discrete clouds of interstellar matter interact much more strongly. Their present dimensions, estimated masses, number density, and mean differential velocity lead to a relaxation time for their motions in the range 10^8 to 10^{10} years, and this time would have been still shorter when clouds were larger and more numerous and moving with greater relative motions. It is assumed that the motions of the clouds were originally much more turbulent than now, with a large velocity dispersion both in the radial direction (highly eccentric orbits) and perpendicular to the plane of general rotation (highly inclined orbits). These motions have been gradually damped out by collisions and close approaches, leaving today a residuum of clouds moving with nearly circular orbits in nearly the same plane (the original plane of rotation), with a small velocity dispersion of about ± 5 to ± 10 km per sec.

A combination of the assumptions above, together with the additional assumption that Population II is the surviving sample of the oldest stellar population while Population I in its purest form (O-B-A stars plus interstellar clouds) is the youngest, accounts for most of the observed facts.

One of the most important parameters describing a stellar population is its luminosity function, i.e., the distribution of the number of stars per cubic parsec as a function of luminosity or absolute magnitude. According to theory, the initial, or "zero-age," luminosity function will be determined by the density distribution in the clouds from which the stars are formed, and to some extent by the chemical composition of the clouds. Since all the stars of a given population need not be formed all at once, this "birth function" is itself a function of the time. Furthermore, the luminosity function at any particular later epoch is changing because of the different relative aging rate of the more massive and less massive stars. The luminosity function at a given time in a given neighborhood (say, today in the neighborhood of the Sun) thus is to be explained in terms of some fairly complex processes. Observationally, the luminosity function in the neighborhood of the Sun shows a broad maximum at a place corresponding to stars with $L = 10^{-3}L_{sun}$. The dropoff in number density at about $10^{-4}L_{sun}$ may be due to the approach to a low-luminosity cutoff corresponding to the minimum mass of the protostars that could have been formed from the original cloud. On the other hand, it may be due to observational incompleteness at the faint end of the luminosity scale. Not only are such stars hard to observe because they are faint (20th magnitude at 100 parsecs), but even when they can be observed, they are extremely troublesome to identify against the background of intrinsically brighter but more distant stars. For the lower end of the main sequence, estimates of the luminosity function depend on extrapolating the inventory of all the stars known to be within 5, 10, 15, etc., parsecs of the Sun, a very small sample which already at very short distances shows signs of incompleteness. For these same reasons, our idea of the number density of white dwarfs is rather sketchy.

Clusters—both open "galactic" clusters like the familiar Pleiades and globular clusters like M3 (Figs. 8 and 9)—are obviously an extremely important source of information in the study of stellar populations and evolution because they are collections of stars that must have formed at very nearly the same time out of the same cloud. They thus had the same initial composition and have aged for the same interval of time. Since the more massive luminous stars have relatively shorter life

FIG. 8. The Pleiades, a typical open galactic cluster of Population I, containing hot bright stars and nebulosity. (*Courtesy of Mount Wilson and Palomar Observatories.*)

expectancies, the effects of aging show much sooner at the upper end of the main sequence and make it a sensitive indicator of age. The H-R diagrams for clusters can be arranged in a monotonic sequence, from youngest to oldest. The dynamic properties, that is, gravitational stability against the disrupting effects of differential galactic rotation, also indicate the same age sequence.

In contrast to the brighter end of the main sequence, hardly any evolutionary effects can be observed in fainter stars because their life expectancy is longer than the hypothetical age of the Galaxy. Furthermore, in globular clusters, stars much fainter than the Sun cannot be observed at all, partly because of their extreme apparent faintness but mostly because of the impossibility of resolving their images against the dense blended background of much brighter stars. (For instance, the Sun at the distance of M3 would look like a 21st-magnitude star.) There is prospect of improving this situation through the use of optically smaller ultraviolet images (see Sec. 3 below).

This brief survey has no more than touched on current ideas of stellar evolution and its relation to element synthesis and chemical composition.

FIG. 9. The globular cluster M3 in Canes Venatici. The brightest resolved stars are yellow giants, the brightest of the perhaps 100,000 Population II stars that make it up. (*Courtesy of Mount Wilson and Palomar Observatories.*)

Readers are referred to M. Schwarzschild's excellent monograph[2] and to various papers by Fowler, E. M. Burbidge, G. R. Burbidge, Hoyle, and Greenstein.[6-10]

2.2 Abundances of the Elements

Because the motion, position in space, and location on the H-R diagram are in the general case only statistical indices of population, astronomers are left with initial chemical composition as the only population-linked characteristic which can be used as an index of population membership for individual stars. It seems likely that differences in the abundance of the elements toward the light end of the periodic table will constitute the best available index. As mentioned above in Sec. 1, their abundances are difficult to determine from the lines in the visible spectrum since, for the most part, they arise from transitions between two excited states, 1 to 4 ev apart. The possibility of observing the resonance lines of these elements in the ultraviolet raises the expectation that more reliable abundances will be derived. On the other hand, the high degree of crowding and blending of the lines in the ultraviolet spectra may make abundance determinations from resonance lines difficult or impossible. Even if this turns out to be so, one may expect other population-linked features in the ultraviolet, such as differences in the continuum or in the intensities of the strongest lines, blends, or bands—differences of the sort whose exploitation in the visible region was pioneered by Chalonge[11] and his students and also pursued by Strömgren.[12] The discovery and systematic application of easily distinguishable population-connected characteristics would disentangle the present somewhat confused picture of stellar populations and would supply the third dimension which the H-R diagram evidently needs to resolve some of its ambiguities. This third dimension might be labeled "relative age," after Schwarzschild's suggestion.[13]

Although in most cases the abundance of the elements in the atmosphere of a star reflects its initial composition and in these cases serves as a rough indication of the star's age, this simple picture may, under certain known circumstances, be complicated by the change in abundances brought about by the energy-production processes within the star itself. For instance, certain stars known to be in an advanced state of evolution have been found to have an abnormally high He/H ratio—white dwarfs, cataclysmic, and ordinary cluster-type variables lying on the trajectory on the H-R diagram, probably representing the decay of red giants into white dwarfs. It is possible that similar effects might be detectable at an even earlier stage (e.g., in the red giants themselves) if the currently accepted model for these stars is correct. Toward the end of the red-giant stage, the shell source may have moved out far enough to allow mixing of the end-products of thermonuclear processes into the lower level of the very extended and turbulent outer envelope. It is suggestive that certain red giants have abnormally high abundances of carbon, others of zirconium, barium, and vanadium. Why should such abundance anomalies exist in red giants but not in red dwarfs?

Other especially interesting cases arise in which abundances at the surface may be related to processes in the interior or to special (not necessarily evolutionary) processes on the surface itself. For example, the abundance of lithium in the Sun, though much lower than on the Earth, is still high enough to indicate that the Sun's surface material has never been involved in its energy-producing core, which would have consumed the lithium almost entirely.[14] Similarly, the short-lived radioactive element technetium has been suspected in the atmosphere of certain peculiar stars; it seems most improbable that it could have been formed anywhere except fairly near the surface because it would have decayed before reaching the surface.

Since the interstellar clouds of gas and dust are believed to be the raw material from which stars have been and are even now being formed and since the medium is believed to be predominantly hydrogen (enriched by injections of heavier elements from supernova explosions and other less violent expulsion of matter from stars), the abundances of elements in the interstellar medium form a link between the stars of the past and those of the future.

The emphasis that has been given to the part that abundances play in unraveling the puzzles of stellar evolution should not be allowed to overshadow the fact that they also enjoy an important role in the equilibrium of structures such as stellar atmospheres and interiors and gaseous nebulae. It is well known that the addition of a slight admixture of some elements to the composition of a gas can have a relatively large effect on its opacity and electron density, with corresponding effects on the transfer of radiant energy. Relatively small differences in abundance can produce relatively large differences in the structure of a star. For example, the difference in position on the H-R diagram between a normal main-sequence star of type K (effective temperature = 5000°K) and a sub-dwarf F (three times as bright, with effective temperature = 7000°K) may be due to the presence or absence of about 1 per cent by weight of the elements heavier than helium.[2] Similar considerations seem to explain the difference in luminosity between Population I and II red giants. The amount of carbon necessary to produce the heavy C_2, CH, and CN absorption bands in the carbon stars need not be great, but the bands nevertheless modify the spectral distribution of the emergent radiation and the atmospheric structure.

2.3 Continuous Spectra of the Stars

Abundances are estimated from the very careful measurement of the amount of energy absorbed or scattered in spectral lines and thus they depend on high-resolution spectral tracings, but much data of great astrophysical interest can be derived from measurements of the continuous spectrum.

Strictly speaking, the expression "continuous spectrum" should refer to a spectrum in which the opacity of the source is a very slowly varying function of the wavelength. In the case of stellar absorption-line spectra, on the other hand, it may refer either to the spectrum between the lines or it may refer to a spectrum in which large variations in opacity are smoothed out, such as one would obtain with a spectrophotometer of low spectral resolution. In what follows, the latter meaning is intended, as the context makes clear.

For convenience, astronomers have customarily used black-body laws with a disposable parameter T (the temperature) as a shorthand way of describing the continuous spectrum of a star. Disagreements among the various values of T derived from the application of the laws of Stefan, Planck, and Wien result from the departure of the radiation from black-body spectral distribution and are, of course, a consequence of various opacity-producing mechanisms in the stellar atmosphere or surrounding medium. The structure of a stellar atmosphere or interior must adjust itself to the damming action of the opacity. Furthermore, as noted above, relatively minor changes in chemical abundance sometimes produce relatively large changes in opacity.

Stars with effective temperatures from, say, 4000 to 9000°K, radiate most of their energy in the visible portion of the spectrum or in the accessible infrared and ultraviolet. Therefore, in photometric studies where an attempt is being made to estimate the total radiation from a star, the correction for the radiation in the unobserved portion of the spectrum lying outside the easily accessible spectral range is small. This so-called "bolometric correction" could itself be in fairly serious error without seriously distorting the estimated total luminosity of the star. The case is quite different, however, for stars hotter than 9000°K or cooler than 4000°K, which radiate most of their energy in invisible regions of the spectrum. The temperatures of the very hot blue stars of spectral Types O-B-A have been estimated (from both their line and continuous spectra in the accessible region) to range from 12,000°K (Type A) through 25,000°K (Type B) to perhaps 50,000°K (Type O5). For these latter stars the estimate of the unobserved ultraviolet radiation is frequently only a black-body extrapolation from the visible spectrum based on the assumption that the ultraviolet spectrum also corresponds to the same high temperature. More sophisticated or refined extrapolations, taking into account the continua of hydrogen and helium on the short-wave-

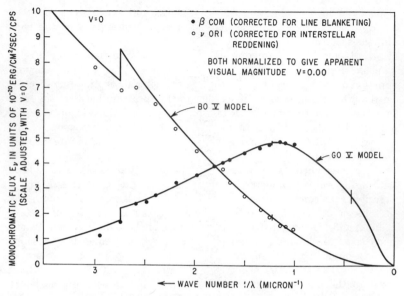

FIG. 10. Observed spectral distribution of the energy radiated in the wavelength interval λ 3000 to 10,000 (0.3 to 1.0 μ) by stars of Type G0 V (∼6000°K) and B0 V (∼25,000°K). (*Courtesy of A. D. Code[15] and the Editors of The Astronomical Journal.*)

length side of the ionization limits, can still lead to serious errors, however, because at these temperatures the bolometric correction for the far ultraviolet is sensitive to temperature and is much larger than the total visible radiation on which it is based (see Figs. 10 and 11).

These considerations become particularly touchy when one is dealing with the question of the physical state (energy balance, electron density, and pressure, etc.) of a nebula associated with a very hot star, since the nebular parameters depend in a very critical way on the amount and detailed distribution of the ultraviolet radiation from the exciting star. For example, in an earlier ultraviolet survey of the night sky conducted by investigators at the Naval Research Laboratory with high-altitude rockets,[16] the sensitivity of the counters in the spectral region 1225 to 1350 Å was such that the radiation in this band from the hot bright star Spica (Alpha Virginis, spectral Type B0) was expected to be thirty times the noise level: in fact, nothing was observed. Certain other stars should also have been detectable. A more recent survey, however, has revealed a number of weak point sources in this wavelength region.[17]

The suspected ultraviolet deficiency of the intrinsically bright stars of spectral Type O-B-A is important for another reason: they are relatively the youngest in the scheme of stellar evolution, and therefore their total luminosity is a datum of great importance in theories of the evolution of galaxies as well as of individual stars. Direct ultraviolet measurements of their luminosities would remove the present uncertainties.

These hot bright stars are also the chief source of the radiation in space, at least in the outer parts of our own Galaxy (e.g. the neighborhood of the Sun) and other spirals. The temperature of both sorts of interstellar matter—gas and dust—depends on the energy density of this dilute bath of radiation. In particular, many elements which certainly or probably occur in gaseous nebulosities have ionization limits in the far ultraviolet; the degree to which these elements are ionized, and hence the electron density, will depend critically not only on the degree to which the interstellar radiation has been attenuated by the Lyman

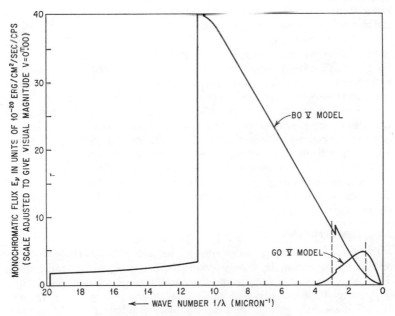

FIG. 11. Spectral distribution of the radiation from stars of Types G0 V and B0 V, extrapolated into the ultraviolet (to λ500) from the observed data of Fig. 10. (*Courtesy of A. D. Code*[15] *and the Editors of The Astronomical Journal.*)

absorption of interstellar hydrogen (see below), but also on the initial amount of ultraviolet and X radiation originating in the hot stars.

The emphasis on very hot stars in the above paragraphs should not be taken to mean that the continuous spectra of cooler stars are of no importance. For example, the effective temperature of the Sun taken from the data of the visible spectrum does not represent the ultraviolet spectral distribution at all well. This should not be regarded as a departure from black-body radiation, which would here be a sheer formalism. We should say, rather, that it is the joint result of crowded absorption lines and molecular bands and of the mixture of radiation from several distinct atmospheric regions at different temperatures.

Spectrograms and spectral scans of the Sun, obtained from rockets[18-20] (see Chap. 17, The Sun) have brought out the following facts about its ultraviolet spectrum. The continuous (i.e., photospheric) spectrum fades below detectable levels at around 1500 to 1600 Å. At shorter wavelengths only separate emission features are present. In the spectral range from $\lambda1600$ down to about $\lambda100$, the emission lines are largely of chromospheric origin and correspond to temperatures of 20,000 to 40,000°K (He, C, N, O, etc., and their ions). At still shorter wavelengths, in the X-ray region, what are evidently unresolved clumps of resonance lines of the multiply ionized metals in the million-degree corona have been detected. The fact that this radiation originates in the corona has been established during two total eclipses of the Sun when the photosphere and chromosphere were blocked from view.[21] We do not know whether a very extended, intensely hot atmosphere like the solar corona is a rare or common phenomenon among the stars in general.[22] A fair guess might be made if we understood better the mechanism causing the Sun's corona; otherwise the problem must await direct observational attack. Since ordinary Sun-like stars are numerous, the answer to this question has considerable bearing on the amount of X radiation in the Galaxy.

2.4 Emission Nebulae

Our knowledge of the gaseous emission nebulae is based almost entirely on optical data and, in a very small number of cases, on radio data. They may be sorted into several general types.[23] Some are diffuse, irregularly shaped objects and are excited or ionized by the ultraviolet radiation emanating from the very hot stars associated with them; this is the type mentioned above (see Fig. 12). The diffuse nebulosities occasionally subtend a large solid angle and show a complicated internal structure, e.g., the Orion Nebula complex, which is about 20° by 30°.

FIG. 12. The Orion Nebula, a typical diffuse nebula of gas and dust which derives its luminous energy from hot stars embedded in it. (*Courtesy of Mount Wilson and Palomar Observatories.*)

The planetary nebulae are by contrast compact, more or less globular objects, centered also on very hot stars of Types O-B-A; these nebulae appear to be, in fact, highly extended atmospheres of their central stars and are excited by their very energetic radiation. The central stars appear to be subluminous; that is, they are intrinsically fainter than main-sequence stars of the same spectral type (see Fig. 13). A third type of gaseous nebula derives its ionization and excitation energy from the shock waves generated in the violent collision of gaseous elements in

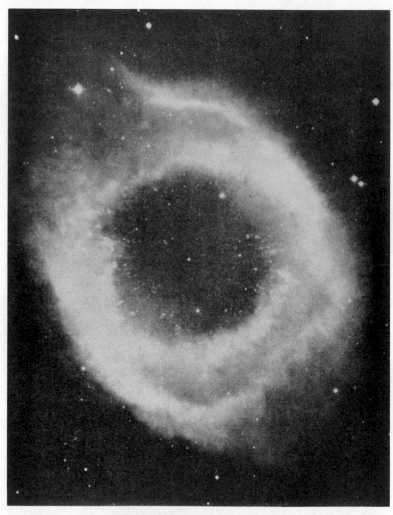

FIG. 13. NGC 7293, a planetary nebula in Aquarius. It derives its energy from the ultraviolet radiation of the central star, which looks very faint in visible light. (*Courtesy of Mount Wilson and Palomar Observatories.*)

very rapid relative motion. The primary elements in the collision may be internal turbulent elements (as in the Crab Nebula, an old supernova; see Fig. 14), an expanding shell of gas and the ambient interstellar medium (e.g., the Cygnus Loop; see Fig. 15), or the gaseous filling of whole galaxies in collision (e.g., Cygnus A). These kinds of objects are also sources of radio-frequency radiation[24] and possibly of X rays (see below).

The optical spectral data from which most of our information about emission nebulosities has been derived consist chiefly of the permitted bright lines of the hydrogen Balmer series and of helium, and forbidden lines of oxygen, carbon, nitrogen, neon, etc., in various stages of ionization. The hydrogen and helium lines are limited to those arising from transitions between two excited states, a circumstance which severely limits the amount of information that can be obtained from them. The uncertainties arise because the gas is very far from thermodynamic equilibrium (because of its extremely low density) and to the very dilute

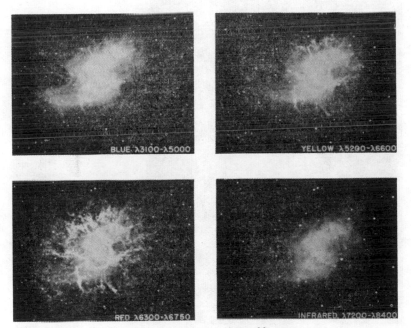

FIG. 14. The Crab Nebula, the remnant of an old supernova explosion. (*Courtesy of Mount Wilson and Palomar Observatories.*)

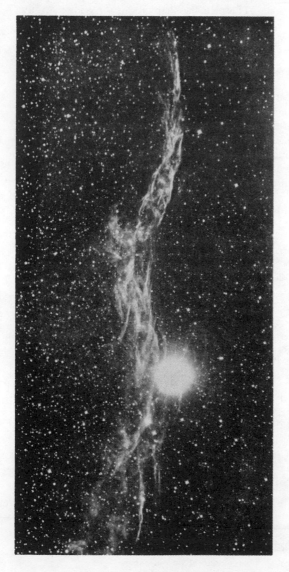

FIG. 15. Part of the
Cygnus Loop of diffuse
nebulosity. It derives its
luminous energy from
collision with the ambi-
ent gas cloud through
which it is moving to
the right. (*Courtesy of
Mount Wilson and Palo-
mar Observatories.*)

radiation field of the embedded hot star (or stars). Furthermore, as we have seen, the ultraviolet and X-ray spectrum of the exciting star is for purposes of calculation extrapolated from the visible spectrum and may be in serious error. These uncertainties can largely be avoided by observing transitions to the ground state, which for the more abundant elements and their ions are almost all in the ultraviolet (e.g., H, He I, He II, C, N, O, the inert gases, the halogens). A knowledge of the ultraviolet emission spectrum is essential to separate such parameters as electron density, temperature, and relative abundance in an unambiguous way. The observation of certain ultraviolet forbidden lines such as those of [Ne IV] would also help. (See Fig. 16 for the expected ultraviolet spectrum of a planetary nebula as computed by T. Daub.[15])

The wavelength region between Lyman-α and λ1350 surveyed by the NRL group,[16,17] in which the ultraviolet radiation of Spica and other hot stars was suspected of being deficient, is of extreme interest for another reason. This same night-sky survey uncovered the existence of at least two large areas of surprisingly intense diffuse emission. One of these,

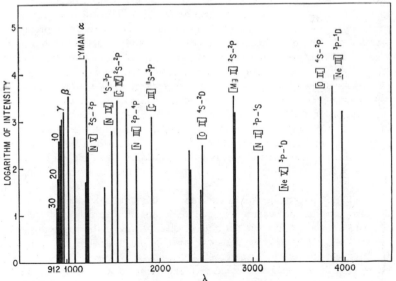

FIG. 16. Expected ultraviolet emission spectrum of a planetary nebula, as predicted by T. Daub. (*Courtesy of A. D. Code*[16] *and the Editors of The Astronomical Journal.*)

about 20° by 30° in Orion, coincides fairly well with an area of visible nebulosity associated with a number of B stars; but in the other region, extending radially about 10° around Spica, there is no visible emission whatsoever. The visible line emission in the Orion region is not of much help, since it does not suggest any very plausible mechanism for the λ1300 radiation. For example, if it were due to neutral oxygen, certain other oxygen lines should also appear, but they do not. It seems that the only source of radiation sufficiently intense to account for the observed nebulosity is Lyman-α widened toward the red. Two suggestions for the red shift are (1) the emission of Doppler-shifted Lyman-α from the fast stellar particles that have been neutralized in the nebular plasma[25] and (2) Raman scattering of Lyman-α by molecular hydrogen.[26] Discovery of the exact nature of this radiation may well await the application of higher-resolution techniques.

2.5 The Interstellar Medium

The mass of the Galaxy can be found from the dynamics of its rotation and its internal stellar motions. It is the equivalent of about 2×10^{11} solar masses, or 4×10^{44} g, and appears to be distributed in comparable quantities between stars and interstellar matter. The diffuse interstellar matter consists chiefly of neutral atomic hydrogen with an appreciable fraction of other elements and probably molecules, together with a non-negligible quantity of minute solid particles, commonly referred to as "dust." The gaseous component can be detected optically by the absorption lines it superposes on the spectra of distant luminous stars and by the emission lines near hot stars. It can also be detected by the neutral hydrogen emission (and, under special circumstances, absorption) of 21-cm radiation in the radio spectrum. The dust component is responsible for the extinction of transmitted starlight and for the partial polarization of transmitted and reflected starlight. Since the extinction is selective with wavelength, it also produces interstellar reddening of starlight.

Although the distribution of the gas and dust in space is by no means uniform (its density varies by several orders of magnitudes from one place to another), nevertheless it is possible to make the following generalizations: (1) the particle density of interstellar hydrogen, as estimated from optical observations and from the 21-cm data, averages about 1 per cubic centimeter near the galactic plane (1 to 2×10^{-23} g per cm³); (2) a mean density of dust of the order of 10^{-25} g per cm³ or less, and suitably distributed, is quite sufficient to explain the observed extinction and reddening of starlight.

The dynamical studies alluded to above call for a total density of matter approximately equal to the combined directly estimated density of the gas, dust, and stars. The estimate of the total mass of the stars is rather uncertain because the observed number density of the stars is based ultimately on counts over a relatively small volume of space in the Sun's immediate neighborhood, which may be observationally incomplete for faint stars. Hence there is still enough room in the estimate of the total mass to allow for the possible presence of hitherto undetected matter: very faint or completely dead stars, cold bodies of planetary dimensions, gas in molecular form such as H_2, etc.

1. *Interstellar Gas.* Except in the neighborhood of a star (the size of the "neighborhood" depending on the temperature of the star), the temperature of interstellar space is very low. In the presence of the very dilute, average radiation field of the stars, the equilibrium blackbody temperature is a few degrees absolute. Thus almost all atoms and molecules are in the ground state, and studies with earth-bound telescopes have been limited to absorption lines of those few atoms and ions whose resonance lines lie in the accessible regions of the spectrum and which at the same time are abundant enough to make an impression. The choice has been limited: Ca, Ca^+, Na, K, K^+, Ti^+, and the molecules CH, CH^+, CN, and possibly NH and OH. The density of hydrogen, where it has not been directly observed in emission near a hot star (the H II regions), has been inferred from rather rough estimates of the above particles together with the application of an assumed hydrogen-metal abundance ratio.

In the ultraviolet, the situation will be quite different. The kinds of question which we may hope to answer by such observations are described in the following excerpt from a sketch of the astronomical space program of Princeton University, contributed by L. Spitzer:[27]

Measurement of the absorption lines produced by interstellar atoms and molecules shortward of 3000 Å should open up a new and highly significant field of astrophysical research. Several decades ago the existence of extensive gas clouds throughout the galaxy was not fully realized. Now it is known that an appreciable percentage of the mass of a galaxy, possibly even more than half, is in such clouds, composed mostly of hydrogen. Radio astronomy studies of the hydrogen line at 21 cm, either in emission or absorption, have given information on the galactic distribution of the hydrogen gas, on the temperature within the denser regions and on the turbulent velocities. Much more detailed velocity information on neighboring gas clouds has been obtained from a study of the interstellar sodium and calcium lines, seen in absorption in the spectra of stars with high surface temperatures. Much theoretical work on interstellar gas dynamics has been based on these observations.

In principle, observations of atomic absorption lines should give detailed information on the physical conditions of the interstellar gas, including level of ionization, electron density, and chemical composition. Such studies are now grossly handicapped by the fact that the only interstellar absorption lines of any strength in the accessible region of the spectrum are those of Na I and of Ca II. These are ultimate lines of relatively scarce elements, in their less abundant states of ionization. Corresponding observations in the far ultraviolet would extend these measures to the more abundant atoms, such as C, N, O, Mg and Fe, in several different states of ionization. Moreover, the much greater strength of these lines would permit research on features which are now not measurable. Finally, ultraviolet measures hold open the possibility of detecting the presence of molecular H_2, which may be almost as abundant as atomic H but which apparently cannot be detected by other means.

Several specific programs of research in this area may be described. One important program would be the measurement of the strength of interstellar Mg I (2852 Å) and Mg II (2796 and 2803 Å) in the spectra of a number of stars of high surface temperature within about 1000 parsecs from the Sun. Since the ionization probability for Mg I can be estimated, these measures would give directly a determination of the electron density in various regions of the interstellar gas. At the present time such estimates are based primarily on the ratio of the Ca I and Ca II lines; the Ca I line is so weak that its strength has been measured in only one star.

Another program would be a measurement of the chemical composition in different interstellar gas clouds, through measurement of the strengths of the Fe II lines (between 2000 and 2700 Å), of C I (1561 Å), C II (1336 Å), and higher members of the Lyman series of neutral H (923 Å to 915 Å). Recent theories on the evolution of stars and of galaxies indicate that heavy elements are formed in supernovae and ejected into the interstellar gas. Direct observation of the chemical composition of the interstellar gas clouds in different spiral arms would give important and perhaps decisive information bearing on these theories.

Yet another program would involve the measurement of the H_2 lines (1108 and 1008 Å). These absorption features may have appreciable strength. The corresponding absorption lines by HD and D_2 molecules a few angstroms away might also be measurable. Analysis of these molecules would close one of the major gaps in accounting for the mass of gas in our galaxy. It is not impossible that in many gas clouds the hydrogen may be almost entirely molecular.

Finally, the analysis of physical conditions in the interstellar gas clouds would be possible from measures of the density, ionization level, chemical composition and detailed velocity distribution. Such studies would be of crucial importance for the analysis of star formation and also for the various hydromagnetic processes that affect the dynamics of these systems.

In the foregoing passage, Spitzer has reference mostly to isolated resonance lines of atoms other than hydrogen and helium. For hydrogen, on account of its overwhelming abundance—and this is true of helium to a lesser degree—the situation is somewhat more complicated. Aller has summarized his findings on the line and continuous absorption of starlight by hydrogen and helium in interstellar space in a paper,[28] excerpts from which follow.

Next, we must mention the role played by the line and continuous absorption of interstellar hydrogen and helium. This will depend on whether we are looking along the plane of the Galaxy or perpendicular thereto.

Consider as an example the nebula and stars in the Orion region. Wade finds 1.5 to 2 × 10^{21} neutral hydrogen atoms/cm^2 in line of sight in the region of λ Orionis.[29] If we assume $T = 100°$K in the neutral hydrogen gas, it follows that the optical depth at the center of the line is about 10^9 and the profile of the Lyman-α absorption line is determined entirely by radiation damping. The line is totally black over a width of about 7 Å and a line of sight velocity of about 700 km/sec would be required to displace an emission line from behind the black-out imposed by the interstellar Lyman α absorption.

The interstellar hydrogen would conceal any chromospheric emission from perhaps all but nearby (or high galactic latitude) stars moving with high radial velocities. Suppose that the average concentration of neutral hydrogen atoms in the neighborhood of the Sun is 0.1/cm^3. The optical depth to Sirius in the center of Lyman-α is 5 × 10^6 and the half-width of the interstellar absorption is about 0.4 Å. Although the wings of the Lyman lines probably will not be strongly modified except in distant stars, the line cores will be affected.

The absorption coefficient in the Lyman continuum may be computed roughly from

$$\alpha_\nu = 6.3 \times 10^{-18} \left(\frac{\nu}{\nu_0}\right)^{-3}$$

where ν_0 is the frequency of the Lyman limit. In the region of Orion where the number of atoms in the line of sight is 10^{21} atoms/cm^2, the optical depth would be 6000 at the Lyman limit, about 6 at 100 Å and about 0.005 at 10 Å. Hence X-rays could escape from the nebula. Next consider the neutral helium absorption. At the series limit $\alpha = 7.6 \times 10^{-18}$, so that with a hydrogen/helium ratio of 7,[30] the optical depth at λ504 is 1000 and the optical depth in hydrogen is about the same. At higher frequencies the helium absorption gradually predominates over the hydrogen absorption. At 20 Å, S. S. Huang[31] finds an absorption coefficient of about 0.0025 × 10^{-18}, and at 10 Å we might expect this to fall to about a quarter of this value. The optical thickness at 20 Å is thus about 0.4 and at 11 Å about 0.1., i.e., considerably greater than for hydrogen. [See Figs. 17 and 18.]

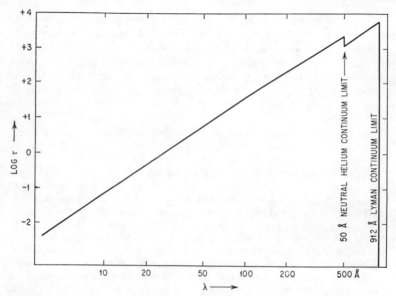

FIG. 17. Absorption of neutral atomic hydrogen and helium, expressed as relative optical depth τ for a fixed geometric depth, as a function of wavelength. (*Courtesy of L. H. Aller and the Editor of the Publications of the Astronomical Society of the Pacific.*)

In the direction of the Crab Nebula we estimate from the 21-cm data about 10^{20} atoms/cm² in the line of sight. Hence there should be no difficulty in detecting X-rays from the Crab Nebula provided they are emitted with a high intensity. We would not expect many regions of space to contain fewer than 10^{20} atoms/cm² in the line of sight.

On the basis of the foregoing considerations we are forced to the unhappy conclusion that the neutral hydrogen in our solar system and in interstellar space will cause serious complications in the observations between the beginning of the Lyman series and the soft X-ray region.

Even in the nearest stars, the profiles of the Lyman lines will be strongly affected by interstellar absorption, and there is almost no hope at all of getting any observations on the Lyman lines in gaseous nebulae or brightline stars.

The strong Lyman continuum will effectively extinguish all the radiation beyond λ912 except perhaps in the spectra of some of the nearest stars. From distant stars and gaseous nebulae we can hope to observe only radiation in the X-ray region.

In connection with Aller's review, the following more hopeful prospect should be noted. The width of the completely black center becomes successively narrower for higher members of the Lyman series (see Spitzer above). Hence one should eventually reach a point in the series where the line width becomes sensitive to the total opacity and, further on, another point where the lines for separate gas clouds with different radial velocities might possibly be resolved. At small distances, or in directions where the interstellar gas is less dense, this whole pattern would move in toward lower members of the Lyman series, a fact which seems to provide the possibility of probing the detailed structure of the interstellar hydrogen in the immediate surroundings of the solar system. It would be necessary to find a sufficient number of nearby stars with a strong enough continuum in the λ912 to 1216 region. Since B stars are scarce and none are very close, probably stars of Type A and possibly F will have to be used, and their own very strong hydrogen absorption lines may confuse the issue a little. Nevertheless, it should be possible to separate the two different contours.

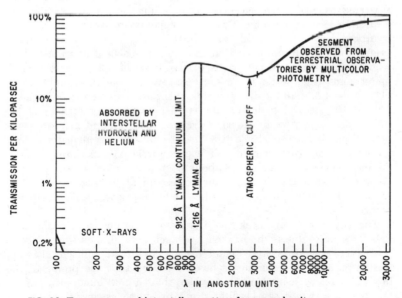

FIG. 18. Transparency of interstellar matter of average density and composition, in the wavelength interval λ100 to 31,000. The heavy segment at λ3000 to 20,000 is the part that has been observed from the ground; its positive slope corresponds to interstellar reddening by selective scattering. (*Courtesy of A. D. Code*[15] *and the Editors of The Astronomical Journal.*)

There remains also the possibility of detecting emission-line radiation from molecular constituents of the interstellar gas or nebulosities in wavelengths from the infrared through the millimeter-wave band: for instance CH, NH, OH, and H_2, the presence of some of which has so far only been suspected. Furthermore, such emissions would correspond to temperatures intermediate between the nebulosities from which visible or ultraviolet emission lines are observed and the neutral hydrogen sources of the 21-cm line (see Sec. 2.7, Radio Sources, below).

2. *Interplanetary or Circumterrestrial Hydrogen.* Closely related to the problem of interstellar hydrogen is that of interplanetary or circumterrestrial hydrogen. The rocket observations of Kupperian, Byram, Chubb, and Friedman[32] have revealed that the entire night sky above heights from 75 to 146 km is aglow with Lyman-α radiation, the total flux from the hemisphere amounting to about 10^{-2} erg per cm^2 per sec. So bright was the radiation that no celestial sources of Lyman-α could be detected through it. The source of this radiation is solar Lyman-α scattered by cold hydrogen gas, but it is not yet certain whether the scattering occurs predominantly in interplanetary space or in an extended hydrogen envelope around the Earth. Friedman originally interpreted these results to mean that radiation is reaching us from a cloud whose neutral particle density is of the order of 0.2 per cubic centimeter and which extends possibly several astronomical units away $(1 \text{ A.U.} = 1.5 \times 10^{13} \text{ cm})$. On this basis, one would expect at least 10^{12} to 10^{13} neutral hydrogen atoms per square centimeter along the line of sight out through the solar system. More recent measurements of the solar Lyman-α profile by Purcell and Tousey[33] reveal a narrow absorption core (uncorrected half width $\sim$0.05 Å) superimposed on a broader one, corresponding to about 2 or 3×10^{12} H atoms per cm^2 column between the Sun and the terrestrial atmosphere at 100 km. Most of this hydrogen appears to be part of a geocorona, i.e., a circumterrestrial cloud.

The sky glow may mask the Lyman-α radiation from stellar and nebular sources unless the neutral hydrogen is telluric as suggested; in this case observations can be made from a satellite at sufficient altitude. Furthermore, later experiments have indicated that the profile of the intense Lyman-α emission is no wider than a few hundredths of an angstrom, so that it can be filtered out by simple means, thereby permitting the broader profile of galactic sources to be readily observed except for the excision of a very narrow core at the center of Lyman-α. Until the intensities and widths of the stellar and nebular Lyman lines are measured, one cannot estimate how serious the masking effects will be.

The considerations discussed in this section do not apply, however, to the Lyman continuum. Furthermore, they should not be confused with the effects of *interstellar* hydrogen discussed by Aller.[28]

3. *Interstellar Dust.* The scattering function of solid grains of radius a for impinging radiation of wavelength λ is a function of the ratio a/λ. For $a/\lambda \ll 1$, the function becomes the familiar λ^{-4} law; but at a/λ near unity, the function becomes more complicated and may have a positive exponent (interstellar "bluing"). Figure 18 shows an estimate of the extinction in stellar magnitudes as a function of wavelength.[15] In the wavelength region $\lambda > 3000$, reddening occurs; in the region $3000 > \lambda > 1000$, interstellar bluing occurs. Particles in the range 0.1 to 0.5μ distributed with a mean density of 10^{-25} g per cm^3 account for observed reddening and extinction in the visible or near-visible spectrum.

Theoretically, it should be possible to deduce the distribution of particle sizes from a detailed knowledge of this function. The actual distribution of particle sizes and number density is somewhat indeterminate, not only because various combinations of these produce nearly indistinguishable effects, but also because the scattering coefficient depends on the index of refraction of the material, about whose nature we can only make plausible guesses. The dependence of the scattering coefficient upon wavelength is deduced by comparing the spectral energy distributions of reddened and unobscured stars of the same spectral class. The extension of the reddening curve into the ultraviolet would give considerably more leverage on the problem of determining particle sizes and indices of refraction of the scatterers. Ultraviolet multicolor photometry is therefore a promising field of investigation for learning about the nature and origin of the interstellar grains. It is an equally important part of the study of gaseous nebulae; much of the uncertainty regarding the composition and temperature of these objects rests upon adequately determining the extent of interstellar reddening, because the absorption alters the relative intensities of nebular emission lines in different parts of the spectrum. Furthermore, the total extinction of integrated starlight in a particular wavelength interval is related to the interstellar reddening coefficient in a simple way, so that once the reddening is known, it is possible to apply the extinction corrections which are necessary to obtain the correct relationship between apparent brightness, absolute luminosity, and distance.

The intensity or surface brightness of the weak thermal radiation from the interstellar dust clouds would, if detectable, be a valuable datum because it would provide another relation between the total cross section of the dust particles in the line of sight and the temperature.

2.6 External Galaxies and Intergalactic Matter

This subject is so enormous that it will be possible only to touch upon a few topics to put possible investigations in their proper context.

The Universe, as far as it is accessible to observation with the most powerful existing instruments, is populated throughout with galaxies. Although the distribution of the galaxies is by no means uniform, but suggests a hierarchy of clustering, their smoothed-out number density can be estimated at about 1 per cubic megaparsec (1 parsec $= 3 \times 10^{18}$ cm). This means that something like 10^9 galaxies should be observable with present telescopes. Thus number density corresponds to a mean matter density of the order of 10^{-29} g per cm^3, or 1 hydrogen atom per cm^3. Although most astronomers think of the reaches of intergalactic space as being nearly void, it must be conceded that the enormous volume of space concerned could be occupied by very tenuous matter that would add up to a very large mass, without necessarily revealing its presence in any conspicuous way. There is some evidence that intergalactic matter is in fact present. Since the mean density of matter in the Universe is a datum of fundamental significance to cosmology, especially that dealing with relativistic models of the Universe, it becomes extremely important not only to establish the statistics of galactic distribution and mass (which involves pursuing all leads to uncover the presence of invisible matter inside of galaxies) but also to detect further evidence of matter between the galaxies.

As mentioned in the discussion of stellar populations above, galaxies are classified into morphological types: Irregular (Population I?), Elliptical (Population II), and Spiral, including the subtype Barred Spiral (both populations). (See Figs. 3 to 5.) Only the nearest galaxies can be resolved into stars with earth-bound telescopes; the population analysis of the more remote ones must be inferred from such data as color, surface brightness, etc. The masses of some of the galaxies may be estimated from their rotation and internal motions. Statistical inferences may be made for some others from their motions and distribution in clusters of galaxies. As in the case of individual stars, the ratio of luminosity to mass is a piece of information very useful in the typing of galaxies, estimating age and the effects of age, and the like. Since our present view of the more remote objects refers to a much earlier time, there is some hope that a more detailed study of the remote galaxies will lead to an actual time sequence of stellar populations.

It is a commonplace that the radiation from distant galaxies shows a systematic red shift that increases with distance. The increase is more or less linear for the closer ones, where one has more confidence in the distance scale. This confidence has been shaken several times in recent years by several discoveries, each tending to show that the galaxies are more remote than had been thought. The Hubble constant of expansion has been successively revised downward from nearly 600 km per sec per megaparsec to about 100 or perhaps even less. The phrase "expansion constant" arises from the widely held view that the red shift is a genuine Doppler shift produced by the galaxies, all receding from us and from each other. Whatever the cause of the observed red shift, it furnishes the only hope that extragalactic radiation in the Lyman series and continuum will not be blotted out by our own interstellar hydrogen.

The following excerpt is taken (with minor revisions in brackets) from a contribution by A. B. Meinel.[54]

The opacity of interstellar hydrogen to light in the Lyman region, while a hindrance to stellar observations, will make galaxies objects of great interest. The light shorter than 912Å from the stars within a galaxy will be completely absorbed by that galaxy's own interstellar medium and scattered as discrete line emissions of the hydrogen atom. The scattered Lyman series lines will be rescattered until all of the radiation is converted into Lyman-α and emission lines of the Balmer and higher level series.

The successive scatterings of the Lyman-α quantum will continue, less inelastic encounters, until the Lyman-α radiation finally escapes from the fringes of the galaxy. The number of quanta that survive depend upon the inelastic collisional cross section of the interstellar dust. It may be that little Lyman-α radiation can survive traversal of a galaxy. If intergalactic space is relatively free from neutral atomic hydrogen, the Lyman-α radiation emitted by the galaxy will arrive at our Galaxy. If the galaxy under observation is sufficiently distant to produce a red-shift of about 1000 km/sec, the radiation will penetrate into our Galaxy and arrive at the solar system.

The study of galaxies [in the spectral region $\lambda > 1215$ Å] should yield considerable knowledge about the distribution of gas within galaxies. Galaxies should be quite conspicuous objects, whose spectra show a rise in intensity well above the [continuum on the long-wavelength side of the spectrum cutoff]. All of the starlight from the stars in the galaxy shorter than 912Å has been converted (less inelastic encounters) into one spectrum line.

In detailed study, galaxies may prove as interesting emission objects as are planetary nebulae. The similarity, but on different scale, to the planetary nebulae is obvious.

In the field of statistical studies, it will be interesting to look for galaxies free of interstellar hydrogen, for instance those that recently experienced a collision with a neighbor. If such occurrences are as good a "sweep" as we now suspect, we may find intergalactic emission clouds of hydrogen with no stars embedded. Such clouds would be rendered visible only by scattering of Lyman-α emitted by neighboring galaxies [except perhaps for a brief interval after the collision].

In the case that a distant galaxy did produce a continuum shorter than $\lambda 1215$ in its own velocity system, either due to free-bound transitions in the outer layers of its interstellar medium or due perchance to the absence of an interstellar medium, in which case the individual stars might contribute to such a continuum, it might be possible to study the distribution of intergalactic hydrogen by observation of the absorption profile if it is [also] red-shifted to the long side of $\lambda 1215$ (terrestrial wavelengths).

Population differences in distance galaxies could be studied by observing the strength of the Lyman-α bump near the short wavelength end of the galaxies' spectra. If hot stars are reasonably abundant (Population I) then considerable energy is available in the starlight with $\lambda \leq 912$Å to form the Lyman-α bump. If the galaxy is free of dust and gas [no bump would form;] or [if the galaxy] is composed of Population II, even though it still might be optically thick in hydrogen, very little energy is available to form the Lyman-α bump.

2.7 Radio Sources

In this section we are concerned with the spectrum of the cosmic radio-frequency radiation and the spatial distribution of its sources.[35] There are several components to cosmic radio-frequency radiation: galactic radiation, extragalactic radiation, and discrete sources of several kinds (radio stars). The diffuse galactic radiation is typically concentrated toward the plane of the Milky Way and to a lesser degree toward the galactic center in Sagittarius. The extragalactic radiation is more or less isotropic, although in low galactic latitudes it is difficult to disentangle from the galactic radiation.

The discrete sources are distributed nearly isotropically also, but it seems likely that they are a mixture of galactic sources showing some concentration toward the galactic plane and extragalactic sources showing no concentration. The majority of that small proportion of the discrete sources that have been optically identified are associated with nebulosity in violent commotion. Some of these sources are galactic (old supernovae like the Crab Nebula or peculiar nebulosities), and others are extragalactic (galaxies in collision and other peculiar galaxies). Some extragalactic discrete sources appear, however, to be normal galaxies when viewed optically. One strong galactic source, Sagittarius A, although not visible, coincides with the center of our Galaxy.

Although the continuous background radiation is known to be a mixture of thermal and nonthermal radiation, the mechanism of its origin and the nature of the bodies emitting it are not known. For instance, we do not know whether it originates in an extended source or is a blend of unresolved, faint, discrete sources. The total radiation received at the Earth is surprisingly intense, about 10^4 times that of the Sun (at the low-frequency end). By contrast the total optical radiation from the stars (received at the Earth) is of the order of 10^{-8} that of the Sun. The equivalent temperature of the radiation is over 100,000°K at the lowest frequencies for which there are unambiguous observations (about 10 Mc), and Reber's and Ellis's temperatures derived from still lower frequencies are even higher[1] (see Fig. 19). The temperature and intensity fall with increasing frequency, and at the highest frequency that has been measured (8000 Mc or so)[36] the temperature is a few degrees absolute and the intensity almost unobservably low.

The implications of these studies for the structure of the Galaxy and of the observable universe are obvious. There remain many studies that can be most easily pursued from the ground. As for radio studies in space, one might infer from the very low intensity of highest-frequency observations that there is perhaps not too much to be gained by attempting for the present to push beyond the short-wavelength atmospheric cutoff ($\sim$4 mm). But the long-wavelength end of the spectrum is another matter (15 m or 20 Mc). Aside from the striking results of Reber and Ellis,[1] we have no data for frequencies lower than 9 Mc. Above our ionosphere, it should be possible to reach a limit somewhere in the neighborhood of 100 kc. If there are as many as 600 electrons per cm^3 in the interplanetary space immediately around the Earth, as some recent results seem to indicate, the cutoff will be as high as 220 kc. In any case, the cutoff frequency will be a datum useful for investigating circumterrestrial electron densities. If the density is less than 600 per cubic centimeter, or if the electron cloud is merely a halo around the Earth so that it can be surmounted by a high enough orbit, the next absorption limit one would expect to encounter is that of the interstellar electron clouds. Not much is known about their densities except in regions exposed to ionizing radiations from hot stars. Since the clouds are concentrated toward the galactic plane, the absorption would set in there at a higher frequency than toward the galactic poles. According to Haddock's estimate,[35] this would show up in the radio spectrum as an intensity maximum near the point where the absorption becomes noticeable, and this maximum would occur at frequencies which would decrease with increasing galactic latitude (see Fig. 19).

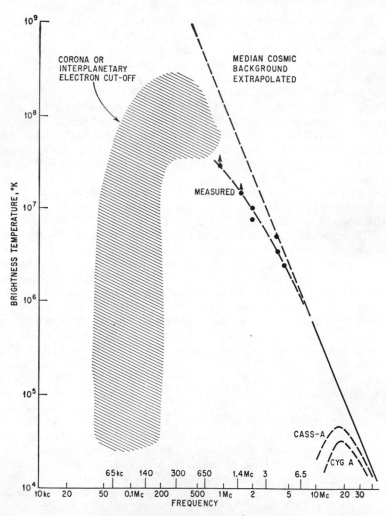

FIG. 19. Cosmic radio background brightness. (*Reproduced from "Final Report—Astronomical Experiments Proposed for Earth Satellites," University of Michigan Research Inst., November, 1958, p. 60.*)

3. RESEARCH PROBLEMS

3.1 Short-wavelength Photometry and Spectroscopy

As with observations in the conventional spectral region from 0.3 to 1μ, research in the ultraviolet and shorter wavelengths will range in dispersion from undispersed images in integrated light at one extreme to the greatest possible resolution at the other. As in conventional observations, the dispersion employed will depend on the particular problem: integrated images for astrometrics, multicolor photometry for color temperature and interstellar reddening, high-dispersion spectra for detailed astrophysical studies, etc.

Logically, perhaps, studies using integrated images might be discussed first, but we shall postpone them because the problems in that field are somewhat different from those treated by spectral studies (see Sec. 3.4, High-resolution Astrometry).

1. *Broad-band Survey for Reconnaissance and for Rough Spectrophotometry.* One of the first types of investigation that is needed is a reconnaissance of the whole sky in limited bands of short-wave radiation inaccessible from the ground. Such a survey would not only be relatively easy to perform compared with other experiments at the present state of the art, but would provide a broad view of the spatial and frequency distribution of the sources and would also approximately locate the regions or objects of greatest interest for later more detailed study. It would serve simply to indicate "what is there."

It is not essential that such a survey be very elaborate or that the angular resolution be high. Although the resolution should be as high as practicable, very valuable information would be obtained from relatively crude systems, say, an angular photometer aperture of several degrees, several passbands with width $\Delta\lambda/\lambda$ of the order of 1/10, and a scan provided by the spin and wobble of the satellite. The example of the NRL rockets has shown that, starting with only a rough knowledge of the orientation of the satellite as a function of the time, it is possible to reconstruct a fairly precise orientation from the signals recorded from known objects or regions; this principle has also been used in the first meteorological satellite (Vanguard II). Both as an aid to identification and as a means of relating the radiation intensities to known standards, it would be well to include a photometric band in the visible region. Photocell instrumentation to monitor the orientation of the satellite axis relative to the Sun is also easily possible.

Such an exploratory survey, besides being useful for purely mapping purposes and for planning future detailed experiments, would yield immediate information of great importance for astrophysics. It would be possible to separate the contributions of the extraterrestrial sources of radiation to the brightness of the sky, once the components of the atmosphere (scattered sunlight, moonlight, and to some extent starlight, airglow, permanent aurora, etc.) have been eliminated. These extraterrestrial sources are distributed very differently on the celestial sphere and in wavelength. For instance, the solar corona is approximately circularly symmetrical around the Sun. The zodiacal light (which some regard as an extension of the outer corona) is symmetrical with respect to the ecliptic and concentrated in celestial longitude toward the Sun. The contributions of integrated starlight (except external galaxies), individual bright stars, reflection (dust) and emission (gas) nebulae are all concentrated toward the galactic equator, but in varying degrees, and local variations in intensity as well as in the spectral distribution can be expected to be quite different. The contribution to the sky surface brightness of the extragalactic nebulae will be more or less isotropic, except for a zone of avoidance centered on the galactic equator where the radiation is absorbed by galactic clouds. The extragalactic surface brightness, as pointed out by Baum, is a special case of Olbers' paradox, which asks why the sky is not as bright a surface as the stars (here, galaxies).

In addition, a coarse survey such as that suggested would provide important astrophysical data relevant to the following problems which were discussed in Sec. 2:

a. The extension to the ultraviolet and X-ray regions of stellar multicolor photometry, as a rough measure of the ultraviolet color temperature of the stars and of interstellar reddening.

b. The distribution and opacity of interstellar neutral hydrogen and helium (in the absence of total absorption) by means of measures at $\lambda1216$ (Lyman-α), $\lambda912$ and shorter (Lyman continuum), $\lambda584$ (resonance line of He I), $\lambda504$ and shorter (He I continuum), and $\lambda304$ (resonance line of He II). These radiations should be included in the first survey, even though the probability of observing them is low.

c. The mapping of bright nebular emissions, at least in the spectral region $\lambda1215$ to 3000.

From the standpoint of reconnaissance, such a survey would serve to guide the selection of a new set of narrower bands for the next series of ultraviolet studies.

The following wavelengths have also been proposed for the reasons stated:

λ1200 for the resonance lines of N I, but this must be separated from Lyman-α

λ1302 to 1306 for the resonance lines of O I

λ1225 to 1350, broken down into narrower bands in order to obtain a more detailed spectral distribution of the radiation discovered by NRL investigators in Virgo and Orion[16,17]

λ1000, between Lyman-α and Lyman-β

λ2700 in the near ultraviolet, but well to the short-wavelength side of the heavy Balmer continuous absorption

λ2100 to 2200, immediately to the long-wavelength side of the point where heavy molecular absorption begins in the spectra of stars of Type G and later (6000°K and cooler)

λ1900, in a molecular absorption band of cooler stars

Suitable standard U, B, V detectors to calibrate the ultraviolet photometry and to help identify stars of known color picked up in an unprecisely controlled or completely uncontrolled scan

The accuracy of pointing and the degree of directional stability determine (1) the narrowest slit width that can be used or the minimum blurring in a slitless spectrum and (2) the length of time that a star image can be kept on the slit. The use of slits or slitless spectra of high dispersion will require long exposures or integration times, and thus a slow scan rate and correspondingly high directional stabilization for the duration of the scan. In an uncontrolled scan, resolution may be somewhat better than the estimate $\Delta\lambda/\lambda \sim 0.1$ given above; but for a real jump in spectral resolving power, accurately stabilized orbiting telescopes with large light-gathering power that can be pointed on command will be required. Designs for such instruments are being developed at several institutions, among which are the University of Wisconsin (Code), the Goddard Space Flight Center (Kupperian), the Princeton University Observatory (Spitzer), the Smithsonian Astrophysical Observatory (Whipple), and the Association of Universities for Research in Astronomy (Meinel).

Broadly speaking, three classes of investigation can be distinguished: (1) a survey of the whole sky with objective-prism or objective-grating spectra, with a resolving power of the order of 10 Å, (2) detailed spectral scans of individual objects, initially with a resolving power of considerably better than 10 Å and possibly as fine as 2 Å, (3) spectra to the limit of the instrumental resolving power. The corresponding requirement for the precision of pointing and maintaining direction would be of the order of minutes of arc for the first of this series, and 0.1 second of arc for the last, in order to equal earth-bound standards.   One may imagine a continuous refinement of all these specifications in successive investigations.

The objective-prism spectral survey may be regarded in some ways as an ultraviolet survey of greater refinement than the broad-band survey discussed above and would serve the following purposes: (1) ultraviolet spectral classification, as a guide to more detailed researches and to reveal features unsuspected from the visual spectrum, (2) a search for population-linked spectral characteristics among the absorption features of elements heavier than He, (3) a mapping of the more conspicuous nebulosities.

Another exciting prospect offered by objective-prism surveys has been pointed out by Greenstein.[22]   This would be the revelation as to whether other stars than the Sun exhibit striking temperature inversions in their atmospheres.   As described in Chap. 17 (The Sun), the temperature of the Sun at first decreases steadily outward from a central value of about 15 million degrees Kelvin to about 4500°K at the top of its photosphere. Thereafter the temperature rather abruptly begins to increase and soon reaches a value on the order of a million degrees in the corona.   The photosphere emits a continuous spectrum which, in the ultraviolet, decreases in intensity with decreasing wavelength and fades out almost entirely beyond 1600 Å.   At shorter wavelengths the solar spectrum consists almost entirely of bright emission lines originating in the hot outer envelope of the Sun.   The survey could answer the question as to whether the phenomenon of the corona is common or confined to relatively few stars.

2. *High-dispersion Studies of Single Objects.*   Problems of the same general type as those mentioned above would be pursued in greater detail in investigations using the highest possible dispersion.   With greater resolving power, however, other possibilities can be realized, for instance, the analysis of the physical state, structure, and abundances, in stellar atmospheres, in emission nebulae, and in interstellar matter. For stellar atmospheres, one would sample the principal spectral types.

The details which astronomers hope to find by such studies were outlined in Sec. 2.   In regard to the emission nebulae, at least in the case of those nebulosities whose details are small and sharp, it would be feasible to employ slitless techniques; this depends on the degree of overlap between neighboring emission features.   In any case it is probably not necessary to use as high resolution as for the stellar spectra, at least in the earliest investigations.   Aller[37] has selected the following nebulae as a representative sample for early investigations: Orion,

Spica, the "Gum" Nebula, and Eta Carinae. Planetary nebulae would also be studied (see Fig. 3).

The following contribution from Spitzer[27] discusses the present technical feasibility of such investigations:

While an instrument capable of such measures is necessarily somewhat complicated, a satellite telescope capable of measuring interstellar absorption lines does not require any completely new techniques. Systems for pointing the telescope by remote control are being worked for balloon-launched instruments. The spectrum can be measured with conventional photoelectric cells, scanning limited regions of the spectrum at a very slow rate (0.1 Å per minute). The problems of data storage and telemetering are well within the capabilities of existing systems. Reflectivities of available surfaces would make possible accurate ultraviolet spectral photometry for stars of high surface temperature down to the 5th magnitude, with a telescope of 24-inch aperture, and for wave lengths longer than about 1200 Å. For wavelengths between 900 and 1200 Å brighter stars would be required, unless more highly reflecting coatings in these wavelengths can be developed for the telescope mirrors.

3. *Line Profiles.* With the kind of spectral resolution that is possible in such refined experiments, the profiles of stellar and interstellar absorption lines are not beyond reach. Preliminary investigations in this field[33] have dealt with the complicated profile of Lyman-α in the solar spectrum, which has superimposed on it the narrow absorption line of interplanetary hydrogen, from which its temperature and the number of atoms per square centimeter in the line of sight may be inferred. Similar studies of stellar and interstellar absorption lines will eventually be possible, which will help unravel the several parameters that affect the line profile: temperature, density, the number of atoms in the line of sight, turbulent-velocity distribution, the mechanism of radiation transfer, etc. If interstellar hydrogen proves to be so abundant that profiles of even the higher members of the Lyman series in stars are completely absorbed, the method will still be applicable to less abundant elements.

4. *X-ray and Gamma-ray Surveys.* The detection and study by Friedman's group of X rays emitted by the quiet corona[21] and of X rays of much greater intensity from active regions associated with flares have lent support to the surmise by Greenstein[22] that since the Sun appears to be in no way an unusual star, most stars may have solar-type coronas and be characterized by activity of the solar type (see Chap. 17, The Sun). It is suggestive that among the red dwarfs at the faint end of the main sequence, one finds "flare stars" which, from the spectroscopic and photometric evidence available, appear to exhibit much the same sort

of activity as the Sun.   Relative to their own total brightness, their flares are more conspicuous than those on the Sun.

Solar X radiation appears to be of two chief distinguishable types: (1) as yet unresolved resonance lines of multiply ionized metals (Fe, Ni, Ca, etc.) in the million-degree corona and (2) bremsstrahlung produced by electrons that have been accelerated to the appropriate energies by fluctuating magnetic fields.   Since the high temperature of the corona may be at least in part the result of magnetic activity and in part the result of the degradation of turbulent energy, X-ray-producing phenomena may well be expected in all normal main-sequence stars.   The low sensitivity of present-day X-ray detectors and the somewhat primitive state of image-forming optics in this spectral region limit our present capacity to pursue these expectations.

In the gamma-ray spectrum of cosmic origin, there are two energy ranges of interest.[38]   Gamma rays in the first region, 0.2 to 5 Mev, result from the radioactive decay of excited nuclei, fusion of light elements, and possibly electron-positron annihilations.   Gamma rays in the second region, 50 to 200 Mev, should result from the decay of neutral π-mesons produced in nuclear interactions with high-energy particles and from the annihilation of matter and antimatter.   The latter high-energy range is of great immediate interest because the hope of finding something is much more definite.

The 100-Mev gamma radiation is expected to originate in the same regions in which cosmic rays are produced, namely, regions where hydromagnetic turbulence accelerates charged particles to very high energies in the presence of gas or dust.   Examples of regions where such conditions probably exist are solar flares, old supernovae like the Crab Nebula, our Galaxy as a whole but particularly the nucleus (identified by some with Sagittarius A[39]), other galaxies (e.g., M31), and galaxies in collision (e.g., Cygnus A).   Furthermore, since turbulent hydromagnetic regions also generate nonthermal radio noise through the synchrotron radiation of energetic electrons, one might expect such radio sources (whether identified optically or not) to emit gamma rays whose characteristics should help us understand the physical nature of these sources.   These same sources may be expected to emit X rays.

Because gamma rays are not deflected by magnetic fields and because they have great penetrating power, the direction of their arrival will indicate the direction of the source.   Because the mass absorption coefficient of 100-Mev gamma rays is less than 0.01 cm² per g for most substances and because the line of sight from the solar system to the far rim of the Galaxy beyond the nucleus contains probably less than

1 g per cm² of gas and dust, the gamma rays will be only slightly attenuated. Tenuous matter in the solar system would have practically no effect. On the other hand, it would be necessary to observe from a point high enough above the Earth to make the residual higher atmosphere much less than 1 g per cm² in order to avoid excessive absorption of the gamma radiation and to minimize the cosmic-ray "albedo."

The first such experiment (proposed by Rossi and Kraushaar[38]) would be relatively coarse as to angular resolving power and counting rate. Its instrumental design will be guided by balloon and rocket results. Provision would be made in the instrumentation for narrowing the cone of acceptance by suitable shielding and for identifying the gamma rays and distinguishing them from high-energy-particle radiation. Like the ultraviolet-X-ray survey discussed earlier, it will serve to map the gamma radiation from the whole sky and to locate regions of particular interest for later detailed study in a second-generation experiment.

3.2 Infrared Investigations

At the outset, it should be emphasized that the potentialities for investigation from the ground or at least from balloon altitudes through the partially transparent atmospheric windows in the infrared between 0.8 to 24 μ are far from being realized, and it would probably be unwise to mount elaborate satellite-borne experiments before these possibilities are exhausted. Furthermore, the nonavailability of sensitive receivers is at present probably a greater obstacle than the atmosphere. For these reasons, only a rather perfunctory survey of some possible infrared investigations will be made here.

A black-body temperature of 3500°K corresponds to peak intensity of about 0.8 μ near the somewhat indefinite boundary between the visible and infrared spectral domains. This immediately tells us that we shall be chiefly concerned with objects cooler than 3500°K. We are also concerned with possible sources of nonthermal radiation in the infrared and with particular spectral features occurring in the infrared. To this must be added the possibility of attempting to observe sources whose visible and shorter-wavelength radiation is heavily obscured by interstellar dust clouds but which emit enough infrared to penetrate them. The following is a sample listing of some of the types of sources or of investigations falling into the categories mentioned:

1. Infrared radiation of ordinary stars of spectral types M, S, late R, and N, ranging from about 3500°K for dwarf M stars to possibly below 2000° for the coolest N stars. These temperatures, at least for the coolest stars, are somewhat artificial constructs based on the spectrum

in the visible region which is subject to heavy absorption by molecular bands in the blue-violet range, thus making the stars redder and therefore apparently "cooler." This situation leads to erroneous "infrared temperatures," like the ultraviolet extrapolation for the very hot O-B-A stars.

2. Obscured Population II regions, like the galactic center which was the subject of a pioneer investigation by Stebbins and Whitford.[40] The rich infrared radiation seems to originate in the denser-than-average cloud of Population II red giants, probably predominantly type K, as in the similar globular clusters. These would then average perhaps somewhat hotter than 3500°K, but their visible radiation is almost completely obscured. It is also possible that there is some other source of infrared radiation in the galactic center, connected with the discrete radio source Sagittarius A, which has recently been tentatively identified as the galactic nucleus itself.[39]

3. A search for "dark objects" of possibly three general types: (a) More or less normal stars cooler than the coolest in the usual spectral classification scheme, i.e., cooler than gM8 and N5, or about 1000 to 1500°K. The huge invisible component of ϵ Aurigae might be such an object. (b) Other less definitely stellar objects, like protostars intermediate in character and temperature between the globules of dark matter seen in silhouette here and there in the Milky Way and a full-fledged star. The effective radiant temperature of such an object might lie almost anywhere in the range from, say, 100 to 1000°K. (c) Cooled-off ex-white dwarfs at any temperature down to that in equilibrium with its surroundings. These will probably be extremely rare, as well as hard to detect, in view of the small number of known white dwarfs and the fairly long cooling times mentioned above.

4. The thermal radiation from interstellar dust clouds, whose temperature in equilibrium with the average, dilute, interstellar-radiation field is thought to be of the order of 100°K.

5. Emission-line spectra from such molecules in the interstellar gas as CH, NH, OH, H_2, etc., under favorable conditions of temperature and optical depth.

6. The possible remote cosmic background of radiation from galaxies with very large red shifts.

7. Detailed studies of the infrared spectra of normal stars cool enough for such molecules as H_2O, CH_4, etc., to exist in their atmospheres. Attention would be concentrated in the region 7 to 30μ.

8. Detailed studies of peculiar stars, where there is some reason to suspect that the infrared spectrum will elucidate their peculiar behavior.

An example of this category is the R Coronae Borealis class of variable stars. Every few years these stars suddenly and unpredictably drop 5 to 8 magnitudes in the visible region for time intervals of the order of weeks. One of the explanations tentatively advanced in the past is that an obscuring cloud of solid particles, possibly of carbon, condenses in the outer atmosphere: the operation of such a mechanism is far from clear, but if this is the cause, it should be accompanied by the formation of many types of molecules.

The following very short table of temperatures and corresponding wavelength of the maximum spectral intensity may be of some help in considering these types of investigations:

Typical objects	Temperature, °K	Wavelength, μ
Obscured Type II gK	4000	0.7
Ordinary cool stars	3000	1.0
Extraordinarily cool stars	2000 1000	1.5 3.0
Protostars, etc.	500	6.0
Interstellar dust	100	30

A search for several of the listed categories would involve some sort of survey covering the sky. It should be noted that the detection of the feeble thermal radiation from interstellar dust or from the hypothetical cosmic background is far beyond the capacity of present-day detectors. Although most of the wavelength regions listed in the table are observable from the ground or from balloons, satellite altitudes may be necessary to get above the airglow.

3.3 Radio-frequency Studies

The types of problem for which radio-frequency studies would provide data were outlined in Sec. 2. In the earliest experiments, probably no attempt to measure the directional distribution of radio sources can be seriously contemplated at frequencies in the range of a few tens of kilocycles to a few megacycles. With a very simple receiver and a proper choice of orbits, however, it should be possible to locate the low-frequency cutoff which may be determined by (1) a geocorona of free electrons surrounding the Earth, (2) an interplanetary electron cloud which may be thought of as an extension of the solar corona, or (3) the electron component of the interstellar clouds in the local spiral arm or a more general galactic halo. The shape, size, and electron density of these structures are at present hardly more than conjectures.

Rudimentary but important information can be acquired with satellites or space probes to determine the low-frequency cutoff and hence the integrated electron concentration between it and cosmic radio sources or the Sun (see Fig. 19): (1) by going out several Earth radii on eccentric Earth-centered orbits to investigate the hypothetical geocorona—its extension and possibly asymmetry between the sides toward and away from the Sun; (2) by launching probes in eccentric circumsolar orbits in or near the ecliptic plane, or in highly inclined orbits, to map the electron component of the interplanetary medium in the inner part of the solar system. This simple class of experiments would also, of course, detect variations of the low-frequency cutoff with time and possible correlations with solar activity or phase of the solar activity cycle. In fact, these data would be gathered by the same probes or satellites designed to measure the low-frequency end of the spectrum of solar bursts (see Chap. 17, The Sun).

Moderately directional antenna would be required in a slightly more sophisticated experiment to determine the low-frequency cutoff as a function of galactic latitude (and possibly longitude) using extragalactic radio-frequency emitters as a source.

Eventually, high angular resolving power will be desirable in order to go beyond simple spectral intensity measurements of the integrated cosmic radio noise. For the frequency range contemplated, this will require very large antennas several kilometers across. Various schemes for unfurling long wire or mesh antennas from satellites and keeping them spread out in the correct configuration are under study.[41] In the event that it ever becomes feasible for man to establish a base on the Moon the possibility has been raised of building very large arrays on the far side, shielded from radio interference of terrestrial origin.

Large rigid antennas with high angular resolution located outside the ionosphere would also be extremely useful at higher frequencies, say, 10 to 1000 Mc. The angular resolving power at these frequencies is limited at the Earth's surface not by the antenna size but by the "poor radio seeing." The different paths of the rays arriving at a large antenna go through regions of the ionosphere of sufficiently different refractivity to destroy the sharpness of the focus.[42]

In discussing the measurements of galactic radio emission at frequencies lower than the ionospheric cutoff, Reber[43] pointed out that although man-made interfering signals and strong terrestrial atmospherics will be shielded from the observing satellite receiver at wavelengths of a few hundred kilometers ($f \lesssim 3$ kc), another kind of phenomenon will be encountered, probably in copious amounts. This is Cherenkov radiation produced in the region from a few hundred to several thousand kilometers. It is caused by low energy particles traveling through regions of very high refractive index. The phenomenon was observed strongly during 1958 at 578 and 2100 meters wavelength (520 and 143 kc). During 1955 it was much less prevalent. Apparently this nuisance rises and falls with solar activity. On this count, also, long wave radio astronomical observations will probably be most successful near solar activity minimum, even with the use of space vehicles.

(The possibility of launching devices to probe directly interplanetary electron concentration and its variation with time and location and to detect the hypothetical electromagnetic "cavities" responsible for the trapping of cosmic rays is discussed in Chaps. 13-15.)

3.4 High-resolution Astrometry

The following discussion is from Meinel:[34]

The preceding discussion has treated the astrophysical properties of radiation. It is not inconceivable that the satellite telescope will progress in time to a point wherein the theoretical resolving power of the telescope can be achieved. The greater intrinsic accuracy offered by a high resolution telescope, unaffected by the atmosphere, would open many new fields for exploration. It is correct that optically perfect resolution can be gained from balloon-borne telescopes. The projects now unfolding in this line are of great importance; they are limited, as are rockets, however, to occasional short glimpses of the sky. Only when optically perfect resolution can be had from a semi-permanent installation above the atmosphere can high angular resolution studies be pushed into the rich field of research that will be dependent upon resolution.

One of the most important gains attendant to an increase in angular resolution is the limiting magnitude of the telescope. On Earth one builds very large telescopes at considerable expense only to gain a single magnitude. In space one can quickly gain five magnitudes by utilizing a star disc 0.10 second of arc diameter as contrasted to the 1.0 second of arc diameter of a terrestrial telescope.

The exact gain to be had from increased angular resolution depends upon the detector. If a device is used having a two-dimensional display, e.g., a photographic plate or an image orthicon, the resolution of the detector must be greater than the size of the image in order to distinguish it with full accuracy above the sky background. If the detector is one-dimensional, as a photocell, the size of the diaphragm must be reduced in accordance with the angular resolution to make a gain in a signal-to-sky.

If we want to use small mirrors (<40-in. aperture) and still to take full advantage of the intrinsically higher resolving power and smaller image size of the order of magnitude mentioned (that is, at least 10:1 better than images made at effective wavelength λ4300 with conventional equipment), we must solve another problem.

To reach a wavelength as short as λ430 (ten times the angular resolution requires working at one-tenth the wavelength, other things being equal), the equipment must remain for extended periods above 300 km, below which the atmosphere is still somewhat opaque. Actually, if one aims for λ430, one must go much farther, because of the interstellar hydrogen and helium absorption in the wavelength range 50 to 912 Å. But at λ ≤ 50 Å, we are already in the X-ray region where conventional photographic optical techniques break down. A present serious technical barrier is the low reflectivity in the X-ray region of most known material from which mirrors might be made. A high-resolution detector carried in the focal plane on precision ways, like a measuring engine, or an image tube with electronic scan might be adapted to measure the coordinates of sharp X-ray images. Any astrometric device naturally demands that the telescope be pointed and guided with a precision equal to that of the angular resolution of the images.

Examples of the types of investigation that come under the heading of astrometrics, requiring the sharpest possible images for the precise measurement of angular coordinates or dimensions, are (1) the parallaxes and proper motions of individual stars, (2) the motions of stars in a binary or multiple system or in a cluster, requiring the resolution of such systems into the component stars, (3) the angular displacement of a light ray by gravitational effects, (4) the internal motions of bright details in a nebula, (5) the diameters and shape of the Sun, planets, and satellites and the surface details of these objects, (6) the search for bodies of planetary size associated with nearby stars. More specifically, it would be tempting to pursue the following problems, most of which are extensions of problems already attacked but for which the data so far acquired are severely incomplete.

1. *Parallaxes and Proper Motions.*[44] We need precise parallaxes and proper motions of selected objects in order to calibrate their luminosities, for instance, white dwarfs and other subluminous hot stars whose radiation should be rich in the ultraviolet. Although perhaps 10 per cent of the stars in the Sun's neighborhood are white dwarfs, we have very few first-class measures of their parallaxes and luminosities because their very low intrinsic brightness makes them inaccessible to precise observation in visible wavelengths unless they are very close.

For objects too remote to exhibit a heliocentric parallax, it is still possible to deduce distances statistically from their angular proper motions, e.g., from the parallactic effects of the motion of the solar system among the stars or from the intercomparison of random angular motions with random radial velocities.   Each method breaks down seriously at a distance corresponding to the point where the measured parallax or proper motion becomes comparable with its errors.   Code has suggested enlarging the base line for heliocentric parallaxes by putting an observatory in a planetary orbit several astronomical units in radius.

For classes of stars that are scarce per unit volume of space (where one must take in a volume with a radius of perhaps several kiloparsecs in order to reach a big enough sample), it will still be necessary to resort to a statistical analysis of motions in order to estimate distances and luminosities.   Examples of such classes of objects, that are at the same time extremely important for evolutionary theories, are subluminous hot stars (other than the white dwarfs already discussed) such as novae in their quiescent state, the nuclei of planetary nebulae, etc.   Another important but scarce class is the classical cepheid variable.   The zero point of luminosities in the period-luminosity relation of these stars, on which the distance scale to neighboring galaxies depends to a large degree, is still not well established after many years of careful effort, partly because the data are barely accessible to classical ground-based techniques and then only if the utmost care in eliminating systematic errors is exercised.

2. *Binary Systems.*   Double stars on the limit of resolution with existing telescopes and many spectroscopic binaries now optically unresolved will be easily separated, and precise measures of separation and position angle as a function of the time will be possible.   This eventuality will of course provide many more first-class determinations of stellar masses and the correlation of mass with other parameters, leading to a firmer observational foundation for theories of stellar constitution and evolution. ' In fact, if some efficient means could be devised to carry it out, it might be well to survey all stars brighter than a certain limiting magnitude to discover those binaries which are now not even suspected.   Such a survey might bring to light many companions with low luminosity or perhaps some with even planetary characteristics.   As Nancy Roman has suggested, in the absence of atmospheric scattering and photographic irradiation, it will be possible to look specifically for planetlike bodies close to the nearest bright stars by masking out the bright but very small stellar images.

3. *Elimination of Earth-connected Systematic Errors.*[45] One of the most troublesome problems in present-day statistical astrometrics is the presence of small persistent systematic errors, mentioned above in connection with cepheids. The analysis of the motions of the stars in our Galaxy and consequent deductions about the nature of the gravitational field in the Galaxy and the distribution of the masses producing it, depend in a surprisingly sensitive way on the treatment of these systematic errors. These systematic errors arise in a complicated way from station and season errors in fundamental star catalogues of position and motion and from uncertainties in the motion of the equatorial coordinate system (precession) that are small, but not small enough to be negligible in comparison with the proper motions. It seems possible that such difficulties might be eliminated in an atmosphere-free observatory— perhaps an orbiting space station, perhaps on the Moon. The diminution of these and of the accidental errors would enable one to measure motions of much more distant stars, i.e., over a larger proportion of the Galaxy, which would immediately lead to a much less ambiguous interpretation of its general gravitational field.

4. *High-resolution Images of Clusters and Galaxies.*[34] The study of the spectrum-luminosity characteristics of the nearby galactic and globular clusters, using high resolution to classify their stars according to astrophysical properties, is of particularly great importance. An extension of 5 magnitudes in these objects should reach the least luminous members of some of them. The problem of separation of cluster members from the general background will be difficult, but colors alone should make possible some degree of separation. The question of the evolution of the least luminous members of a cluster would prove most interesting. It could lead to the determination of a minimum mass cutoff point to the population of a cluster that should reflect back upon the mean density of the gas cloud that presumably gave rise to the star cluster.

Many persons have contributed to the material in this chapter, either directly with ideas or analysis of expected effects or indirectly through having made successful observations and achieved some definite preliminary results or through having offered concrete proposals on which work has in some cases actually started. We are particularly indebted to L. H. Aller (University of Michigan); H. W. Babcock (Mount Wilson and Palomar Observatories); A. D. Code (University of Wisconsin); H. K. J. Eichhorn (Wesleyan University); J. Findlay (National Radio Astronomy Observatory); H. Friedman (Naval Research Laboratory); F. T. Haddock, Jr. (University of Michigan); H. E. Hinteregger (Air

Force Cambridge Research Center); P. van de Kamp (Swarthmore College); William Kraushaar (Massachusetts Institute of Technology); A. B. Meinel (Association of Universities for Research in Astronomy); B. Rossi (Massachusetts Institute of Technology); and L. Spitzer (Princeton University). We are grateful to the Editors of *The Astronomical Journal* for permission to reprint several figures from Ref. 15, to the Editor of *The Publications of the Astronomical Society of the Pacific* for permission to reprint excerpts of Ref. 28, and to Mount Wilson and Palomar Observatories for photographs.

REFERENCES

1. G. Reber and G. R. Ellis: *J. Geophys. Res.*, *61*, 1 (1956). See also G. Reber: *J. Geophys. Res.*, *63*, 109 (1958).
2. M. Schwarzschild: *Structure and Evolution of the Stars*, Princeton University Press, 1958.
3. E. M. Burbidge and G. R. Burbidge: "Stellar Evolution," in S. Flügge (ed.), *Handbuch der Physik*, *51*, 134, Springer-Verlag, Berlin-Göttingen-Heidelberg, 1959.
4. E. M. Burbidge, G. R. Burbidge, W. A, Fowler, and F Hoyle: "Synthesis of the Elements in Stars," *Rev. Mod. Phys.*, *29*, 547 (1957). Contains extensive bibliography.
5. M. Schwarzschild: Section 27 of Ref. 2, above.
6. F. Hoyle and M. Schwarzschild: *Astrophys. J.* Suppl. 2, 1 (1955).
7. W. A. Fowler: *Men. Soc. Roy. Sci. Liège*, *14*, 88 (1954).
8. W. A. Fowler, G. R. Burbidge, and E. M. Burbidge: "Stellar Evolution and Synthesis of the Elements," *Astrophys. J.*, *122*, 271 (1955).
9. W. A. Fowler, G. R. Burbidge, and E. Margaret Burbidge. "Nuclear Reactions and Element Synthesis in the Surfaces of Stars," *Astrophys. J.* Suppl. 2, 167 (1955).
10. W. A. Fowler and J. Greenstein: *Proc. N.A.S.*, *42*, 173 (1956).
11. D. Chalonge: Paper in *Stellar Populations*, D. J. K. O'Connell, S. J. (ed.), (Proceedings of the conf. sponsored by Pont. Acad. of Sci. & the Vatican Obsy., Rome, May 20–28, 1957), North-Holland Publishing Co., Amsterdam, and Interscience Publishers, Inc., New York, 1958. See also *Ricerche Astronomiche*, *5* (1958).
12. B. Strömgren: Papers in *Stellar Populations* (see Ref. 11), 245, 385.
13. M. Schwarzschild: Remark following paper by H. L. Johnson, NSF Conference on the Cosmic Distance Scale, University of Virginia, *Astron. J.*, *63*, 149ff. (1958).
14. M. Schwarzschild: Ref. 2, p. 87 above, referring to some work by J. Greenstein.
15. A. D. Code: "Stellar Astronomy from a Space Vehicle," paper given at the Conference on Astronomical Observations from Above the Earth's Atmosphere, *Astron, J.*, *65*, 239ff. (1960).
16. J. E. Kupperian, A. Boggess III, and J. E. Milligan: *Astrophys. J.*, *128*, 453 (1958).

17. E. T. Byram, T. A. Chubb, and H. Friedman: "Ultraviolet Radiation from Celestial Sources," in H. Kallmann Bijl (ed.), *Space Research*, p. 599 (Proc. 1st International Space Science Symposium, Nice, Jan., 1960), North-Holland Publishing Co., Amsterdam, 1960.

18. W. A. Rense: "Solar Ultraviolet Spectroscopy and Applications to Problems of the Upper Atmosphere and the Solar Corona," *Space Research*, p. 608 (see Ref. 17). See also earlier papers: A. Aboud, W. E. Behring, and W. A. Rense: *Astrophys. J., 130*, 381 (1959); T. Violett and W. A. Rense: *Astrophys. J., 130*, 954 (1959).

19. H. E. Hinteregger, K. R. Damon, L. Heroux, and L. A. Hall: "Telemetering Monochromator Measurements of Solar 304 Å Radiation and Its Attenuation in the Upper Atmosphere," *Space Research*, p. 615 (see Ref. 17).

20. J. D. Purcell, D. M. Packer, and R. Tousey: "The Ultraviolet Spectrum of the Sun," *Space Research*, p. 581 (see Ref. 17). See also an earlier paper, F. S. Johnson, H. Malitson, J. D. Purcell, and R. Tousey: *Astrophys. J., 127*, 80 (1958).

21. H. Friedman: *J. Geophys. Res., 64*, 1751 (1959). See also H. Friedman: "Rocket Astronomy," *Sci. Amer., 200*, 52 (1959); H. Friedman et al.: "Reports of the IGY Solar Eclipse Expedition," *IGY Bull.* No. 19, 2 (Jan., 1959).

22. J. Greenstein: unpublished address, *Am. Rocket Soc.*, Los Angeles, May 11, 1960.

23. See, for example, L. H. Aller: *Gaseous Nebulae*, John Wiley & Sons, Inc., 1956.

24. See, for example, in R. N. Bracewell (ed.): *Paris Symposium on Radio Astronomy*, Stanford University Press, Palo Alto, 1959; R. Minkowski: Paper 61, "Optical Observations of Non-thermal Galactic Radio Sources," p. 314; E. M. Burbidge and G. R. Burbidge: Paper 62, "The Radio Sources in the Cygnus Loop and IC 443," p. 323.

25. I. S. Shklovsky: *Astron. J. U.S.S.R., 36*, 579 (1959).

26. Max Krook and T. Gold: Private communication, unpublished.

27. L. Spitzer: Private communication to Committee for Optical and Radio Astronomy of the Space Science Board.

28. L. H. Aller: *Publ. Astron. Soc. Pacific, 71*, 324 (1959). References 29 to 31 in our text were 7 to 9 in the original; figure 17 was Aller's Fig. 3.

29. C. M. Wade: Dissertation, Harvard University, 1957, quoted by T. K. Menon, *Proc. Inst. Radio Engrs., 46*, 232 (1958).

30. J. S. Mathis: *Astrophys. J., 125*, 328 (1957).

31. S. S. Huang: *Astrophys. J., 108*, 354 (1948).

32. E. T. Byram, T. A. Chubb, H. Friedman, J. E. Kupperian, Jr., and R. W. Kreplin: *Astrophys. J., 128*, 738 (1958). See also J. E. Kupperian, Jr., E. T. Byram, T. A. Chubb, and H. Friedman: *Planet. & Space Sci.*, 1, 3 (1959).

33. J. D. Purcell and R. Tousey: "The Profile of Solar Lyman Alpha," in *Space Research*, p. 590 (see Ref. 17). See also abstract, J. D. Purcell and R. Tousey: *Astron. J., 65*, 56 (1960).

34. A. B. Meinel: Private communication to the Committee on Optical and Radio Astronomy of the Space Science Board.

35. This section is based partly on material from F. T. Haddock: "Astronomical Experiments Proposed for Earth Satellites," Final Report of University of Michigan Research Institute, Sec. 50, 1958, and also on private communications from F. T. Haddock.

36. J. H. Oort: "Radio-frequency Studies of Galactic Structure," in S. Flügge (ed.), *Handbuch der Physik, 53*, 100, Springer-Verlag, Berlin-Göttingen-Heidelberg, (1959).

37. L. H. Aller: Paper in "Astronomical Experiments Proposed for Earth Satellites," p. 45 (see Ref. 28).
38. B. Rossi and W. L. Kraushaar: Mass. Institute of Technology proposal to NASA, 1959.
39. G. Westerhout: "The Radio Galaxy," *Sci. Amer.*, *201*, 44 (1959) (see Ref. 3). See also R. X. McGee and J. G. Bolton: *Nature*, *175*, 1079 (1955); R. Hanbury Brown: *Handbuch der Physik*, *53*, 208 (1959).
40. J. Stebbins and A. E. Whitford: *Astron. J.*, *51*, 130 (1947); *Astrophys. J.*, *106*, 235 (1947).
41. F. T. Haddock: Private communication.
42. J. Findlay: Private communication to the Committee on Optical and Radio Astronomy of the Space Science Board.
43. G. Reber: Private communication to O. Struve, Oct. 24, 1959, "Radio Astronomy from Space Vehicles."
44. Much of this section is based on material in a letter from P. van de Kamp.
45. Section based on material in a letter from H. K. J. Eichhorn.

SUPPLEMENTARY READING

General

F. Hoyle: *Frontiers of Astronomy*, Harper & Bros., or Mentor Books, MD200, 1957.

J. L. Pawsey and R. N. Bracewell: *Radio Astronomy*, Oxford University Press, 1955.

M. Schwarzschild: *Structure and Evolution of the Stars*, Princeton University Press, 1958.

S. Flügge (ed.): *Handbuch der Physik*, vols. 51–53, Springer-Verlag, Berlin-Göttingen-Heidelberg, 1959.

D. J. K. O'Connell, S. J. (ed.): *Stellar Populations* (Proceedings of Conference sponsored by the Pontifical Academy of Science and the Vatican Observatory, May 20–28, 1957), North-Holland Publishing Co., Amsterdam, or Interscience Publishers, Inc., New York, 1958. Contains papers by W. Baade, J. H. Oort, B. Lindblad, A. Sandage, A. D. Thackeray, D. J. K. O'Connell, S. J., A. Blaauw, G. H. Herbig, J. J. Nassau, M. Schwarzschild, F. Hoyle, E. E. Salpeter, B. Strömgren, W. A. Fowler, W. W. Morgan, D. Chalonge, L. Spitzer, and G. Lemaître.

Astronomy and Space Science

Conference on Astronomical Observations from Above the Earth's Atmosphere, *Astron. J.*, *65*, 239ff. (1960). Contains Nancy Roman: "Vehicles and Plans," p. 240; Lyman Spitzer: "Space Telescopes and Components," p. 242; Herbert Friedman: "Recent Experiments from Rockets and Satellites," p. 264; G. M. Clemence: "Controlled Experiments in Celestial Mechanics," p. 272; Leo Goldberg: "Solar Experiments," p. 274; Arthur D. Code: "Stellar Astronomy from a Space Vehicle," p. 278; Fred L. Whipple and Robert J. Davis: "Proposed Stellar and Interstellar Survey," p. 285.

Selected papers in:

J. A. Van Allen (ed.): *Scientific Uses of Earth Satellites*, 2d rev. ed., University of Michigan Press, 1958.

Hilde Kallmann Bijl (ed.): *Space Research* (Proceedings of the 1st International Space Science Symposium, sponsored by COSPAR), North-Holland Publishing Co., Amsterdam, 1960.

PART 7

THE LIFE SCIENCES

19 ≡

THE BIOLOGICAL SCIENCES AND SPACE RESEARCH

Joshua Lederberg and H. Keffer Hartline

1. INTRODUCTION

Historically, space biology and space medicine are successors to the fruitful work of four decades of aviation medicine. In accord with this tradition, the most extensive activity in biology related to space exploration at the present time concerns the problems of human space flight. "Space biology" has thus tended to become identified with the technical support of "man in space" and related problems. However, it is becoming apparent that space flight may furnish a unique instrument for studying the most fundamental problems of biology: the origin of life and its progress in independent evolutionary systems. To distinguish this aspect of space biology—the evolution of life beyond our own planet—the term "exobiology" has been introduced.

Until now, payload and range limitations of space vehicles have sharply restricted the scope of significant biological experimentation, and it has been difficult to identify experiments of fundamental import that could command high priorities on such flights. However, larger payloads in orbital satellites, their recovery, and the programming of space flight to the Moon and the planets pose unique and exciting challenges to experimental biology. Space research is extraordinarily (and obviously) expensive. Apart from the immense costs of the rocket vehicles and their operation, experiments must be meticulously designed to function in spacecraft payloads—to withstand the hazards of launching and of the space environment, perhaps also of landing and retrieval, and in most instances to be rigidly programmed and to maintain useful communication with the data-control stations. To justify such costs in money and in human talent and effort, the experiments must be clearly important to fundamental biology (or to a definite technological requirement). Many biological experiments that have been proposed could be done as well or better in the laboratory; others may well justify inclusion in spacecraft payloads when necessary supporting work has been completed. Sober, well-thought-out experiments should have little difficulty in attaining financial support and priorities for accommodation on scientific space flights.

At the present time, orbital flights appear to offer significant opportunities in the following areas: physiological and psychological effects of weightlessness, verification of biological actions of some forms of corpuscular and ionizing radiations, and biological rhythms in an environment which is unequivocally disconnected from the rotation of the Earth. The wider recognition of realistic possibilities of satellite experiments may uncover other opportunities, not yet appreciated, and should at least give the most critical appraisal and efficient exploitation of the lines already indicated. We invite our colleagues in the life sciences to study the general specifications for satellite experiments which are summarized in "Research in Space" (*Science, 130,* 195–202 (1959).)

These lines of investigation represent the use of extraterrestrial environments to isolate specific physical effects on terrestrial organisms. In many cases, these environments can be simulated, or their effects predicted to a large degree. For example, since most cells can tolerate violent disorganization of their apparent gravitational fields (e.g., the tumbling of bacteria or tissue cells in agitated liquid cultures), weightlessness should have a much more profound effect on the orientation of complex organisms than it does on basic cellular processes.

One of the principal aims of space exploration is to secure detailed scientific knowledge of the other planets of the solar system, for comparison with the physics, chemistry, and natural history of the Earth. This knowledge is expected to give us new insights into the origin and evolution of the physical universe and of the chemical phenomena that constitute life. This extension of earth-bound science already 'suffices to justify the cost and effort that are entailed by space exploration; we have no doubt that the economic costs will also be amply repaid in the long run by technological applications of space science, in the same fashion as has always been true of pure science in other fields.

The capability of space vehicles has, until now, been the main limiting factor in the acquisition of new knowledge of the planets. However, the possibilities of telescopic studies from the Earth, and from earth-based balloons have by no means been exhausted. Further, the development of telescopes mounted on satellite platforms in orbit above the Earth's atmosphere should be very fruitful of new data on planetary chemistry. Many avenues of ground-based research can lead to important insight into the origin and cosmic distribution of life, for example, the analysis of meteorites for biochemically interesting components.

As we consider the prospects of direct communication with the planets by long-range spacecraft, new issues present themselves, issues of cautionary wisdom as well as capability. These are of particular concern to biology, having to do with the unique capacity of living organisms, especially microorganisms, to proliferate rapidly and occupy new habitats. Our judgment as to the wisdom of direct communication must follow a careful assessment of the consequences of (1) the implantation of terrestrial organisms on a planetary habitat and (2) the converse, the "back contamination" of the Earth by planetary organisms carried by a returning spacecraft.

Within the foreseeable future, the cost of sending an experimental device through space and receiving information from it will be many times that of using comparable analytical instruments in the laboratory. For many other reasons, the retrieval of samples of the planets would ultimately be the most informative means for the advancement of planetary science. This self-evident design has been and should continue to be foremost in long-range planning. The retrieval missions will introduce the risk of back contamination, a risk that cannot be decisively evaluated within the framework of our present knowledge of planetary biology. The same missions, as well as the one-way probes that will precede them, might also contaminate the targets; however, these missions can be programmed so as to minimize the carriage of "samples" of the Earth and to disinfect the spacecraft by methods of known efficacy for terrestrial organisms. Furthermore, as a matter of policy, acceptable risk figures for contaminating a planetary target must be substantially higher than for bringing trouble home.

From this standpoint, it may be fortunate that the vehicles for one-way missions will (as is obvious) become available first.   We must make every effort to develop experiments that can be flown on such missions and give telemetered information on planetary life and life habitats.

20

EXOBIOLOGY: EXPERIMENTAL APPROACHES TO LIFE BEYOND THE EARTH

Joshua Lederberg

As the close investigation of the planets approaches reality, few inquisitive minds can fail to be intrigued by what these studies will tell of the cosmic distribution of life. To conform to the best of our contemporary science, much thoughtful insight, meticulous planning, and laboratory testing must still be invested in the experimental approaches to this problem. This may require international cooperation and also, perhaps more difficult, mutual understanding among scientific disciplines as isolated as biochemical genetics and planetary astronomy.

Many discussions of space exploration have assumed that exobiological studies might await the full development of the technology for manned space flight and for the return of planetary samples to the terrestrial laboratory. To be sure, these might be preceded by some casual experiments on some instrumented landings. Such a program would allow time for exobiological experiments to be planned with composure and deliberation, based on improved knowledge, from closer approaches, of the chemistry and physics of planetary habitats. Unfortunately, this orderly and otherwise desirable program takes insufficient account of the capacity of living organisms to grow and spread throughout a new environment. This unique capacity of life, which engages our deep interest, also generates our grave concerns in the scientific management of missions beyond the Earth. We are thus obliged to weigh the most productive experiments that we can do by remote instrumentation in early flights, whether or not manned space flight eventually plays a role in scientific exploration.

1.1 Motivations for Exobiological Research

The demons which lurk beyond the Pillars of Hercules have colored the folklore and literature of ages past and present, not always to the benefit of fruitful exploration and dispassionate scientific analysis. Apart from such adventuresome amusements and the amateur delights of a cosmically enlarged natural history, how does exobiology relate to contemporary science and culture? The exploration of space may seem to have very little to do with fundamental questions in biology or medicine, with the mechanisms of gene action, embryological development, protein synthesis, the biology of viruses, or the evolution of species. To answer this question we may consider one aspect of the history of the physical sciences.

Twenty-five centuries of scientific astronomy have so widened the horizons of the physical world that the casual place of the planet Earth in the expanding universe is a central theme in our modern scientific culture. The dynamics of celestial bodies, as can be observed from the Earth, is the richest inspiration for the generalization of our concepts of mass and energy throughout the universe. The spectra of the stars likewise testify to the universality of our concepts in chemistry. But biology has lacked tools of such extension, and *life* until now has meant only *terrestrial life*. This disparity in the domains of the physical versus the biological sciences attenuates most of our efforts to construct a theoretical biology as a cognate of theoretical physics or chemistry. For the most part, biological science has been the rationalization of particular facts which give too limited a basis for the construction and testing of meaningful axioms to support a universal theory of life. The Darwinian concept of evolution through the natural selection of random hereditary fluctuations is the chief element of contemporary biological theory. This may preclude any other effort to systematize the actual manifestation of life as it actually, by accident, evolved. While Darwinian evolution may thus account for the differences among living forms, we may still ask about their common features, especially their biochemical mechanisms. Are these also earth-adapted choices among numberless possibilities? Or is only one biochemical system possible for life, one that we must meet again wherever life shall have evolved or spread?

Some chemical attributes of terrestrial life might support a claim to be basic principles: for example, polyphosphates (adenylpyrophosphate) occur in all organisms as coupling agents for the storage and transfer of metabolic energy. But at least in principle, we can imagine that organisms may have found alternative solutions to the same problem. Only the perspective of comparative biology on a cosmic scale could tell whether this device is an indispensable element of all life or a particular attribute of its local occurrence on this planet.

An important aim of theoretical biology is an abstract definition of life. Our only consensus so far is that such a definition must be arbitrary. If life has gradually evolved from inanimate matter, the demarcation of chemical from biological evolution is one of useful judgement. For a working principle, we might again rely upon the evolutionary concept: a living system has those properties (of self-replication and metabolism) from which we may with more or less confidence deduce an evolutionary scheme that would encompass self-evidently living organisms. But we cannot propose this as a rote formula for the assessment of other celestial bodies and certainly not before we have some empirical knowledge of the diversities of chemical evolution.

From this standpoint the overriding objective of exobiological research is to compare the over-all patterns of chemical evolution of the planets, stressing those features which are globally characteristic of each of them.

The question "Is there life on Mars?" properly dominates exobiological speculation. To answer it may require a careful reassessment of our meaning of "life" and matching this with the accumulation of hard-won evidence on chemical composition of that planet. On the other hand, our first probe might be confronted with an object obviously analogous to an earthly plant, animal, or microbe. But even this abrupt answer should be just the start of biochemical analysis of the organism and its habitat for comparison with the fundamentals of terrestrial life.

In our first approaches to the nearby planets we shall wish to design experiments which have some tangible foundation in the present accumulation of biochemical knowledge. The aqueous environment, and its corollary of moderate temperatures in which large carbonaceous molecules are reasonably stable, are implicit in terrestrial biochemistry. This is not to reject the abstract possibility of nonaqueous life, or noncarbonaceous molecules that might characterize temperatures of <200 or $>500°K$. However, we can defer our concern for such exotic biological systems until we have gotten full value from our searches for the more familiar

and have learned enough of the exotic chemistry to judge how to
proceed.

Within the bounds of its aqueous environment, what are the most
nearly universal features of terrestrial life? In fact, our plants, animals,
and bacteria share a remarkable list of biochemical components, and a
biochemist cannot easily distinguish extracts of yeast cells and beef
muscle. Among these components, the *nucleic acids* warrant first attention. Although they constitute the hereditary material, so that all the
variety of terrestrial life can be referred to subtle differences in the
nucleic acids, the same basic structure is found in the nuclei of all cells.
This is a long, linear polymer fabricated from a sugar-phosphate repeating unit:

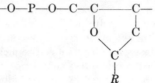

where R is a purine side group:

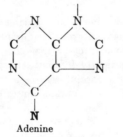   or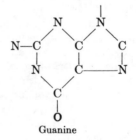

Adenine   Guanine

or a pyrimidine side group:

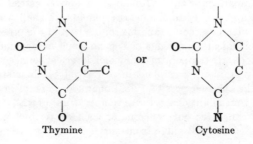

Thymine   Cytosine

The meaningful variety of nucleic acids depends on the specific order of the side group attached to each sugar of this monotonous backbone, a linear message written in a language of four letters, T, C, A, and G. The bacteria, which are the simplest free-living organisms, contain nucleotide sequences about 5,000,000 units long; man has about 5,000,000,000—this content being one of our best, objective measures of biological complexity. On the other hand, the simplest viruses, which can multiply only inside living cells and come close to being single genes, have about 2500 units per particle. Playing a central role in the unification of terrestrial biology, nucleic acids underlie both heredity and (through their control of protein synthesis) development. Are they the only linear polymers which can take on these functions or will many other fundamental types have evolved, to be found on other celestial bodies?

Equally general among the constituents of living cells are the proteins, which are also polymers but of a more diverse set of constituents, some 20 amino acids. The fundamental backbone of a protein is a poly-amino acid chain:

$$\text{H---NH---CH---CO---NH---CH---CO} \ldots \text{NH---CH---CO---OH}$$
$$\quad\quad\quad R \quad\quad\quad\quad\quad R \quad\quad\quad\quad\quad\quad\quad R$$

where R may be any one of 20 different groups. Proteins assume a wide variety of three-dimensional shapes, through coiling and cross-linking of the polymer chains. They are in this way suited to perform such diverse functions as those of enzymes, structural elements, and antibodies. Not only do we find just the same 20 amino acids among the proteins of all terrestrial organisms, but these are all the levo-isomers, although dextro-amino acids are found to have other metabolic functions. Next only to the incidence of nucleic acids, we would ask whether exobiota make analogous use of these amino acid polymers, in hopes of understanding what seem to be random choices in the sculpture of our own living form.

Common to terrestrial life are also a number of smaller molecules which are involved in the working metabolism of the cells; for example, most of the B vitamins have a perfectly general distribution. They are vitamins for us only because we have learned, in our evolutionary history, to rely on their production by green plants, rather than to synthesize them within our own cells. But once formed, these vitamins, and similar categories of substances such as porphyrins, play entirely analogous roles in the metabolism of all cells.

A few substances, such as the steroid hormones, do play special roles in the metabolism of higher organisms and testify to some progress in biochemical evolution. In fact, objective evidence points to many losses of specific functions: microorganisms are certainly more versatile and less dependent than man is on a specific nutrient milieu. The main burden of evolution has been not to develop new biochemical unit processes, but to coordinate them in time and space.

While we propose to give first priority to these most general questions, they by no means exhaust our interest in the peculiarities of extra-terrestrial organisms, any more than they would for a newly discovered phylum of the Earth's own repertoire. Nor should we even preclude the possibility of finding new organisms that might be economically useful to man, just as they were among the fruits of geographic exploration.

1.2 Theories of the Origin of Life

At this point, a consideration of contemporary theory on the origin of life is justified for two reasons: (1) exobiological research gives us a unique, fresh approach to this problem; and (2) we can find some encouragement that the recurrent evolution of life is more probable than was once believed.

The interval just after Pasteur's work on spontaneous generation was especially difficult for the mechanistic interpretation of the origin of life. Before Pasteur's time, many investigators could believe that simple microorganisms arose spontaneously in nutrient media. His demonstration that such media remained sterile if properly sterilized and protected seemed to disqualify any possibility of "spontaneous generation." His conclusion was of course overdrawn, since life must have evolved at least once, and might again on a scale that would still loom large in geological time spans. Meanwhile, the problem was compounded by the growth of biochemical knowledge. We now realize that bacteria, small as they are, are still extremely complex, well-ordered, and repre-sentative organisms. The first organisms must have been far simpler than present-day free-living bacteria.

With the growth of genetics since 1900 and the recognition of the self-replicating gene as the elementary basis of life, the question could focus on the origin of the first genetic molecule: given the power of self-replica-tion and incidents of stochastic variation, Darwin's principle could account for the eventual emergence of any degree of biological complexity.

An immense amount of fruitful genetic work was completed in a period when "genetic molecule" was an abstraction and "self-replica-tion" an axiomatic principle whose chemical basis seemed beyond the possibility of human understanding. Now we recognize that the nucleic acids are the material basis of heredity, and we can begin to construct mechanistic models of their replication. The first principle, as already stated, is that the gene is a string of nucleotides, each position in the string being marked by one of the four nucleotide units A, T, C, and G. The polymerization of such strings by the union of the monomeric units presents no fundamental problems, but self-replication would necessitate the assembly of the units in a specific order, the one dictated by the order of the nucleotides in the parent molecule. The key to the solution of this problem was the realization by Watson and Crick that the complete nucleic acid molecule is a rigid, duplex structure in which two strings are united. In that rigid structure, as can be shown by suitable molecular models, adenine occupies a space which is just complementary to that of thymine, and cytosine is likewise complementary to guanine. A string can therefore replicate, i.e., direct the assembly of another daughter string, in the following way. The nutrient mix of the cell contains all four nucleotide units. However, at any position of the parent nucleic acid molecule, only one of these four can make a suitable fit and will therefore be accepted. After being accepted, the daughter units are firmly bound together by new chemical linkages, giving a well-defined daughter string. Kornberg has reconstructed most of these events in some detail, by means of extracts from bacteria, to the very verge of proven duplication of genes in a chemically defined system in the test tube.

However, the media in which such syntheses can occur, in the cell or even in the test tube, are extremely complex. Given that the simplest organisms would be the most dependent on their environments for raw materials, where did these precursors come from before living organisms had evolved the enzymes to manufacture them?

Thanks to the insight of Haldane, Oparin, Horowitz, and others, we now realize that this paradox is a false one, though it dates to the confusion between "carbon chemistry" and "organic chemistry" which still exists in English terminology. In fact, in 1828, Wohler had already shown that an organic compound, urea, could be formed experimentally from an inorganic salt, ammonium cyanate. A hundred years later, a number of routes for synthesis of geochemically significant amounts of complex organic materials were pointed out, for example, the hydrolysis of metallic carbides and subsequent reactions of olefins with water and ammonia. More recently, Miller and Urey demonstrated the actual production of amino acids by the action of electric discharges on gas mixtures containing the hydrides NH_3, OH_2, and CH_4. This demonstration converges with other arguments that the primitive atmosphere of the earth had just such a reduced composition, becoming oxidized secondarily (and in part through photosynthetic separation of C from O_2).

An alternative origin of carbonaceous molecules is even more pervasive. Perhaps we associate carbon with life, and rocks and metals with physical phenomena: beyond doubt we tend to connote the latter with the predominant substance of the universe. In fact, as a glance at tables of cosmic abundance (see Table 1) will show, the lighter elements by far

Table 1. Relative Abundance

Element	Cosmos*	Terrestrial atmosphere† and hydrosphere†	Earth's crust‡
H	1600	2	0.03
He	160		
O	0.378	0.978	0.623
N	0.269	0.003	
Ne	0.168 ±		
C	0.135	0.0001	0.0005
Si	0.017		0.211
Mg	0.015		0.018
Fe	0.012		0.019
S	0.003	0.0005	
Ca	0.002		0.019
A	0.002		
Al	0.002		0.064
Na	0.001	0.008	0.026
Ni	0.0005		
Others	0.002	0.011	0.020

* After Urey.

† After Hutchinson, in *The Earth as a Planet*, (G. P. Kuiper, ed., Univ. of Chicago Press, Chicago, 1954.)

‡ After Mason, in *The Earth as a Planet*, (G. P. Kuiper, ed., Univ. of Chicago Press, Chicago, 1954.)

are the most prevalent, and after the dispersed H and He, these are C, O, and N. The primitive condensation of free atoms to form the interstellar smoke, and eventually the stars themselves, must entail the molecular aggregation of $H + C + O + N$; i.e., a large fraction of the condensed mass of the universe must consist, or once have consisted, of organic macromolecules of great complexity. The chief problem for their synthesis is in fact not a source of chemical energy, but how to dissipate the excess energy of reactions of free atoms and radicals,

This aspect of astrophysics may have place for a remote biological analogy: once a few molecules have formed, the energy of subsequent impacts can be dissipated among the vibrational degrees of freedom; that is, such molecules can function as nuclei of condensation. Those molecules will be favored, as seeds for further condensation, which (1) most readily dissipate the energy of successive impacts and (2) can undergo molecular fission to increase the number of nuclei. The actual molecular chemistry of the interstellar (or prestellar) smoke is thus subject to a kind of natural selection and cannot be a purely random sampling of available atoms.

Whether the Earth has retained remnants of this chemistry is hard to say. There is at least some evidence of it in the spectra of comets, and fragments from these continue to form part of the meteoroidal infall. These particles, unless associated with larger meteorites, would be unrecognizable after traversing the Earth's atmosphere: they are among the possible treasures to find buried in protected crevices on the Moon.

Light traversing the interstellar smoke has been found to be polarized. If primitive aggregation plays some role in furnishing precursors for biological evolution, this polarization furnishes at least one bias for a decision between levo- and dextro-isomers. The choice between these is perhaps not altogether random.

At any rate, possible sources for probiotic nutrition no longer pose a problem. Before the appearance of voracious organisms, organic compounds would accumulate until they reached equilibrium with thermal and radiative decomposition, from which the oceans would furnish ample cover. Locally, the concentration of the soup would be augmented by selective evaporation and by adsorption onto other minerals. The main gap in the theory, not yet bridged by any experiment, is the actual formation of a *replicating* polymer in such a morass. We are beginning to visualize the essential conditions for chemical replication, and its ultimate realization is foreshadowed both by biochemical studies of nucleic acids and by industrial syntheses of stereospecific polymers.

There is some controversy whether nucleic acids were the first genes, partly because they are so complex, partly because their perfection hints at an interval of chemical evolution rather than one master stroke. The advantage of the nucleic hypothesis is that no other self-replicating polymers have so far been found. But as an alternative speculation, a simplified protein might replicate by the complementary attachment of acidic versus basic units, perhaps the crudest possible method of assembly. The nucleic acids would be perfections on this theme for replication. The existent proteins do not replicate; with their variety of amino acids, they would have evolved as better adaptations for assuming specific shapes. A comparative view of independent evolutionary systems may at least serve to check such speculations.

Although many steps in the generation of living molecules remain to be recreated, we can state this as a relevant problem for exobiological study, with considerable optimism for the prevalence of life elsewhere. A sterile planet, too, would still be of extraordinary interest to biology for the insight it should give on the actual progress of probiotic chemical evolution.

1.3 Natural and Artificial Panspermia

The foregoing discussion tacitly assumed that the evolution of planetary life was a local phenomenon, independent of its incidence elsewhere. But at a time when *de novo* generation seemed less plausible than it does now, Arrhenius defended another hypothesis: *panspermia*, the migration of spores through space from one planet to another. The credibility of the panspermia hypothesis has been eroded mainly for two reasons: (1) the lack of a plausible natural mechanism for impelling a spore-bearing particle out of the gravitational field of a planet as large as the Earth or any planet large enough to sustain a significant atmosphere and (2) the vulnerability of such a particle to destruction by solar radiation. In any case, panspermia could be disparaged, for evading the fundamental problem, by transposing it to an unknown, perhaps scientifically unknowable, site. These difficulties have impeached the standing of panspermia as an experimentally useful hypothesis, but not its immense significance for cosmic biology. In its defense, it might be indicated that the hazards of exposure to space may be exaggerated, taking account of the dormancy of microorganisms in high vacuum and low temperatures and their relatively low cross section for ionizing radiations. The chief hazard to microorganisms might come from solar ultraviolet and the proton wind, but a thin layer of overlying material would shield a spore from these. For the impulsion of particles we might possibly appeal to impacts with other heliocentric bodies, be they grazing meteorites or planetoids in cataclysmic encounters—suggestions not more remote than those invoked for other astronomical phenomena. Nor can we be sure that all the electrokinetic mechanisms which Arrhenius may have had in mind can be excluded from applying to any single particle. In testing for panspermia, we should be concerned first of all for evidence of interplanetary transport of any material. The Moon suggests itself as a nearby trap for particles of terrestrial origin, among which living spores or biochemical fragments of them might be the most characteristic markers. At one spore per kilogram of sample, a weight ratio of 10^{-15}, the sensitivity of easy biological detection partly compensates for the vulnerability of spores to physical hazards.

The development of rocket-impelled spacecraft has, of course, furnished a mechanism for *artificial panspermia*. Several authors have recently revived Haldane's passing suggestion that life might even have been disseminated by intelligent beings from other stellar systems. That another century of productive science and technology could give the human species this capability would be hard to dispute. The hypothesis is connected with the age or agelessness of the Universe: if the Universe has lasted only some ten billion years, there could not be time for very many cycles of evolution of intelligence and technology. Whether any stellar system, or even other planets in the solar system, has or has not evolved intelligent life could be the subject of endless a priori speculation. At least for the solar system, the lack of any reliable evidence has rightly discouraged such speculations. Final answers await the experimental flights.

Communication by radio with other stellar systems would be far more readily accomplished than material transport. The technical problem of such communication has been introduced lately by, Cocconi and Morrison. Whether it would be desirable, from our own standpoint, to establish such communication might be pondered very carefully in the light of the historical facts of intercultural conflict on this planet.

1.4 Planetary Targets

The suitability for life of the accessible bodies of the solar system has already received ample attention. Mars is, of course, the likeliest target, most nearly resembling the habitat of the Earth. The indicated scarcity of free moisture and oxygen would severely limit the occupation of Mars by man or most terrestrial animals. However, there seems little doubt that many simpler, earthly organisms could thrive there. Indeed, many students have concluded that Mars does have a biota of its own. The most pertinent evidence is perhaps the infrared reflection spectrum recorded by Sinton, which indicates an accumulation of hydrocarbonaceous materials in the dark areas. This is complemented by Dollfus' report (First International Space Science Symposium, Nice) on the seasonal changes of granularity of these areas. The main reservation that must be registered is that these might be meteorological phenomena involving masses of material which may be carbonaceous but not necessarily living. Most such material on the Earth's surface is associated with life. However, this may be connected with the greedy utilization of such compounds by organisms rather than their production by vital synthesis. Yet the most plausible explanation of the astronomical data is that Mars is a living planet. (The term "vegetation" is often used: this should be discouraged if it implies that Martian biota will necessarily fall into the taxonomic divisions that we know on Earth.)

The habitability of Venus is connected with its temperature, which is still controversial, although many measurements indicate a very high temperature under the clouds. Perhaps the most useful first contribution to the exobiology of this planet would be a definitive measurement of its temperature profile. Even should the surface be unbearably hot, this need not preclude a more temperate zone at another layer.

The exposure of the Moon's surface to solar radiation and its absence of a significant atmosphere have discounted the possibility of a lunar biology. However, the composition of the Moon's deeper layers, from even a few meters beneath the surface, is very much an open question (see Urey, First International Space Science Symposium, Nice), particularly in the light of Kozyrev's recent reports of gaseous emissions. Realistic plans for the biological study of the Moon probably must await the results of chemical analyses. Apart from the remote possibility of indigenous life, the Moon is a gravitational trap for meteoroidal material. We may eventually be able to screen large quantities of this virgin material for what Haldane called astroplankton—the cosmically distributed spores that would be the empirical test of the panspermia hypothesis. While exposed deposits would be subject to solar degradation, shaded refuges must also exist. Mercury may be analogous to the Moon, except in so far as its dark side may furnish an even more reliable, though much remoter, refuge of this kind.

It may be academic to discuss the exploration of the major planets in view of their distance and the difficulty of deceleration in the Jovian field. However, their wealth of light elements, subject to solar irradiation at temperatures and in gravitational fields very different from the Earth's, offers the most exciting prospects for novel biochemical systems.

1.5 Experimental Approaches

Our treatment of this topic warrants the utmost humility from a realistic view of our limitations. Useful landings on planetary targets are fraught with difficulties and hazards; experiments that can already be conducted at some distance from their targets should not now be overlooked in the excitement of planning for more adventurous missions. Balloon- and satellite-mounted telescopes can tell much about planetary chemistry, and hence biology, and probes to the vicinity of the planets can furnish additional information prior to actual landing.

It is instructive to ask ourselves how we might diagnose the existence of life on the Earth from distant observations. If we may judge from the photographs so far obtained from high-altitude rockets, we could hope to detect only large-scale manifestations of organized culture—cities, roads, rockets. This reserve may not give due credit to the possibilities of high-resolution photography and sensitive infrared spectrometry and reasonable implications from seasonal changes in the color and texture of terrain. However, we may conclude that distant approaches will be invaluable for preparatory chemical information, but probably will not be conclusive for a decision on the presence of life. Even if we could more surely decide that the Martian cycle involved living organisms rather than inanimate chemical transformations, we should still have little insight into the intimate biochemical details which are a major objective of exobiological research. On the other hand, like our own extensive deserts and deep waters, a planet could harbor an extensive biota that would defy detection from a distance.

Microorganisms, for many reasons, are the best prospects on which to concentrate marginal capabilities of experimental detection by spacecraft instruments. They are more likely to flourish in a minimal environment than larger organisms. The microbes would precede the macrobes in evolutionary sequence. The Earth is well endowed with both kinds of organisms. We can imagine another world with only microbes, but we cannot conceive of one lacking microbes if it bears any form of life at all. Likewise, taking the Earth as a whole, we find that large organisms occupy only a small fraction of the surface. However, we can reasonably expect to find evidence of microscopic life in any drop of water, pinch of soil, or gust of wind. Given a limited sample for study, microbiological analysis will certainly give the most reliable diagnosis for the presence of life anywhere on the planet. By the same odds, the greatest diversity of biochemical mechanisms will be represented among the *micro*biota of a small sample.

Microbiological probes also offer distinct advantages for the collection and analysis of living material. Starting from a single particle, microbes can easily be cultivated within the confines of an experimental device. In this they remain accessible to physiological and chemical experiments that would be extremely cumbersome for larger organisms. (Compare, for example, the automatic instrumentation that would be needed to catch a hare and then to determine its nutritional requirements!) The techniques of cytochemistry, as have already been developed for the chemical analysis of microscopic cells and organisms, appear to be the most readily adaptable to automation and telemetric recording, an important advantage under the existing pressure of time, talent, and cost. Important issues of policy cannot be decisively settled without factual information on the growth capacity of the microorganisms that might be exchanged among the planets. Accordingly, the methodological precedents in terrestrial science for exobiology are most evident in microbial biochemistry. The conceptual aims are equally close to those of biochemical genetics. Needless to say, no other resource or objective of serious biological science can be neglected in the development of an experimental program.

Aside from the experimental designs, the pace of exobiological research may be regulated by advances in vehicular and guidance capabilities and data communication. In the expectation that these will remain in reasonable balance—for static or real-time television communication with the planetary probe—the microscope may be the most efficient sensory instrument. The redundancy of a pictorial image is not altogether wasted: would we confide in a one-bit pulse from an efficient black box to answer our cosmic queries?

According to this experimental concept, the terminal microscope-vidicon chain must be supported by three types of development: (1) for collection and transport of specimens to the aperture of the microscope, (2) for cytochemical processing of the samples, and (3) for protection of the device from environmental hazards, its apt location after landing, provision for illumination, focusing, and perhaps preliminary image selection. Detailed studies of these problems are only just under way, and the following suggestions are only tentative.

The easiest specimens to obtain may be atmospheric dust and samples of surface soil once the device has been landed. These are collected on a traveling ribbon of transparent tape which is thrown out and then rewound into the device. Larger samples, collected by a soil auger, could be subjected to a preliminary concentration of nonmineral components by flotation in a dense liquid. The use of such a tape simplifies the problem of treating the samples with a succession of reagents, for example, specific enzymes and fluorescent stains which allow for the detection of nucleic acids and proteins. Microscopy with ultraviolet light, particularly at 2600 and 2800 Å, because of its selectivity for nucleic acids and proteins, may be the most direct way to distinguish microorganisms from mineral particles. Generally speaking, the microscope can be adapted to many simple analytical procedures whose construction on a larger scale would present formidable problems for automatic technique.

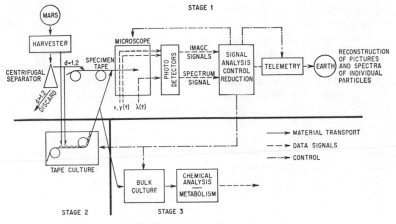

FIG. 1. Schematic diagram of an automatic microscope system
for use on a planet (e.g., Mars).

The adaptation of the microscope system to a payload can be undertaken more realistically when laboratory prototypes have been built and
tested. For example, we shall have to decide between accurate pre-
focusing of a microscope (whose lenses and entry slit are mounted in a
rigid structure) and continuous control of focus by an optically controlled servo system (an innovation that would be far from useless in the
biological laboratory). This automatic discrimination can also conserve
radio power: the traveling ribbon can be stopped and the vidicon-trans-
mitter activated just when a significant object is in view.

These preliminary experiments can indicate some of the general features
of the planetary microbiota. The data they furnish will support more
intensive studies of the growth characteristics, chemical composition,
and enzymatic capabilities of organisms cultivated on a larger scale.
The interaction of these organisms with tissue cultures of animal cells
can also be considered. From the results of these initial probes we can
better deduce how to anticipate the long-range consequences of the
intercourse of planetary biota.

2.6 Conservation of Natural Resources

A corollary of interplanetary communication is the artificial dissemination of terrestrial life to new habitats. History shows how the exploitation of newly found resources has enriched the human experience;
equally often we have seen great waste and needless misery follow from
the thoughtless spread of disease and other ecological disturbances. The

human species has a vital stake in the orderly, careful, and well-reasoned extension of the cosmic frontier. How we react to the adventuresome and perplexing challenges of space flight will be a crucial measure of the maturity of our national consciences and their concern for posterity.

The introduction of microbial life to a previously barren planet, or to one occupied by a less adapted form, can result in the explosive growth of the implant with consequences of geochemical scope. With a generation time of 30 min and easy dissemination by winds and currents, common bacteria could occupy a nutrient medium the size of the Earth in a few days or weeks, being limited only by the exhaustion of available nutrients. It follows that we must *rigorously* exclude terrestrial contaminants from our spacecraft. This stricture must hold until we have acquired the factual information from which we can assuredly assess the detriments of free traffic and whether these detriments are small enough to warrant the relaxation of the controls.

At the present time, the most obvious values that would be threatened by contamination are scientific ones. The overgrowth of terrestrial bacteria on Mars would destroy an inestimable prize for the understanding of our own living nature. Even if an intemperate mission has not contaminated a planet, the threat of its having done so will confuse later studies, if earthlike organisms are then found. However, other values are in question. Quite apart from strictly scientific concerns, would we not deplore a heedless intrusion on other life systems? It would be rash to predict too narrowly the ways in which undisturbed planetary surfaces, their indigenous organisms, their molecular resources may ultimately serve human needs. If we have cause to prejudice these values, we surely would not wish to do so by inadvertence.

To do this effectively requires a nice appreciation for the ubiquity and durability of bacterial spores, which are well preserved in high vacua and at low temperatures and are only rapidly destroyed when kept at temperatures over 160°C. It is probable that spacecraft can be disinfected by the conscientious application of gaseous disinfectants, especially ethylene oxide, but this will succeed only if the procedure is carried out meticulously and with controlled tests of its effectiveness. Sealed components, if found to be potential sources of contamination, can be disinfected by chemicals, prior to sealing, or subsequently by heat or by irradiation at very high doses. The technology of disinfection is an expert one, and personnel already experienced in it should be delegated supervisory control.

The assessment of this problem involves a concept of risk that has not always been perceptively realized. The hazards of space flight itself or of hard impact or the planetary environment *might* suffice to neutralize any contaminants: but can we afford to rely on any uncertain suppositions when the stakes are so high and when we have practical means at hand for conservative protection? We must be especially sensitive to the extreme variations in the environments of spacecraft or of planetary surfaces which might furnish refuges for microbial survival no matter how hostile the *average* conditions.

The indications by agencies both in the United States and in the U.S.S.R. that adequate precautions will be exercised on all relevant missions are an important step in the realization of constructive exobiology.

Scientists everywhere will call for the application of these measures with the same care and enthusiasm as the more positive, exciting, and patently rewarding aspects of space research. Scientific microbiology in the laboratory is absolutely dependent on the rigorous application of the special technique of pure culture with aseptic control. If we do not exercise the same rigor in space science, we might as well save ourselves the trouble of thinking about and planning for exobiological research.

While early traffic to the planets will be one-way, we must anticipate the capability of round trip and even of manned space flight. Undoubtedly, planetary samples can be analyzed for any scientific purpose more conveniently and more exactly in the terrestrial laboratory than by remote devices. For each step of analysis, special devices can be used (or, if need be, newly designed and constructed) and a constant give-and-take between human judgment and instrumental datum is possible.

However, the return of such samples to the Earth exposes *us* to a hazard of contamination by foreign organisms. Since we are not yet quite certain of the real existence of planetary (e.g., Martian) organisms and know nothing of their properties, it is extremely difficult to assess the risk of the event. The most dramatic hazard would be the introduction of a new disease, imperiling human health. What we know of the biology of infection makes this an extremely doubtful possibility: most disease-producing organisms must evolve very elaborate adaptations to enable them to resist the active defenses of the human body, to attack our cells, and to pass from one person to another. That a microorganism should have evolved such a capacity in the absence of experience with human hosts or similar organisms seems quite unlikely. However, a converse argument can also be put: that we have evolved our specific defenses against terrestrial bacteria, and we might be less capable of coping with organisms that lacked the proteins and carbohydrates by which they could be recognized as foreign. Furthermore, a few diseases are already known (e.g., psittacosis, botulism, aspergillosis) whose involvement of man seems to be a biological accident. These arguments can only be resolved by more explicit data. Nonetheless, if they are harmful at all, exobiota are more likely to be weeds than parasites, to act on our agriculture and the general comfort of our environment, and to be pervasive nuisances than acute aggressors. But even the remotest risk of pandemic disease, and the greater likelihood of serious economic nuisance, must dictate a stringent embargo on the premature return of planetary samples or craft that might inadvertently carry them. Again, our preliminary experiments must give us the foundation of knowledge to cope with exoorganisms, even select those which may be of economic benefit. A parallel development of technique for disinfection may mitigate some of these problems; at present the prospects for treating a *returning* vehicle to neutralize any possible hazard are at best marginal by comparison with the immensity of the risks.

Of the possible payloads for interplanetary travel, living man of course excites the widest popular interest. In due course, he may be supported by a sufficient payload to accomplish useful tasks in exploration beyond the capacities of instrumentation. However, he is a teeming reservoir of microbial contamination, the most difficult to neutralize, and an especially apt vehicle for infectious organisms. In view of these difficulties, and in so far as manned space flight is predicated on the return of the crew, a sound basis of scientific knowledge from instrumented experiments is a *sine qua non* for the planning of such missions.

Timely effort now to devise and build instrumented experiments is essential to keep pace with the technical capacities of space vehicles.

Many of the ideas presented in this statement are not new. In the scientific literature, they have been treated only occasionally, for example, in a remarkable article by J. B. S. Haldane (1954). They are also anticipated in the classic works of science fiction, e.g., H. G. Wells' *War of the Worlds*, and by a flood of derivative fantasies of less certain quality either as science or as fiction. This kind of attention has not necessarily helped the realistic evaluation of the biological aspects of space travel, which may still be dismissed as overimaginative by some of our colleagues. However, exobiology is no more fantastic than is the realization of space travel itself, and we have a grave responsibility to explore its implications for science and for human welfare with our best scientific insights and knowledge.

The continued interest and advice of M. Calvin, R. Davies, N. Horowitz, S. E. Luria, A. G. Marr, D. Mazia, A. Novick, C. Sagan, G. Stent, H. C. Urey, C. B. van Niel, and H. Weaver, among many others, have made this discussion possible.

REFERENCES

V. Alpatov: "The Rocket, the Moon and Life," *Izvest. Akad. Nauk S.S.S.R. Ser. Biol.*, 1959 (Sept. 18, 1959).

C. B. Anfinsen: *The Molecular Basis of Evolution* (Wiley, 1959).

G. Cocconi and P. Morrison: "Searching for Interstellar Communications," *Nature*, *184*, 844 (1959).

R. W. Davies and M. G. Comuntzis: "The Sterilization of Space Vehicles to Prevent Extraterrestrial Biological Contamination," *Intern. Astronaut. Congr. Proc.*, *10th Congr., London*, 1959.

A. Dollfus: "Resultats d'observations indiquant la vie sur la planète Mars," *Space Research*, Proceedings of the First International Space Science Symposium, Nice, 1960 (North-Holland Publishing Co., Amsterdam, 1960).

J. Dufay: *Nebuleuses galactiques et matière interstellaire*, translated by A. J. Pomerans as *Galactic Nebulae and Interstellar Matter* (Hutchinsons, London, 1957),

C. S. Elton: *The Ecology of Invasions by Animals and Plants* (Methuen, London, 1958).

S. W. Fox: "How Did Life Begin?," *Science, 132*, 200 (1960).

J. B. S. Haldane: "The Origins of Life," in *New Biology*, vol. 16 (Penguin, London, 1954).

N. Horowitz: "The Origin of Life," in E. Hutchings, Jr. (ed.), *Frontiers of Science*, (Basic Books, 1958).

H. Spencer Jones: *Life on Other Worlds* (New American Library, 1949).

A. Kornberg: "Biologic Synthesis of Deoxyribonucleic Acid," *Science, 131*, 1503 (1960).

J. Lederberg: "A View of Genetics," *Science, 131*, 269 (1960),

—— and D. B. Cowie: "Moondust," *Science, 127*, 1473 (1958).

S. L. Miller and H. C. Urey: "Organic Compound Synthesis on the Primitive Earth," *Science, 130*, 245 (1959).

A. I. Oparin: *The Origin of Life*, S. Morgulis, translator (Macmillan, 2d ed., 1938); (Dover, 3d ed., 1953); A. Synge, translator (Oliver and Boyd, London, 1957).

W. M. Sinton: "Further Evidence of Vegetation on Mars," *Science, 130*, 1234 (1959).

H. C. Urey: "Lines of Evidence Regarding the Composition of the Moon," *Space Research*, Proceedings of the First International Space Science Symposium, Nice, 1960 (North-Holland Publishing Co., Amsterdam, 1960).

The Origin of Life on the Earth, Reports on the International Symposium, August, 1957, Moscow (Academy of Sciences of the U.S.S.R., Moscow).

"Report of the Committee on the Exploration of Extraterrestrial Space (CETEX) 1959," *ICSU Rev., 1*, 100 (1959); second report, *Nature, 183*, 925 (1959).

C. R. Phillips and K. K. Hoffman: "Sterilization of Interplanetary Vehicles," *Science, 132*, 991 (1960).

C. Sagan: "Biological Contamination of the Moon," *Proc. National Acad. Sci.*, U.S. *46*, 396 (1960).

PART **8** =

APPENDIX

APPENDIX

A NOTE ON THE SPACE SCIENCE BOARD

The Space Science Board of the National Academy of Sciences serves science in several ways. It is advisory to government agencies charged by the Congress with executive responsibilities in the field of space activity. It provides a focus for the interests of American science and a voice for the scientific community. It serves as the national means, through the Academy, for cooperation with the international community as represented by the International Council of Scientific Unions (ICSU) and specifically, the Council's Committee on Space Research (COSPAR). The historical roots of these functions are to be found in the IGY.

Before the IGY came to a close, the Academy's IGY Committee and its Satellite Panel became concerned with the continuity of scientific work in space. Similar concerns were expressed by officials in the government, particularly by the Director of the National Advisory Committee for Aeronautics, which later became the NASA, and by the Director of the National Science Foundation, who expressed their interest in the establishment of a Space Science Board by the Academy. It was also known that the ICSU expected to establish COSPAR and that it would then call upon adhering academies to provide appropriate means for their participation in the work of this committee.

The President of the Academy, Dr. Detlev W. Bronk, accordingly established the Space Science Board in June 1958 and delineated its functions as follows:

" . . . It is my hope that the Board will give the fullest possible attention to every aspect of space science, including both the physical and the life sciences. I believe that we have a unique opportunity to bring together scientists from many fields to survey in concert the problems, the opportunities, and the implications of man's advance into space, and to find ways to further a wise and vigorous national scientific program in this field.

"We have talked of the main task of the Board in three parts—the immediate program, the long-range program, and the international aspects of both. In all three we shall look to the Board to be the focus of the interests and responsibilities of the Academy-Research Council in space science; to establish necessary relationships with civilian science and with governmental scientific activities, particularly the proposed new space agency, the National Science Foundation, and the Advanced Research Projects Agency; to represent the Academy-Research Council in our international relations in this field on behalf of American science and scientists; to seek ways to stimulate needed research; to promote necessary co-ordination of scientific effort; and to provide such advice and recommendations to appropriate individuals and agencies with regard to space science as may in the Board's judgment be desirable.

"As we have already agreed, the Board is intended to be an advisory, consultative, correlating, evaluating body and not an operating agency in the field of space science. It should avoid responsibility as a Board for the conduct of any programs of space research and for the formulation of budgets relative thereto. Advice to agencies properly responsible for these matters, on the other hand, would be within its purview to provide
. . . ."

The membership of the Space Science Board consists of L. V. Berkner (chairman), Harrison S. Brown, Leo Goldberg, H. Keffer Hartline, Donald F. Hornig, William W. Kellogg, Christian J. Lambertsen, Joshua Lederberg, Colin S. Pittendrigh, Richard W. Porter, Bruno B. Rossi, Alan H. Shapley, John A. Simpson, Harold C. Urey, James A. Van Allen, O. G. Villard, Jr., Harry Wexler, George P. Woollard, Hugh Odishaw (executive director), and R. C. Peavey (secretary).

To examine various fields of science, in terms of research, a number of committees and panels have been established by the Board:

Chemistry of Space and Exploration of Moon and Planets: Harold C. Urey (chairman), Harrison S. Brown (vice-chairman), Harry H. Hess,

A. R. Hibbs, Mark Inghram, Zdenek Kopal, Gordon J. F. MacDonald, Frank Press, William M. Sinton, G. de Vaucouleurs, Fred L. Whipple, George A. Derbyshire (secretary).

Optical and Radio Astronomy: Leo Goldberg (chairman), Lawrence H. Aller, Horace W. Babcock, Gerald M. Clemence, A. D. Code, John W. Evans, Jr., John Findlay, Herbert Friedman, Roger Gallet, G. H. Herbig, Frederick T. Haddock, Jr., Walter Orr Roberts, Lyman Spitzer, Jr., Martin Schwarzschild, Edward R. Dyer, Jr. (secretary).

Future Vehicular Development: Donald F. Hornig (chairman), J. P. T. Pearman (secretary), ad hoc membership depending upon the subject.

International Relations: Richard W. Porter (chairman), Herbert Friedman, Leo Goldberg, Hugh Odishaw, Homer E. Newell, Jr., Howard P. Robertson, Alan H. Shapley, Harry Wexler, Joel Orlen (secretary).

Space Projects: Bruno B. Rossi (chairman), Thomas Gold, Salvador E. Luria, Philip Morrison, J. P. T. Pearman (secretary).

The Atmospheres of the Earth and Planets: Alan H. Shapley (chairman), Henry G. Booker, Joseph W Chamberlain, Robert Jastrow, C. Gordon Little, Laurence A. Manning, A. H. Waynick, R. C. Peavey (secretary).

Physics of Fields and Particles in Space: John A. Simpson (chairman), James A. Van Allen (vice-chairman), Joseph W. Chamberlain, William Kraushaar, Eugene N. Parker, E. H. Vestine, John Winckler, J. P. T. Pearman (secretary).

General Engineering Service and Co-ordination: O. G. Villard, Jr. (chairman), J. P. T. Pearman (secretary), ad hoc membership depending upon the subject.

Meteorological Aspects of Satellites: Harry Wexler (chairman), Charles C. Bates, George Benton, Sigmund Fritz, William W. Kellogg, Norman Phillips, Ernst Stuhlinger, Verner E. Suomi, William K. Widger, Jr., Edward R. Dyer, Jr. (secretary).

Biological Research: H. Keffer Hartline (chairman), Howard J. Curtis, L. E. Farr, Thomas Francis, Christian J. Lambertsen, Joshua Lederberg, E. F. MacNichol, Colin S. Pittendrigh, Otto H. Schmitt, Edward L. Tatum, George A. Derbyshire (secretary).

Geodesy: G. P. Woollard (chairman), R. K. C. Johns, D. A. Lautman, William Markowitz, W. J. O'Sullivan, Donald A. Rice, Hellmut Schmid, Charles A. Whitten, Edward R. Dyer, Jr. (secretary).

Upper Atmosphere Rocket Research: W. W. Kellogg (chairman), H. J. aufm Kampe, Warren W. Berning, W. W. Elam, Robert D. Fletcher, Herbert Friedman, Stanley M. Greenfield, John E. Masterson, Willis Webb, Harry Wexler, George A. Derbyshire (secretary).

Exobiology: Joshua Lederberg (chairman), Paul Berg, Melvin Calvin,

Richard Davies, Norman Horowitz, A. G. Marr, Daniel Mazia, Aaron Novick, Carl Sagan, C. B. van Niel, Harold F. Weaver, George A. Derbyshire (secretary).

Environmental Biology: Colin S. Pittendrigh (chairman), Alan H. Brown, Theodore H. Bullock, George A. Derbyshire (secretary). Ad hoc working groups and additional members are called upon as needed.

Man in Space: C. J. Lambertsen (chairman), Howard J. Curtis, James D. Hardy, H. Keffer Hartline, James Henry, Joshua Lederberg, Norton Nelson, Colin S. Pittendrigh, Richard W. Porter, John W. Senders, George A. Derbyshire (secretary).

In addition, expert panels and working groups have been created from time to time for the examination of special topics.

The Board has provided advice and recommendations on a variety of subjects relating to basic research; it has served to represent the interests of scientists broadly; and it has sought to provide a broad scientific base for current and future United States space science efforts by stimulating the interests of leading scientists in space and by affording a forum for discussion of research problems by the scientific community.

Immediately upon its establishment the Board collected proposals and suggestions from the national scientific community for additional projects in space science research which should follow upon the accomplishment of the IGY satellite and rocket program. The Board's committees assessed some 200 proposals and provided recommendations concerning these projects to the National Aeronautics and Space Administration and the National Science Foundation in the fall of 1958 and early 1959. These studies proved especially valuable by enabling the NASA, promptly upon its establishment, to organize the initial program of post-IGY space research. They also provided for an orderly transition from the IGY period to the post-IGY effort.

The Board has regularly reviewed space programs and plans of the various government agencies and has inspected vehicle development and launching facilities as well as laboratories. Following the initial activities noted in the preceding paragraph, the Board and its committees have conducted systematic studies of the interests of science in space, field by field. These studies have occupied most of the energies of the Board; extensive recommendations have been submitted to the government; and the chapters of this book are suggestive of the scientific findings of the Board and its committees.

In addition to this basic activity, the Board has considered a variety of special topics, of which the following are illustrative: the problem of contamination of extraterrestrial bodies and of back contamination of the Earth, the need for exclusive allocation of radio frequencies for use in space research, ground-based radar astronomy, photochemical aspects of space (especially the photochemistry of the far ultraviolet), the analysis of meteorites, laboratory astrophysics, nuclear propulsion, rocket launching sites, aspects of mathematics and its potential contributions to a variety of space problems, and experiments concerned with artificial ionospheres. The Board has also provided guidance to the rocket and satellite subcenter of World Data Center A, located in the Academy and charged with international interchange of geophysical data. The subcenter, established during the IGY, has issued two series of reports, listed at the end of this note.

The Board has participated extensively in the activities of the Committee on Space Research (COSPAR), established by the International Council of Scientific Unions (ICSU) to continue and extend international cooperation in space research along the lines of the IGY. Dr. Richard W. Porter, Board member and chairman of its Committee on International Relations, has served as the Academy's chief delegate to COSPAR. He is a vice president of COSPAR and a member of its Executive Council.

In this area the Board has served to represent the scientific community of the United States and has coordinated national interests and contributions relevant to the activities of COSPAR. It compiles, and submits annually to COSPAR, the national contribution in space research. It arranges for U.S. participation in the assemblies, symposia and scientific working groups of COSPAR and in such programs as the annual COSPAR international rocket intervals.

LIST OF ROCKET AND SATELLITE REPORTS

These series of reports were initiated during the IGY in partial fulfillment of the international data interchange agreements. The series are continuing under the national auspices of the Rocket and Satellite Subcenter of World Data Center A at the Academy and the international aegis of COSPAR. Requests for the reports, each costing one dollar, may be addressed to the Publications Office, National Academy of Sciences, Washington 25, D.C.

Rocket Series

No. 1. *Experimental Results of the U.S. Rocket Program for the International Geophysical Year to 1 July, 1958*, edited by John Hanessian, Jr. and Ilene Guttmacher. 236 pp., July, 1958. Thirty papers on: summary results of the US-IGY rocket program to 1 July 1958; atmospheric structure; ion composition of the arctic ionosphere; ionospheric measurements; auroral particles and soft radiation; solar radiation, cosmic rays, and the earth's magnetic field; U.S. Air Force and BRL rocket programs for the IGY.

No. 2. *Flight Summaries for the U.S. Rocketry Program for the International Geophysical Year, Part 1: 5 July, 1956–30 June, 1958*, compiled by Pembroke J. Hart and Ilene Guttmacher. 193 pp., March 1959. Launching information (time, place, date), objectives, instrumentation, and preliminary report on performance of the rocket and instrumentation.

No. 3. *Flight Summaries for the U.S. Rocketry Program for the International Geophysical Year, Part II: 23 May–31 December 1958*, compiled by Pembroke J. Hart and Ilene Guttmacher. 120 pp., Sept. 1959. Includes 20 pre-IGY rockets not in Part I and 5 rockets planned as part of the IGY program but postponed to 1959. Launching information (time, place, date), objectives, instrumentation, and preliminary report on performance of the rocket and instrumentation.

No. 4. *Magnetic Exploration of the Upper Atmosphere*, by Laurence J. Cahill, Jr. 87 pp., October, 1959. A report on the program of shipboard launchings of rocket-borne magnetometers conducted by the State University of Iowa.

No. 5. *Upper Air Densities and Temperatures from Eight IGY Rocket Flights by the Falling-Sphere Method*, by L. M. Jones, J. W. Peterson, E. J. Schaefer, and H. F. Schulte. 102 pp., December, 1959. Thirty pages of text, 11 tables, 68 figures. A technical report on experimental techniques and tabulations of observations and results obtained from falling-sphere experiments on board eight IGY rockets, conducted by the University of Michigan. (Included in a pocket is a reprint from the *Journal of Geophysical Research*, December, 1959, of an article by the same authors, based on the results of these and other rocket flights.)

No. 6. *A Second Compilation of U.S. IGY Rocket Program Results*, compiled by J. P. T. Pearman and Ilene Guttmacher. 198 pp., November, 1960. Twenty-two papers on: physical properties of the atmosphere; atmospheric composition; electron densities and collision frequencies; energetic particles and auroras; terrestrial magnetism; solar radiation. Reprinted from several journals and symposia.

Satellite Series

No. 1. *Processed Observational Data for USSR Satellites 1957 Alpha and 1957 Beta*, by R. N. Adams, N. McCumber, and M. Brinkman. 120 pp.,

March, 1958. Four-page introduction on sources and processing of data; 116 pages of catalogue of observations and station coordinate list.

No. 2. *Status Reports on Optical Observations of Satellites 1958 Alpha and 1958 Beta*, edited by G. F. Schilling. 41 pp., April, 1958. Twelve papers on: preliminary results from optical tracking of the U.S. earth satellites; optical satellite observations; scientific results; use and distribution of satellite predictions; and Harvard announcement cards.

No. 3. *Some Preliminary Reports of Experiments in Satellites 1958 Alpha and 1958 Gamma*, by various authors. 100 pp., May, 1958. Five articles: Status Reports on Optical Observations of Satellites 1958 Alpha and 1958 Beta; Determination of the Orbit of 1958 Alpha at Vanguard Computing Center; Satellite Micrometeorite Measurements; Satellite Temperature Measurements for 1958 Alpha; The Observation of High Intensity Radiation by Satellites 1958 Alpha and Gamma.

No. 4. *Observational Information on Artificial Earth Satellites*, by J. A. Hynek and G. F. Schilling. 38 pp., July, 1958. Nine papers on: the USSR satellites; the U.S. satellites; satellite characteristics and scientific results.

No. 5. *Radio Observations of Soviet Satellites 1957 Alpha 2 and 1957 Beta 1*, by James W. Warwick. 50 pp., July, 1958. Three parts: Determination of Passage Parameters from Simple Interferometer Records; Preliminary Results of the Analysis of Ionospheric Fading and Interferometer Effects; Spin Fading.

No. 6. *Reports and Analyses of Satellite Observations*, by various authors. 60 pp., Aug. 1958. Four papers: Moonwatch Catalogue (tables); Preliminary Note on the Mass-Area Ratios of Satellites 1958 Delta 1 and 1958 Delta 2; The Descent of Satellite 1957 Beta 1; Positions of Satellite 1957 Beta 1 during the First 100 Revolutions (tables).

No. 7. *Simplified Satellite Prediction from Modified Orbital Elements*, by Leonard N. Cormier, Norton Goodwin, and Reginald K. Squires. 54 pp., January, 1959. This report is intended primarily to serve the needs of participating observers of satellites. Orbital elements are disseminated by IGY World Warning stations, and by the volunteer organizations for tracking IGY satellites—*Moonbeam* (radio), *Moonwatch* (telescope) and *Phototrack* (camera)—and are not available through World Data Center A.

No. 8. *Ephemeris of Satellite 1957 Alpha 2 and Collected Reports on Satellite Observations*, by various authors. 122 pp., June, 1959. Part I:

Ephemeris (3-minute read-out), Part II: Ten papers dealing with technical parameters and orbital acceleration of satellites, earth's gravitational potential, effects of sun and moon on satellites, empirical formula for ephemerides, atmospheric structure.

No. 9. *Symposium on Scientific Effects of Artificially Introduced Radiations at High Altitudes.* 88 pp., September, 1959. A reprint from the Proceedings of the National Academy of Sciences, August 1959, pp. 1141–1228, containing seven papers presented at a symposium of the National Academy of Sciences. Topics include the Argus experiment; satellite observations of electrons artificially injected into the geomagnetic field; Project Jason measurement of trapped electrons from a nuclear device by sounding rockets; theory of geomagnetically trapped electrons from an artificial source; optical, electromagnetic, and satellite observations of high-altitude nuclear detonations.

No. 10. *The Determination of Ionospheric Electron Content and Distribution from Satellite Observations,* by O. K. Garriott. 65 pp., January, 1960. Analysis of 20 mc telemetry and 40 mc second harmonic from satellite 1958 Delta 2 (Sputnik III) for the period September 1958–April 1959.

No. 11. *Observations of Corpuscular Radiation with Satellites and Space Probes,* by various authors. 125 pp., June, 1960. Contains 14 articles reprinted from several journals and symposia.

No. 12. *IGY Satellite Ionospheric Research, based on observations of 1957 Alpha 2 and 1958 Delta 2,* by various authors. 80 pp., December, 1960. Three papers on: Ionospheric electron content from the Faraday-rotation fading and dispersive Doppler effect of transmissions from 1958 Delta 2 (Sputnik III), and analysis of scintillation of signals from 1957 Alpha 2 and 1958 Delta 2 (Sputniks I and III).

No. 13. *Satellites 1958 Alpha and Gamma: High Intensity Radiation Research and Instrumentation,* by various authors. 106 pp., January, 1961. Unedited transcript of the presentation on May 1, 1958, by James A. Van Allen of the first results of high-intensity radiation observations made by satellites 1958 Alpha and Gamma (Explorers I and III); and descriptions of the related instrumentation carried by these satellites.

NAME INDEX